GELS Handbook

Fundamentals, Properties and Applications

GELS Handbook

Fundamentals, Properties and Applications

Volume 1: Fundamentals of Hydrogels

Qi Wen and **Yi Dong** *Volume Editors*

Editors

Utkan Demirci
Stanford

Ali Khademhosseini
Harvard

World Scientific

NEW JERSEY • LONDON • SINGAPORE • BEIJING • SHANGHAI • HONG KONG • TAIPEI • CHENNAI • TOKYO

Published by

World Scientific Publishing Co. Pte. Ltd.
5 Toh Tuck Link, Singapore 596224
USA office: 27 Warren Street, Suite 401-402, Hackensack, NJ 07601
UK office: 57 Shelton Street, Covent Garden, London WC2H 9HE

British Library Cataloguing-in-Publication Data
A catalogue record for this book is available from the British Library.

GELS HANDBOOK
Fundamentals, Properties and Applications
(In 3 Volumes)

Volume 1: Fundamentals of Hydrogels
Volume 2: Applications of Hydrogels in Regenerative Medicine
Volume 3: Applications of Hydrogels in Drug Delivery and Biosensing

ISBN 978-981-4656-10-8 (Set)
ISBN 978-981-4656-13-9 (Vol 1)
ISBN 978-981-4656-14-6 (Vol 2)
ISBN 978-981-4656-15-3 (Vol 3)

In-house Editors: Rhaimie Wahap/Dipasri Sardar

Typeset by Stallion Press
Email: enquire@stallionpress.com

Printed in Singapore

Contents

Chapter 1

Natural Hydrogels

Shangyou-Tee
Department of Physics, Nanyang Technological University, Singapore

1. Introduction

Gels are ubiquitous materials that can be found all around our everyday lives. In fact most of our tissues and organs are gels. Most gels are made up of a network of polymers or colloids that is filled by a fluid.[1] At steady state when the gel is neither stressed nor strained, it will not flow.[2] That is, a gel's elastic modulus, *G*', is greater than its loss modulus, *G*''; a gel is thus a solid albeit a soft and squishy one. Even though the network of polymers or colloids that form a continuous 3D network in a gel can be very dilute (less than 1% by weight), this dilute network is enough to support shear stresses and thus gives the gel its solid-like material properties.[3]

1.1. Types and chemistry of natural hydrogels

A hydrogel is simply a gel where the fluid discontinuous phase is water whereas the solid continuous phase is still a network of polymers or colloids.[4] Hydrogels can be characterized by how their networks are held together. "Physical" hydrogels have their polymer network linked together by entanglements, ionic, hydrogen bonds or other forces. "Chemical" hydrogels, on the other hand, have their networks linked by permanent chemical bonds. In general, the links or connections of physical hydrogels are transient in nature and are therefore weaker than those of chemical hydrogels. These transient connections are also sometimes reversible compared to the covalent chemical connections.[5]

Natural hydrogels that are formed from protein such as collagen or fibrin or from polysaccharides such as agarose or alginate are all around us and have been known for a long time. Synthetic hydrogels have to be polymerized in the laboratory and are first reported in 1954.[6] Such artificial hydrogels are highly customizable and can be tailored to specific applications by fine-tuning their mesh size,[7–9] polymer length,[10,11] water content,[12] mechanical and chemical properties, etc.[13–15] However, natural hydrogels have the strong advantage of being biocompatible[16–19] and biodegradable.[20–22]

1.2. Classify hydrogels based on their formation

Yet another way to classify hydrogels is by how they are synthesized. The hydrogel research field is quite diverse. Here we will briefly discuss two new very exciting developments. One, smart hydrogels are materials that change their properties in response to a change to external stimuli or inputs.[23,24] Some possible inputs are changes in pH,[25,26] temperature,[27,28] salt content,[29–31] chemical or biochemical contents, etc.[32,33] Possible outputs or changes in the hydrogel properties include changes in mechanical properties,[34,35] shapes, swelling, etc.[23,36] These "smart" properties can be exploited for many important industrial and biochemical applications. For example, drug-laden hydrogels microparticles can be allowed to circulate the blood stream to only release upon encountering particular temperature,[37] pH or biochemical situations.[38] Second, self-healing hydrogels are materials that can automatically "repair" themselves when defects such as cracks, changes in mechanical properties, etc. are encountered.[39–41] Typically, such healing occurs because of spontaneous formation of new bonds.[42] Intuitively, it is not hard to envision the utility of such self-healing materials in tissue engineering, organ regeneration, etc.[43,44]

Due to their high water content, hydrogels has wide ranging applications in a variety of areas. In a research setting, hydrogels have been used for cell culture and tissue scaffold bioengineering.[45–47] In the medical area, hydrogels have been used as drug delivery systems, wound dressing scaffolds, biosensors, etc.[48–50] Moreover, hydrogels are used widely in diapers[51,52] and contact lens.[53–55] As a rule of thumb, natural hydrogels are biocompatible and are rapidly finding more and more uses in the biomedical setting.

2. Hydrogel Synthesis

In this chapter, we describe methods that are most commonly used to synthesis hydrogels. In general, physical and radiation crosslink techniques are prefer in medical application compare with chemical crosslink and grafting techniques due to non-toxicity in preparation process.

2.1. Physical crosslink

2.1.1. *Heating or cooling process*

A sol-gel formation bases on temperature alteration of polymer solution is a process without using chemical crosslink agents. Phase transition occurs at a distinct temperature of polymer solution is called low critical solution temperature (LCST) and form a reversible hydrogels. Natural polymers such as agarose[56] or polyethylene glycol (PEG)–polylactic acid[57] dissolve in water as random coils, and then form helix structure if solution temperature is lower than LCST and reversible. Upon cooling the structure aggregates to form a rigid hydrogels (Fig. 1). A similar example is from Yoshioka group that dissolved gelatin in warm water at 37°C and form hydrogels at 27°C.[58]

2.1.2. *Ionic interaction*

Ionic interaction occurs between ionic polymer chains containing opposite charges with multivalent ions that plays a role as crosslinkers.[59] In the case of chitosan, ammonium groups with positively charges on chitosan form ionic bonds with Pt (II) which is commonly used as crosslinker (Fig. 2).[60]

2.1.3. *Complex coacervation*

The interaction between an anionic polymer solutions with a cationic polymer solution forms a complex coacervation gel (Fig. 3). Gotoh group developed alginate-chitosan

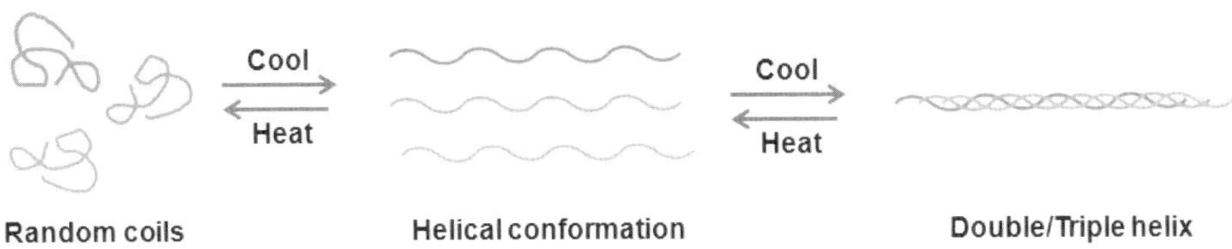

Fig. 1. Gel formation due to phase transition upon changing temperature.

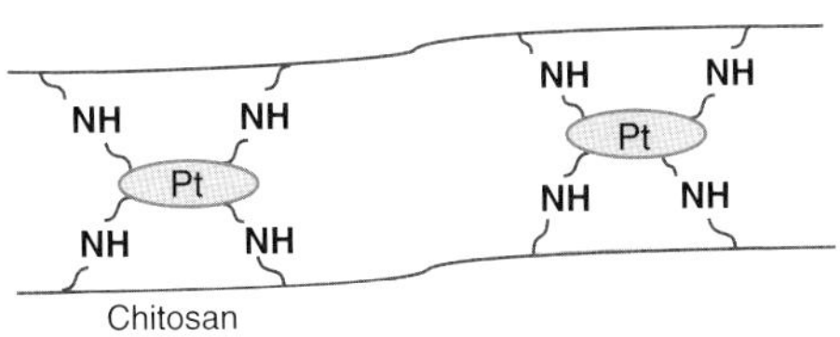

Fig. 2. Gelation based on ion interaction between charged ammonium groups of chitosan with divalent Platinum ions.

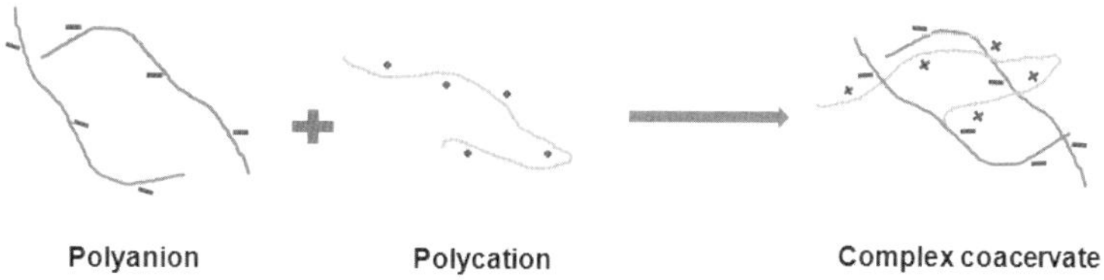

Fig. 3. Schematic of complex coacervation process.

hybrid gels by mixed anionic polysaccharide alginate acid, which contains carboxyl group, and cationic polysaccharide chitosan, which contains amino groups in neutral aqueous solution. The polyelectrolyte complexes were synthesized provide a good substance to absorb Cu (II), Co (II), and Cd (II) in drug delivery system.[61]

2.1.4. *Freeze-thaw process*

Freeze-thaw is one of the gelation techniques occur in mild condition without chemically crosslink agents. Polymeric solution is frozen and thawed to form cryogels. The method was first reported on aqueous poly(vinyl alcohol) solutions by Peppas group in 1975.[62] Continuously repetition of freeze-thaw process leads to form crystallites as a crosslink region. Crystallites degree has associated with aqueous solution concentration, freeze and thaw time.[63–65] Starch (amylose, amylopectin and their mixtures), agarose, hyaluronan (HA), maltodextrins (MDs) that are natural materials are able to form hydrogels upon freeze-thaw technique.[66,67]

2.2. Chemical crosslink

Chemical crosslink is the predominant method in hydrogel synthesis, in which natural or artificial crosslinkers form covalent bonds to functional groups on side chain of polymer (such as –OH, –COOH, and NH_2).[68–72] Mincheva *et al.* developed a network hydrogel net-chitosan-ι-PEG-$(COOH)_2$ by using PEG diacid as an agent to crosslink chitosan. The amide bonds formed between carboxyl groups of chitosan react with the amine groups of PEG diacid PEG-$(COOH)_2$ in low pH and high temperature aqueous solution (Fig. 4). The highly equilibrium degree of swelling of networks serves effectively as a matrix of the regenerating processes in artificial bone defects.[73]

Similarly, Wang group used genipin as a natural agent for crosslinking the lysine groups in the poly(l-lysine)-block-polyglycine (PLL-b-PGly) polypeptides to constitute genipin-crosslinked hydrogels in a short time.[74] The novel hydrogels were biocompatible on support cell attachment or proliferation. Additionally, PEG, Polypropylene glycol (PPG) and Isophorone diisocyanate (IPDI) were combined to form pre-polymer with polyurethane (PU) serving as crosslinker in

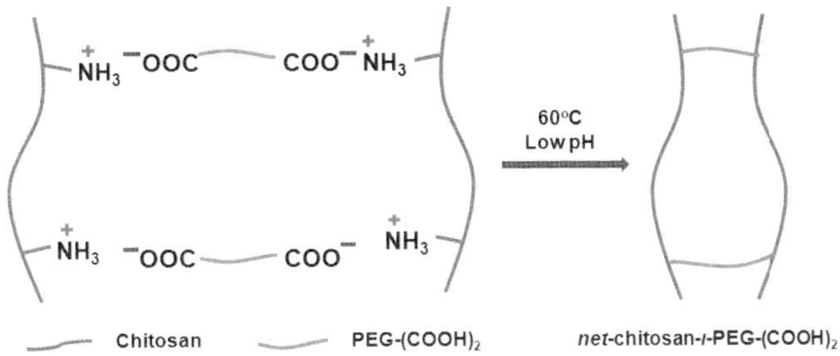

Fig. 4. Formation of covalently crosslinked network net-chitosan-ι- PEG-$(COOH)_2$.

Huang group.[75] PU chain not only provided –NCO groups to form covalently bond with $-NH_2$ and –OH groups on silk fibroin (SF) chains but also interacted to form hydrogen bonds makingmup a crosslinked network of silk fibroin-polyurethane (SF-PU) hydrogels. The permanent structures show good properties in swell-deswell and sensitive to pH, temperature and ionic strength.

2.3. *Grafting*

The polymerization of monomers or polymers on to the chains of a polymeric material is called grafting crosslink. The polymers are treated by high energy radiation or chemical reagents to expose functional groups on monomers or polymers as well as polymeric material. As a result, the process leads to branching and crosslink to synthesize stable hydrogels (Fig. 5).

Amin group developed bacterial cellulose/acrylic acid hydrogel by grafting bacterial cellulose on acrylic acids that were ionized radiation.[76] In another case, a conventional polyethylene was grafted with a chelate agent function was done by Tamada group. The amidoxime fibrous absorbent was obtained after crosslinking

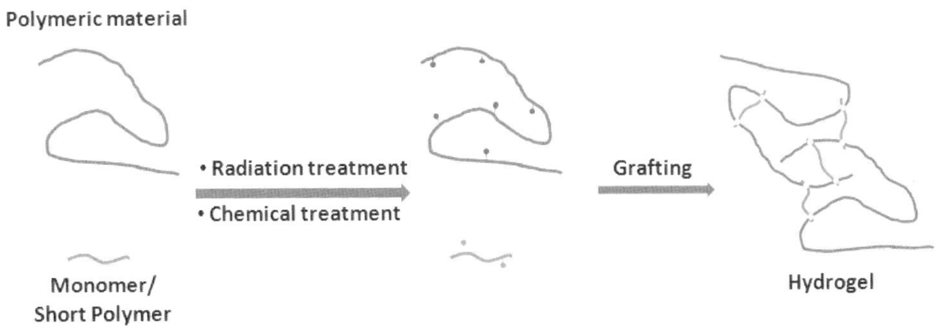

Fig. 5. Preformed monomers or short polymers graft on and crosslink preformed polymeric material.

process.[77] Similarly, Yazdani-Pedram and Retuert de la Torre introduced carboxylic groups onto chitosan by grafting process with poly(acrylic acid) to form a swelling network hygrogels.[78]

2.4. Crosslinking by ionizing radiation or radiation crosslinking

Radiation crosslinking technique has been widely used as an effective approach to modify the structure of natural polymers and induce the hydrogel formation. In principle, the hydrogel can be obtained when exposed interest polymer in solid or aqueous solution state under ionizing radiation with high energy such as gamma radiation.[79,80] As a result, there are two main events to be achieved (i) direct energy transfer to the polymer to generate a lot of free radicals called macroradicals which are important for the recombination of inter-molecules and (ii) the direct or indirect effect of water induces polymer chains mobility or radiolysis macromolecules products, respectively.[81]

2.4.1. *Radiation crosslinking between natural polymers*

The application of this technique has been recently reported for the hydrogels preparation of several natural polymers used in biomedical studies such as carboxymethyl-chitosan (CMCTS)/gelatin hydrogel, methylcellulose hydrogel, hydroxyethyl metacryate (HEMA)-agar and hydroxyethyl metacryate (HEMA)-gelatin hydrogel.[82–85] In brief, the mechanism for the formation of hydrogels was proposed to be

$$H_2O \xrightarrow{\text{Ionizing radiation}} {}^{\bullet}OH,\ {}^{\bullet}H,\ H_2O_2,\ H_3O^+,\ H_2,\ e^-_{aq}, \quad (1)$$

$$RH + {}^{\bullet}OH\ (H^{\bullet}) \leftrightarrow {}^{\bullet}R + H_2O\ (H_2), \quad (2)$$

$${}^{\bullet}R + {}^{\bullet}R \rightarrow R\text{–}R, \quad (3)$$

where RH represent as gelatin or carboxymethyl chitosan molecule.[84]

In the study on CMCTS/gelatin hydrogel, these sterilized protein/polysaccharide polymers were mixed at different weight ratio to form homogenous solution in the absence of additives (crosslinking reagents). By using a ^{60}Co facility, the polymer complex solution was then gamma-irradiated with 30 kGy absorbed dose. The crosslinked hydrogel products were used for implantation experiment or wound healing experiment. The CMCTS/gelatin CG4:6 hydrogel was optimally applied in clinical techniques due to the biodegradation behavior, swelling property and integration ability. More interestingly, the application of hydrogels to mouse cutaneous wound model leaded to thicker granulation tissue in the skin recovery process.[84]

2.4.2. *Radiation crosslinking between synthetic polymers and natural polymers*

The same technique is currently applied on plenty of complex systems of water-soluble polymers crosslinking between synthetic and natural materials. Most of these radiated hydrogels are more benefit and effective than one synthesized by chemical crosslinkers. Even though the treatments by chemical reagents such as glutaraldehyde, D,L-glutaraldehyde or genipin[86–88] were shown to have high degree of crosslinked products, the chemical compounds could be highly toxic to the cells or mouse models *in vivo* which is the main limitation for biomedical applications. In contrast, hydrogels achieved from radiation crosslinking technique are considered biocompatible due to whole sample was prepared in a system of pure water. There is an interest example for the radiated hydrogel of mixture of polyvinyl pyrrolidone (PVP) and CMCTS. The final hydrogel membranes of PVP and CMCTS are reported to non-toxicity, biocompatibility and pH sensitivity. These blend hydrogels enhanced reported to have the potential ability of protein absorption and immobilization. The increasing CMCTS content to the blend system indicated the improvement in the surface property and the BSA adsorptive property.[89]

3. Application of Hydrogel

Hydrogels broadly exist in natural conditions such as animal, plant and widely used in a lot of therapeutics due to their high water affinity and biocompatibility. For example, natural hydrogels can be used in health care, such as tissue scaffolds, wound dressing, dental materials, and implants, injectable polymeric systems. Furthermore, hydrogels were also studied in biomedical research, such as biosensor, or used as matrices for control of macromolecules release. Especially, they are applied as the potential carrier for drug delivery systems based on their peculiar characteristics and high sensitivity towards temperature and some other stimuli.[90,91]

Interestingly, we could easily find hydrogels in our diet and in popular molecular gastronomy, such as pectin, gelatin, guargum, and starch. Moreover, natural hydrogels can be combined with artificial polymers to achieve better control of material ability; also the molecular system of natural hydrogel can be tailored to intelligently match with environment conditions, which we will not discuss further in this chapter. Table 1 lists the most common natural hydrogels with their corresponding applications.

Table 1. Various applications for appropriate natural polymers.

Tissue engineering, transplantation, microencapsulation	
	Collagen,[92–94] fibrins,[95] alginate,[96] agarose,[97,98] hyaluronic acid hydrogels[99]
Controlled drug delivery	
	Polysaccharide,[100] gelatin,[101] cellulose,[102,103] starch,[104,105] chitosan,[106,107] pectin,[108,109] zein[110,111]
Wound dressing	
	Agar, collagen,[112] cellulose, chitosan,[113,114] gelatin,[115,116] polysaccharide,[117,118] fibrin[119]
Bio-sensor	
	Dextran,[120,121] gelatin,[122] alginate[123]
Injectable polymers	
	Chitosan,[124,125] alginate[123] fibrin[126]
Food industry	
	Pectin, gelatin,[127] starch[128]
Micro patterning, Nano patterning	
	Collagen,[129] gelatin[130]

4. Future Perspective and Challenge

Nowadays, natural hydrogels have already been employed effectively in tissue engineering and drug delivery due to their unique mechanical and chemical properties. Thanks to advantages of widely existence and great biocompatibility compared to synthetic polymer, natural hydrogels are expected as essential materials for present and future biomedical applications. Furthermore, researchers are attempting to modify natural hydrogel or incorporate with other artificial polymers to form novel materials with highly desired properties. In the case of drug delivery, a fine-tuned hydrogel drug release mechanism is indispensable for controlled release of drugs, because the efficiency of delivering medical active molecules is influenced by various factors, like drug loading, hydrogel breakdown, interactions between drug and hydrogel. Recent days, most of works focus on developing intelligent materials which are not only sensitive but also able to respond to the surrounding environment. Even though it is assumed that natural hydrogels are biocompatible with human body, there are still some impacting factors involved, such as physicochemical and biological properties of polymer, nano assembly drug carriers, controllable drug release rate, bioactivity and maximum cytotoxicity of drug payloads upon polymer degradation, so it is a great challenge for hydrogel drug carrier design to simultaneously optimize all of them. At this moment the synthesis of multidisciplinary technologies, which is urgently needed in intelligent drug-carrier design, seems overly complicated. Moreover, relatively easy degradation without any toxic effect should be taken into consideration during intelligent drug delivery system based on natural hydrogels.

Regarding tissue engineering, the ultimate goal is to fabricate functional tissues and even organs that can successfully replace original organ after implantation, in which extracellular matrix deposition, various remodeling tests, and maybe high shape fidelity maintenance are involved. For example, the fabricated cartilage tissue with natural hydrogels should be able to not only transmit and respond to the mechanical signals, but also be bio-sensitive to the chemical signals. To achieve this goal, desired mechanical, chemical, and biological properties should be engineered into the modified natural hydrogels.[131] It is promising to construct building blocks for a tissue entity and scaffolds with natural or modified hydrogels, however, lacking comprehensive knowledge of bio-inks from physical and rheological perspective to some extent may block the progress of generating larger construct which is expected to replicate tissue organization.[132] Moreover, potential toxicity of bio-inks and possible change of rheological properties of hydrogels should be taken into consideration as well. Another challenge associated with tissue engineering is the trade-off between resolution and speed during biofabrication, especially for the constructs of clinical sizes.[132]

Natural hydrogels can be utilized themselves or modified to fit the requirement for promoting biomedical research and make personalize drug delivery plans. There is already a growing number of routine clinics adopting polymer therapeutics, like the nano-sized medicine.[133] So we can hope that with the development of study on the mechanical properties of natural hydrogels, novel methods of biofabrication and relevant micro-manipulation, natural hydrogels will continue play an important role in biomedical applications.

References

1. R. G. Jones, *Compendium of Polymer Terminology and Nomenclature: IUPAC Recommendations*, 2008. Cambridge: Royal Society of Chemistry (2009).
2. J. D. Ferry, *Viscoelastic Properties of Polymers*. New York: Wiley (1980).
3. M. F. Refojo and H. Yasuda, Hydrogels from 2-hydroxyethyl methacrylate and propylene glycol monoacrylate. *J. Appl. Polym. Sci.*, **9**(7), 2425–2435 (1965).
4. C.-C. Lin and A. T. Metters, Hydrogels in controlled release formulations: Network design and mathematical modeling. *Adv. Drug Deliver. Rev.*, **58**(12–13), 1379–1408 (2006).
5. S. K. Gulrez, S. Al-Assaf, and G. O. Phillips, Hydrogels: Methods of preparation, characterisation and applications. In *Progresses in Molecular and Environmental Bioengineering*, Ed. A. Carpi. Croatia: Creative Commons (2011).
6. O. Wichterle and D. Lim, Hydrophilic gels for biological use. *Nature*, **185**(4706), 117–118 (1960).
7. H. Liao *et al.*, Influence of hydrogel mechanical properties and mesh size on vocal fold fibroblast extracellular matrix production and phenotype. *Acta Biomaterialia*, **4**(5), 1161–1171 (2008).

8. M. J. Mahoney and K. S. Anseth, Three-dimensional growth and function of neural tissue in degradable PEG hydrogels. *Biomaterials*, **27**(10), 2265–2274 (2006).
9. S. Sutton *et al.*, Controlled release from modified amino acid hydrogels governed by molecular size or network dynamics. *Langmuir*, **25**(17), 10285–10291 (2009).
10. D. Fournier, R. Hoogenboom, and U. S. Schubert, Clicking polymers: A straightforward approach to novel macromolecular architectures. *Chem. Soc. Rev.*, **36**(8), 1369–1380 (2007).
11. W. Shen *et al.*, Tuning the erosion rate of artificial protein hydrogels through control of network topology. *Nat. Mater.*, **5**(2), 153–158 (2006).
12. M. E. Byrne, K. Park, and N. A. Peppas, Molecular imprinting within hydrogels. *Adv. Drug Deliver. Rev.*, **54**(1), 149–161 (2002).
13. T. R. Hoare and D. S. Kohane, Hydrogels in drug delivery: Progress and challenges. *Polymer*, **49**(8), 1993–2007 (2008).
14. A. M. Kloxin *et al.*, Photodegradable hydrogels for dynamic tuning of physical and chemical properties. *Science*, **324**(5923), 59–63 (2009).
15. J. ZacháHilt, Hydrogel nanocomposites: A review of applications as remote controlled biomaterials. *Soft Matter*, **6**(11), 2364–2371 (2010).
16. S. Dumitriu, P. F. Vidal, and E. Chornet, *Hydrogels based on Polysaccharides. Polysaccharides in Medical Applications.* New York: Marcel Dekker Inc, pp. 125–242 (1996).
17. J.-K Francis Suh and H. W. Matthew, Application of chitosan-based polysaccharide biomaterials in cartilage tissue engineering: A review. *Biomaterials*, **21**(24), 2589–2598 (2000).
18. M. Risbud *et al.*, *In vitro* expression of cartilage-specific markers by chondrocytes on a biocompatible hydrogel: Implications for engineering cartilage tissue. *Cell Transplant.*, **10**(8), 755–763 (2001).
19. D. Seliktar, Designing cell compatible hydrogels for biomedical applications. *Science*, **336**(6085), 1124–1128 (2012).
20. J. Baier Leach *et al.*, Photocross-linked hyaluronic acid hydrogels: Natural, biodegradable tissue engineering scaffolds. *Biotechnol. Bioeng.*, **82**(5), 578–589 (2003).
21. G. D. Nicodemus and S. J. Bryant, Cell encapsulation in biodegradable hydrogels for tissue engineering applications. *Tissue Eng. Part B Rev.*, **14**(2), 149–165 (2008).
22. H. Park, K. Park, and W. S. Shalaby, *Biodegradable Hydrogels for Drug Delivery.* Florida: CRC Press (2011).
23. Y. Qiu and K. Park, Environment-sensitive hydrogels for drug delivery. *Adv. Drug Deliver. Rev.*, **53**(3), 321–339 (2001).
24. A. S Hoffman, "Intelligent" polymers in medicine and biotechnology. *Macromol. Symp.*, **98**(1), 645–664 (1995).
25. I. Y. Galaev and B. Mattiasson, 'Smart' polymers and what they could do in biotechnology and medicine. *Trends Biotechnol.*, **17**(8), 335–340 (1999).
26. P. Gupta, K. Vermani, and S. Garg, Hydrogels: From controlled release to pH-responsive drug delivery. *Drug Discov. Today*, **7**(10), 569–579 (2002).
27. R. Yoshida *et al.*, Comb-type grafted hydrogels with rapid deswelling response to temperature changes. *Nature*, **374**(6519), 240–242 (1995).

28. E. Ruel-Gariépy and J.-C. Leroux, *In situ*-forming hydrogels — review of temperature-sensitive systems. *Eur. J. Pharm. Biopharm.*, **58**(2), 409–426 (2004).
29. G. R. Mahdavinia, M. J. Zohuriaan-Mehr, and A. Pourjavadi, Modified chitosan III, superabsorbency, salt- and pH-sensitivity of smart ampholytic hydrogels from chitosan-g-PAN. *Polym. Adv. Technol.*, **15**(4), 173–180 (2004).
30. G. R. Mahdavinia *et al.*, Modified chitosan 4. Superabsorbent hydrogels from poly (acrylic acid-co-acrylamide) grafted chitosan with salt- and pH-responsiveness properties. *Eur. Polym. J.*, **40**(7), 1399–1407 (2004).
31. C. Chang *et al.*, Superabsorbent hydrogels based on cellulose for smart swelling and controllable delivery. *Eur. Polym. J.*, **46**(1), 92–100 (2010).
32. N. A. Peppas *et al.*, Physicochemical foundations and structural design of hydrogels in medicine amd biology. *Annu. Rev. Biomed. Eng.*, **2**(1), 9–29 (2000).
33. Y. Murakami and M. Maeda, DNA-responsive hydrogels that can shrink or swell. *Biomacromolecules*, **6**(6), 2927–2929 (2005).
34. B. D. Johnson, D. J. Beebe, and W. C. Crone, Effects of swelling on the mechanical properties of a pH-sensitive hydrogel for use in microfluidic devices. *Mater. Sci. Eng. C*, **24**(4), 575–581 (2004).
35. K. Haraguchi and H.-J. Li, Control of the coil-to-globule transition and ultrahigh mechanical properties of PNIPA in nanocomposite hydrogels. *Angew. Chem. Int. Edit.*, **44**(40), 6500–6504 (2005).
36. A. Emileh, E. Vasheghani-Farahani, and M. Imani, Swelling behavior, mechanical properties and network parameters of pH- and temperature-sensitive hydrogels of poly ((2-dimethyl amino) ethyl methacrylate-co-butyl methacrylate). *Eur. Polym. J.*, **43**(5), 1986–1995 (2007).
37. C. D. Landon *et al.*, Nanoscale drug delivery and hyperthermia: The materials design and preclinical and clinical testing of low temperature-sensitive liposomes used in combination with mild hyperthermia in the treatment of local cancer. *Open Nanomed. J.*, **3**, 38 (2011).
38. S. C. Owen *et al.*, Correlation of tissue drug concentrations with *in vivo* magnetic resonance images of polymer drug depot around arteriovenous graft. *J. Control Release*, **146**(1), 23–30 (2010).
39. A. B. South and L. A. Lyon, Autonomic self-healing of hydrogel thin films. *Angew. Chem.*, **122**(4), 779–783 (2010).
40. M. Nakahata *et al.*, Redox-responsive self-healing materials formed from host–guest polymers. *Nat. Commun.*, **2**, 511 (2011).
41. D. Y. Wu, S. Meure, and D. Solomon, Self-healing polymeric materials: A review of recent developments. *Prog. Polym. Sci.*, **33**(5), 479–522 (2008).
42. J. Cui and A. D. Campo, Multivalent H-bonds for self-healing hydrogels. *Chem. Commun.*, **48**(74), 9302–9304 (2012).
43. Y. Tabata, The importance of drug delivery systems in tissue engineering. *Pharm. Sci. Technol.*, **3**(3), 80–89 (2000).
44. Y. Tabata, Biomaterial technology for tissue engineering applications. *J. R. Soc. Interface*, **6**(Suppl 3), S311–S324 (2009).

45. A. S. Hoffman, Hydrogels for biomedical applications. *Adv. Drug Deliver. Rev.*, **54**(1), 3–12 (2002).
46. V. Jayawarna *et al.*, Nanostructured hydrogels for three-dimensional cell culture through self-assembly of fluorenylmethoxycarbonyl–dipeptides. *Adv. Mater.*, **18**(5), 611–614 (2006).
47. S. Zhang, Fabrication of novel biomaterials through molecular self-assembly. *Nat. Biotechnol.*, **21**(10), 1171–1178 (2003).
48. S. Brahim, D. Narinesingh, and A. Guiseppi-Elie, Amperometric determination of cholesterol in serum using a biosensor of cholesterol oxidase contained within a polypyrrole–hydrogel membrane. *Anal. Chim. Acta*, **448**(1–2), 27–36 (2001).
49. K. Madhumathi *et al.*, Development of novel chitin/nanosilver composite scaffolds for wound dressing applications. *J. Mater. Sci.-Mater. M.*, **21**(2), 807–813 (2010).
50. N. A. Peppas *et al.*, *Biomedical Applications of Hydrogels Handbook.* NewYork: Springer (2010).
51. A. Sannino, C. Demitri, and M. Madaghiele, Biodegradable cellulose-based hydrogels: Design and applications. *Materials*, **2**(2), 353–373 (2009).
52. O. Pohl, Now, diaper technology takes on a desert. *The New York Times*, Science Desk, (2004).
53. J. Michalek *et al.*, Hydrogels contact lenses. In *Biomedical Applications of Hydrogels Handbook*, Eds. R.M. Ottenbrite, K. Park, and T. Okano, New York: Springer, pp. 303–315 (2010).
54. P. C. Nicolson and J. Vogt, Soft contact lens polymers: An evolution. *Biomaterials*, **22**(24), 3273–3283 (2001).
55. L. Xinming *et al.*, Polymeric hydrogels for novel contact lens-based ophthalmic drug delivery systems: A review. *Contact Lens and Anterior Eye*, **31**(2), 57–64 (2008).
56. S. Arnott *et al.*, The agarose double helix and its function in agarose gel structure. *J. Mol. Biol.*, **90**(2), 269–284 (1974).
57. W. E. Hennink and C. F. van Nostrum, Novel cross-linking methods to design hydrogels. *Adv. Drug Deliver. Rev.*, **54**(1), 13–36 (2002).
58. H. Yoshika *et al.*, Thermoreversible gelation on cooling and on heating of an aqueous gelatin± poly (N-isopropylacrylamide) conjugate. *Polym*er *Adv. Tech.*, **9**, 155–158 (1998).
59. C. F. Roff and E. A. Foegeding, Dicationic-induced gelation of pre-denatured whey protein isolate. *Food Hydrocolloid.*, **10**(2), 193–198 (1996).
60. J. Berger *et al.*, Structure and interactions in covalently and ionically cross-linked chitosan hydrogels for biomedical applications. *Eur. J. Pharm. Biopharm.*, **57**(1), 19–34 (2004).
61. T. Gotoh, K. Matsushima, and K. Kikuchi, Preparation of alginate-chitosan hybrid gel beads and adsorption of divalent metal ions. *Chemosphere*, **55**(1), 135–140 (2004).
62. N. A. Peppas, Turbidimetric studies of aqueous poly (vinyl alcohol) solutions. *Die Makromolekulare Chemie*, **176**(11), 3433–3440 (1975).
63. C. Hassan and N. Peppas, Structure and applications of poly (vinyl alcohol) hydrogels p produced by conventional cross-linking or by freezing/thawing methods. In

Biopolymers. PVA Hydrogels, Anionic Polymerisation Nanocomposites. Berlin-Heidelberg: Springer, pp. 37–65 (2000).
64. P. J. Willcox *et al.*, Microstructure of poly (vinyl alcohol) hydrogels produced by freeze/thaw cycling. *J. Polym. Sci. Part B Polym. Phys.*, **37**(24), 3438–3454 (1999).
65. R. Ricciardi *et al.*, Investigation of the crystallinity of freeze/thaw poly (vinyl alcohol) hydrogels by different techniques. *Macromolecules*, **37**(25), 9510–9516 (2004).
66. H. Zhang, F. Zhang, and J. Wu, Physically cross-linked hydrogels from polysaccharides prepared by freeze–thaw technique. *React. Funct. Polym.*, **73**, 923–928 (2013).
67. C. Xiao and Y. Gao, Preparation and properties of physically cross-linked sodium carboxymethylcellulose/poly (vinyl alcohol) complex hydrogels. *J. Appl. Polym. Sci.*, **107**(3), 1568–1572 (2008).
68. H. Hezaveh and I. I. Muhamad, Modification and swelling kinetic study of kappa-carrageenan-based hydrogel for controlled release study. *Journal of the Taiwan Institute of Chemical Engineers*, **44**(22), 182–191(2013).
69. J. Berger *et al.*, Structure and interactions in covalently and ionically cross-linked chitosan hydrogels for biomedical applications. *Eur. J. Pharm. Biopharm.*, **57**(1), 19–34 (2004).
70. K. H. Bouhadira, D. S. Hausmana, and D. J. Mooney, Synthesis of cross-linked poly (aldehyde guluronate) hydrogels. *Polymer*, **40**, 3575–3584 (1999).
71. J. A. Rowley, G. Madlambayan, and D. J. Mooney, Alginate hydrogels as synthetic extracellular matrix materials. *Biomaterials*, **20**(1), 45–53 (1999).
72. D. Ciolacu *et al.*, New cellulose–lignin hydrogels and their application in controlled release of polyphenols. *Mater. Sci. Eng. C*, **32**(3), 452–463 (2012).
73. R. Mincheva *et al.*, Hydrogels from chitosan cross-linked with PEG-$(COOH)_2$ as bone regeneration materials. *e-Polymers*, **58**, 11 (2004).
74. S. S Wang *et al.*, Genipin-cross-linked poly (l-lysine)-based hydrogels: Synthesis, characterization, and drug encapsulation. *Colloid. surface. B, Biointerfaces*, **111C**, 423–431 (2013).
75. Y. Huang *et,al.*, Swelling behaviours and mechanical properties of silk fibroin–polyurethane composite hydrogels. *Compos. Sci. Technol.*, **84**, 8 (2013).
76. M. C. I. M. Amina *et al.*, Synthesis and characterization of thermo- and pH-responsive bacterial cellulose/acrylic acid hydrogels for drug delivery. *Carbohyd. Polym.*, **88**, 465–473 (2012).
77. M. Tamada, N. Seko, and F. Yoshii, Application of radiation-graft material for metal absorbent and cross-linked natural polymer for healthcare product. *Radiat. Phys. Chem.*, **71**(1–2), 223–227 (2004).
78. M. Yazdani-Pedram and J. Retuert de la Torre, Hydrogels based on modified chitosan, 1 — Synthesis and swelling behavior of poly (acrylic acid) grafted chitosan. *Macromol. Chem. Physic.*, **201**(9), 923–930 (2000).
79. H. E. Allcock *et al.*, Hydrophilic polyphosphazenes as hydrogels: Radiation cross-linking and hydrogel characteristics of poly [bis (methoxyethoxyethoxy)phosphazene]. *Biomaterials*, **9**(6), 509–513 (1988).
80. J. M. Rosiak *et al.*, Radiation formation of hydrogels for biomedical purposes. Some remarks and comments. *Radiat. Phys. Chem.*, **46**(2), 161–168 (1995).

81. L. Zhao, H. Mitomo, N. Nagasawa, F. Yoshii, and T. Kume, Radiation synthesis and characteristic of the hydrogels based on the carboxymethylated chitin derivatives. *Carbohyd. Polym.*, **51**, 169–175 (2003).
82. C. Yang, L. Xu, Y. Zhou, X. Zhang, H. Xin, W. Min, H. Ye, M. Zhai, S. Wei, and J. Li, A green fabrication approach of gelatin/CMCTS hybrid hydrogel for wound healing. *Carbohyd. Polym.*, **82**, 9 (2010).
83. S. Rimdusit, K. Somsaeng, P. Kewsuwan, C. Jubsilp, and S. Tiptippakorn, Comparison of gamma radiation cross-linking and chemical cross-linking on properties of methylcellulose hydrogel. *Eng. J.*, **16**(4), 15–28 (2012).
84. X. Huang *et al.*, Influence of radiation cross-linked CMCTS/gelatin hydrogel on cutaneous wound healing. *Mater. Sci. Eng. C Mater. Biol. Appl.*, **33**(8), 4816–4824 (2013).
85. M. Eid, Preparation and characterization of natural polymers as stabilizer for magnetic nanoparticles by gamma irradiation. *J. Polym. Res.*, **20**,11 (2013).
86. S. Q. Liu *et al.*, Biodegradable poly (ethylene glycol)-peptide hydrogels with well-defined structure and properties for cell delivery. *Biomaterials*, **30**(8), 1453–1461 (2009).
87. J. D. Kosmala, D. B. Henthorn, and L. Brannon-Peppas, Preparation of interpenetrating networks of gelatin and dextran as degradable biomaterials. *Biomaterials*, **21**(20), 2019–2023 (2000).
88. A. Bigi *et al.*, Stabilization of gelatin films by cross-linking with genipin. *Biomaterials*, **23**(24), 4827–4832 (2002).
89. L. Zhao, L. Xu, H. Mitomo, and F. Yoshii, Synthesis of pH-sentive PVP/CMCTS hydrogels with improved surface property by irradiation. *Carbohyd. Polym.*, **64**, 473–480 (2006).
90. S. Amin, S. Rajabnezhad, and K. Kohli, Hydrogels as potential drug delivery systems. *Scientific Research and Essays*, **4**(11), 1175–1183 (2009).
91. F. Brandl *et al.*, Hydrogel-based drug delivery systems: Comparison of drug diffusivity and release kinetics. *J. Control. Release*, **142**(2), 221–228(2010).
92. B. P. Chan *et al.*, Mesenchymal stem cell-encapsulated collagen microspheres for bone tissue engineering. *Tissue Eng. Part C Methods*, **16**(2), 225–235 (2010).
93. C. M. R. Perez, A. Panitch, and J. Chmielewski, A collagen peptide-based physical hydrogel for cell encapsulation. *Macromol. Bioscience*, **11**(10), 1426–1431 (2011).
94. J. Glowacki and S. Mizuno, Collagen scaffolds for tissue engineering. *Biopolymers*, **89**(5), 338–344 (2008).
95. T. A. E. Ahmed, E. V. Dare, and M. Hincke, Fibrin: A versatile scaffold for tissue engineering applications. *Tissue Eng. Part B Rev.*, **14**(2), 199–215 (2008).
96. F. Lim and A. M. Sun, Microencapsulated islets as bioartificial endocrine pancreas. *Science*, **210**(4472), 908–910 (1980).
97. S. Sakai, I. Hashimoto, and K. Kawakami, Synthesis of an agarose-gelatin conjugate for use as a tissue engineering scaffold. *J. Biosci. Bioeng.*, **103**(1), 22–26 (2007).
98. R. L. Mauck *et al.*, Functional tissue engineering of articular cartilage through dynamic loading of chondrocyte-seeded agarose gels. *J. Biomech. Eng. T Asme*, **122**(3), 252–260 (2000).

99. J. A. Burdick *et al.*, Controlled degradation and mechanical behavior of photopolymerized hyaluronic acid networks. *Biomacromolecules*, **6**(1), 386–391 (2005).
100. A. Jain, Y. Gupta, and S. K. Jain, Perspectives of biodegradable natural polysaccharides for site-specific drug delivery to the colon. *J. Pharm. Pharm. Sci.*, **10**(1), 86–128 (2007).
101. A. K. Bajpai and J. Choubey, Release study of sulphamethoxazole controlled by swelling of gelatin nanoparticles and drug-biopolymer interaction. *J. Macromol. Sci. Pure*, **A42**(3), 253–275 (2005).
102. R. Kolakovic *et al.*, Nanofibrillar cellulose films for controlled drug delivery. *Eur. J. Pharm. Biopharm.*, **82**(2), 308–315 (2012).
103. J. K. Jackson *et al.*, The use of nanocrystalline cellulose for the binding and controlled release of drugs. *Int. J. Nanomed.*, **6,** 321–330 (2011).
104. P. B. Malafaya *et al.*, Porous starch-based drug delivery systems processed by a microwave route. *J. Biomat. Sci. Polym. E.*, **12**(11), 1227–1241 (2001).
105. M. J. Santander-Ortega *et al.*, Nanoparticles made from novel starch derivatives for transdermal drug delivery. *J. Control. Release*, **141**(1), 85–92 (2010).
106. N. Bhattarai, J. Gunn, and M. Q. Zhang, Chitosan-based hydrogels for controlled, localized drug delivery. *Adv. Drug Deliver. Rev.*, **62**(1), 83–99 (2010).
107. S. Chopra *et al.*, Advances and potential applications of chitosan derivatives as mucoadhesive biomaterials in modern drug delivery. *J. Pharm. Pharmacol.*, **58**(8), 1021–1032 (2006).
108. L. S. Liu *et al.*, Pectin-based systems for colon-specific drug delivery via oral route. *Biomaterials*, **24**(19), 3333–3343 (2003).
109. L. S. Liu *et al.*, Pectin/zein beads for potential colon-specific drug delivery: Synthesis and *in vitro* evaluation. *Drug Deliver.*, **13**(6), 417–423 (2006).
110. X. M. Liu *et al.*, Microspheres of corn protein, zein, for an ivermectin drug delivery system. *Biomaterials*, **26**(1), 109–115 (2005).
111. S. Lee, N. S. A. Alwahab, and Z. M. Moazzam, Zein-based oral drug delivery system targeting activated macrophages. *Int. J. Pharm.*, **454**(1), 388–393 (2013).
112. L. Bao *et al.*, Agar/collagen membrane as skin dressing for wounds. *Biomed. Mater.*, **3**(4), (2008).
113. D. R. Solway, M. Consalter, and D. J. Levinson, Microbial cellulose wound dressing in the treatment of skin tears in the frail elderly. *Wounds*, **22**(1), 17–19 (2010).
114. W. C. Lin *et al.*, Bacterial cellulose and bacterial cellulose-chitosan membranes for wound dressing applications. *Carbohyd. Polym.*, **94**(1), 603–611 (2013).
115. S. Kanokpanont *et al.*, An innovative bi-layered wound dressing made of silk and gelatin for accelerated wound healing. *Int. J. Pharm.*, **436**(1–2), 141–153 (2012).
116. W. H. Chang *et al.*, A genipin-cross-linked gelatin membrane as wound-dressing material: *In vitro* and *in vivo* studies. *J. Biomat. Sci.-Polym. E.*, **14**(5), 481–495 (2003).
117. H. N. Li *et al.*, Superabsorbent polysaccharide hydrogels based on pullulan derivate as antibacterial release wound dressing. *J. Biomed. Mater. Res. Part A*, **98A**(1), 31–39 (2011).

118. S. Wittaya-areekul and C. Prahsarn, Development and *in vitro* evaluation of chitosan-polysaccharides composite wound dressings. *Int. J. Pharm.*, **313**(1–2), 123–128 (2006).
119. S. E. Bishara, D. L. Zeitler, and C. R. Kremenak, Effects of a fibrin-sealant wound dressing on the healing of full-thickness wounds of the hard palate — preliminary-report. *Cleft Palate J.*, **23**(2), 144–152 (1986).
120. W. C. Chen and Y. Y. Lin, Glucose biosensor based on dextran-Fe_3O_4 nanocomposite modified SPCEs. *Biomed. Eng. App. Bas. C.*, **21**(6), 437–440 (2009).
121. R. J. Russell *et al.*, A fluorescence-based glucose biosensor using concanavalin A and dextran encapsulated in a PEG hydrogel. *Anal. Chem.*, **71**(15), 3126–3132 (1999).
122. S. Sungur *et al.*, New glucose biosensor based on glucose oxidase-immobilized gelatin film coated electrodes. *J. Biomater. Appl.*, **18**(4), 265–277 (2004).
123. J. Prasad *et al.*, Cholesterol biosensors based on oxygen sensing alginate-silica microspheres. *Biotechnol. Bioeng.*, **108**(9), 2011–2021 (2011).
124. Q. X. Ji *et al.*, Injectable thermosensitive hydrogel based on chitosan and quaternized chitosan and the biomedical properties. *J. Mater. Sci.-Mater. M*, **20**(8), 1603–1610 (2009).
125. M. Aliaghaie *et al.*, Investigation of gelation mechanism of an injectable hydrogel based on chitosan by rheological measurements for a drug delivery application. *Soft Matter*, **8**(27), 7128–7137 (2012).
126. R. P. Silverman *et al.*, Injectable tissue-engineered cartilage using a fibrin glue polymer. *Plast. and Reconstr. Surg.*, **103**(7), 1809–1818 (1999).
127. D. Baziwane and Q. A. He, Gelatin: The Paramount food additive. *Food Rev. Int.*, **19**(4), 423–435 (2003).
128. S. Jobling, Improving starch for food and industrial applications. *Curr. Opin. Plant Biol.*, **7**(2), 210–218 (2004).
129. M. D. Tang, A. P. Golden, and J. Tien, Fabrication of collagen gels that contain patterned, micrometer-scale cavities. *Adv. Mater.*, **16**(15) 1345–1348 (2004).
130. T. J. Qu and X. H. Liu, Nano-structured gelatin/bioactive glass hybrid scaffolds for the enhancement of odontogenic differentiation of human dental pulp stem cells. *J. Mater. Chem., B* **1**(37), 4764–4772 (2013).
131. N. A. Peppas *et al.*, Hydrogels in biology and medicine: From molecular principles to bionanotechnology. *Adv. Mater.*, **18**(11), 1345–1360 (2006).
132. J. V. Jos Malda, F. P. Melchels, T. Jüngst, W.E. Hennink, W. J. A. Dhert, J. Groll, and D. W. Hutmacher, 25th anniversary article: Engineering hydrogels for biofabrication. *Adv. Mater.*, **25**(36), 18 (2013).
133. R. Duncan, Polymer therapeutics as nanomedicines: New perspectives. *Curr. Opin. Biotechnol.*, **22**(4), 492–501 (2011).

Chapter 2

Types and Chemistry of Synthetic Hydrogels

John Garner* and Kinam Park†
**Akina, Inc., West Lafayette, IN 47906, USA*
†Purdue University, Departments of Biomedical Engineering & Pharmaceutics, West Lafayette, Indiana 47907, USA

1. Introduction

Hydrogels are materials which interact with water but do not dissolve due to chemical or physical crosslinks forming a network of chains. There are a variety of natural as well as synthetic hydrogels. Synthetic hydrogels have occupied an important place in science ever since the pioneering work of Wichterle and Lim in 1960 for the use of poly (hydroxyethyl methacrylate) (HEMA) as a soft contact lens material.[1] Synthetic hydrogels offer many advantages, such as precise control of chemical, mechanical, and physical properties as well as flexibility to design features that can be easily manipulated for intended applications.

Hydrogels can be broadly divided into physical and chemical hydrogels. In physical gels, polymer chains are crosslinked by physical interactions. On the other hand, chemical gels are made by covalent crosslinking of polymer chains, making them difficult to alter their forms and shapes. Only physical gels can undergo gel-sol phase transition upon changes in environmental conditions, while chemical gels cannot.

Hydrogels can also be made to respond to minute changes in environmental conditions, such as pH, temperature, salt, solute, electric current, etc., and those are collectively called "smart" (or "intelligent") hydrogels. Smart hydrogels respond to environmental changes in the form of shrinking/swelling, bending, or degradation. This chapter focuses on the types and chemistry of synthetic hydrogels.

2. Physically Crosslinked Hydrogels

Physically crosslinked hydrogels are made by linking polymer chains through physical interactions. These hydrogels are popular due to their ability to form solids without need for additional chemical reagent. The absence of additional chemically active agent makes them ideal for applications in pharmaceutical and biomedical applications. Physical gels can be classified based on the mechanism of their crosslinking, such as crystallinity, hydrogen bonding, ionic interaction, stereocomplex domains, and hydrophobic association. Of course, physical gels can also be formed by multiple mechanisms.[2]

2.1. Crystallinity

In polymers crystallinity refers to the alignment of polymer chains into regularly ordered regions called lamellae. This orderly conformation requires a polymer which has strong affinity to itself as well as a highly regular structure, allowing for close proximity of polymer chains without steric hindrance. One classic example of a hydrogel held together by crystalline domains is poly (vinyl alcohol) (PVA). The presence of pendant hydroxyl groups on PVA allows this polymer to form crystallites by strong inter-chain bonding. Aqueous solutions of PVA will, over time, form soft gels. More useful, however, is the capacity of PVA to form highly elastic gels by undergoing freeze-thaw cycling.[2] Often PVA is mixed with another material to impart additional strength or functionality to the gel state. For example, Liu *et al.* recently reported on the formation of highly strong PVA-gelatin gels. Solutions of PVA and gelatin (with the weight ratio of PVA: gelatin = 9:1) were prepared by dissolving at 121°C for 1 h. These solutions were then crosslinked by freeze-thaw cycles (freezing at −20°C for 12 h and thawing at 21°C for 12 h). These freeze-thawed hydrogels were then additionally crosslinked using different chemistry by being submerged in a constantly stirred coagulation bath (7.5% KOH and 1 M Na_2SO_4) for 1 h to further crosslink the gelatin, thus forming strong hydrogels by physical and chemical crosslinking.[3] Similar techniques have also been applied to chitosan and starch mixtures with PVA[4]. The crystalline properties of freeze-thaw PVA can also be adapted by using modifiers. Freeze thaw combinations of PVA and dextran have shown that incorporation of dextran generated PVA with a broader crystalline size distribution than with PVA alone.[5] Additionally incorporation of chitosan into PVA imparts pH sensitivity to the hydrogel matrix as a whole due to the pH sensitive nature of chitosan. Wei *et al.* utilized PVA/chitosan hydrogels along with micelles made of poly (glutamic acid)-b-poly (ethylene glycol)-b-poly (glutamic acid) (PGA-PEG-PGA) to create a pH sensitive system for the controlled delivery of both aspirin and doxorubicin.[6] PVA represents a group of hydrogels that are held together by crystalline domains.

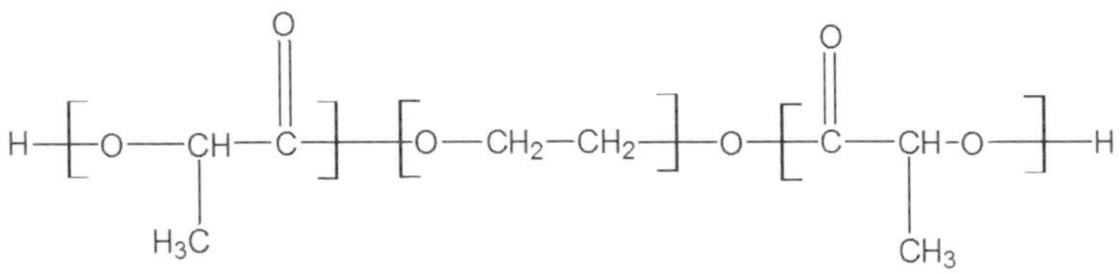

Fig. 1. PLA–PEG–PLA triblock copolymer.

The crystalline blocks holding the hydrogel together can be hydrophobic. For example, poly (L-lactic acid) (PLLA), one of several distinct forms of poly (lactic acid) (PLA), is well known to form strong tight crystalline domains due to its preferential arrangement of the methyl side chain allowing the chains to interact with each other tightly. This is a feature which is different from the racemic form poly (D, L-lactic acid) (PDLLA) which does not interact nearly as tightly into crystalline domains due to steric hindrance. PLLA was utilized recently as a part of a triblock copolymer (Fig. 1) to generate hydrogels with higher elastic modulus than typically achieved by controlling the stereochemistry of the ABA-type triblock copolymers. Normally, PDLLA–PEG–PDLLA forms soft gels, but addition of the chirally controlled stereochemistry allows formation of gels with a much higher elastic modulus (in the 1–10 kPa range) than that achieved with the racemic lactide blocks. The gels can be further strengthened by incorporation of laponite which serves as binding points to the middle PEG block.[7]

2.2. Hydrogen bonding

Hydrogen bonding is a strong electromagnetic attraction between the polar hydrogen and an atom with a loose pair of electrons, such as oxygen and nitrogen. Hydrogen bonding occurs in many synthetic hydrogels due to the presence of an acid or an amine group interacting with neutrally charged oxygen units. One classic example of strong hydrogen bonding is the attractive force between the carboxylic acid hydrogen of poly (acrylic acid) (PAA) and the lone-pair electrons on PVA (Fig. 2(A)).[8,9] Hydrogen bonding generally serves as a good target for generation of environmentally sensitive hydrogels as these bonds are highly sensitive to changes in pH[9] and applied electric fields.[8] Amine groups, such as those present on polyamidoamine (PAMAM), can form hydrogen bonding (Fig. 2(B)). When the PAMAM dendrimers are incorporated into PVA to form hydrogels by freeze/thaw cycling, the resultant gels display a higher swelling than the PVA alone due to the hydrophilicity of the PAMAM.[10] Additionally, hydrogels formed by interaction between PAA and poly (N-vinylpyrrolidinone) (PVP) also display hydrogen bonding between the carbonyl group of PVP and the carboxylic acid group of PAA.[11]

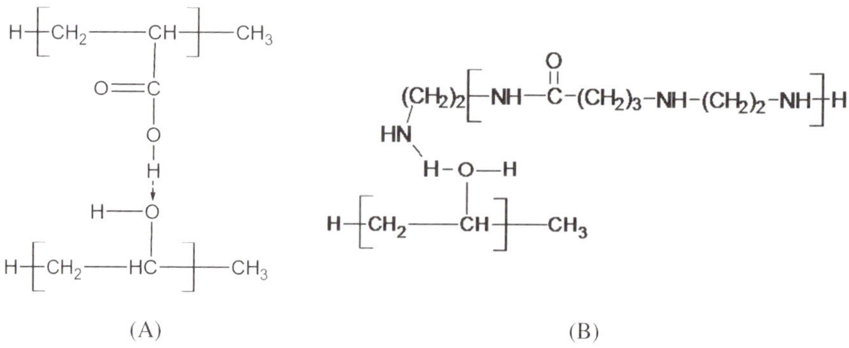

Fig. 2. (A) The acid-based hydrogen bonding between PAA and PVA and (B) the amine-based hydrogen bonding between PVA and PAMAM. Arrow indicates hydrogen bonding.

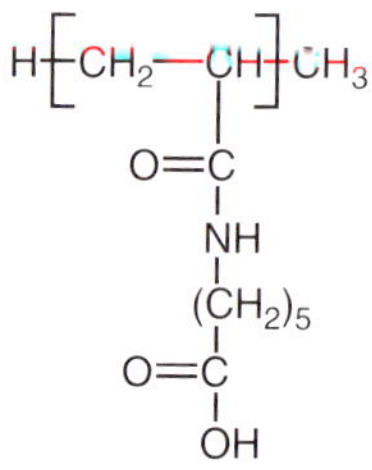

Fig. 3. Structure of Poly (A6ACA).

Recently, "self-healing" hydrogels were prepared based on poly (acryloyl-6-aminocaproic acid) (Poly (A6ACA) Fig. 3) which have flexible pendant side chains terminating in carboxylic acids.[12] Although the hydrogel itself is held together by chemical crosslinks, the "healing" feature is achieved by hydrogen bonding. When in an acidic aqueous environment (pH < 3), pieces of the hydrogel will spontaneously attach to each other by hydrogen bonding, thus "healing". This effect was so strong that coating a punctured polypropylene container with Poly (A6ACA) prevented leaking of hydrochloric acid from the container. This property is pH-dependent, and the healing effect disappears at high pH where the carboxylic acid groups are ionized. In addition to pH, hydrogen bonding is also susceptible to disruption by chemicals such as urea.

Additional examples of hydrogels held together by hydrogen bonding include mixtures of PAA or poly (methacrylic acid) (PMA) and PEG as well as synthetic polymers based on oligonucleotides. Synthetic, complementary oligonucleotides have been used to generate hydrogels held together by hydrogen bonding between base pairs. The importance of pH for all hydrogels held together by hydrogen bonding cannot be stressed enough, as protonation of the acid groups is critical for hydrogen bonding to occur. Hydrogels based on crosslinking through hydrogen bonding change their swelling property, ranging from no swelling to complete dissolution, depending on the environmental pH.[2]

2.3. Ionic interaction

Ionic interaction occurs through electrostatic attraction between cationic (positively charged) and anionic (negatively charged) moieties. Hydrogels formed through ionic crosslinking require a carefully controlled quantity of ionic functional groups. Excess ionic groups may result in dissolution of polymer chains in aqueous solution, while too few does not allow polymer chains to interact and form crosslinks[13]. Ionic attraction as a form of physical crosslinking is relatively uncommon in synthetic hydrogels, but is better known to occur in natural hydrogels, such as sodium alginate mixed with calcium[14] and tripolyphosphate combined with chitosan.[15] there are, however, some synthetic hydrogels which also display this mode of attraction. One commercial example is Nafion®, an ionomer sold by Dupont, which has a range of properties resultant from the incorporation of sulfonate groups along its chain (Fig. 4). Notably, when hydrated, this material in combination with a platinum coating has the capacity to physically flex in the direction of an applied electric field.[16] Another synthetic hydrogel crosslinked by ionic interaction is poly-[di(carboxylatophenoxy)phosphazene] (PCPP) which, like alginate, has the capacity to crosslink in the presence of calcium ions.[2]

2.4. Stereocomplex domains

Stereocomplex domains are regions of tightly bound material which orient in a unique manner relative to each other based on the physical shape of the material. One of the most common example is the formation of stereocomplex domains between regions of "D" and "L" enantiomeric PLA, i.e., poly (D-lactic acid) (PDLA) and PLLA (Fig. 5). Stereocomplex formation between PDLA and PLLA is different from crystalline formation between two PLLA chains. In the formation of a stereocomplex domain, the D and L chiral versions of PLA interact with each other based on the preferential interlocking of their shapes. Because of the hydrophobic nature,

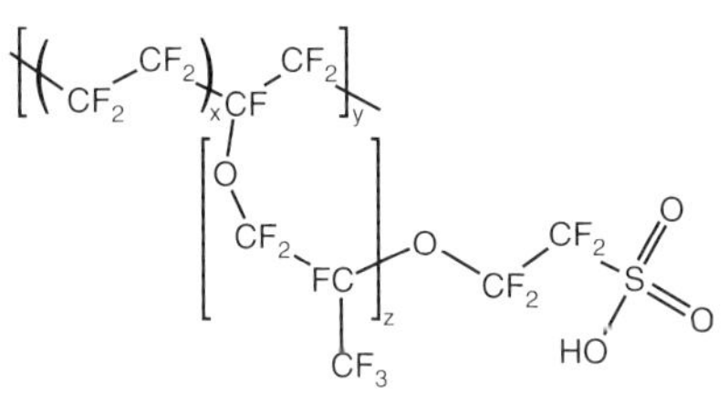

Fig. 4. Nafion® chemical structure

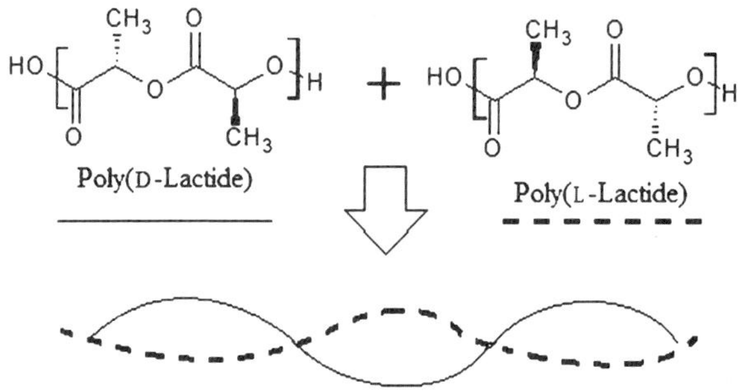

Fig. 5. Formation of a stereocomplex domain between PDLA and PLLA.

PDLA and PLLA themselves cannot form hydrogels. For this reason, they are usually react as either graft or block polymers with hydrophilic components, such as PEG,[17] dextran,[18] or poly (HEMA)[2] to form biodegradable hydrogels with strong physical bonds.[18] Stereocomplex domains are sensitive to temperature. They often form into strong junctures at room temperature, but tend to break down at higher temperatures. Dextran hydrogels based on PDLA and PLLA stereocomplex are known to lose their elastic modulus upon heating to 80°C, but regain it upon cooling back to room temperature.[19]

Stereocomplex domains also form in high molecular weight blends and racemic mixtures of PLA leading to a higher melting point (T_m) of 230°C rather than typical 170°C). The stereocomplex domains also occur in low molecular weight residues (~11 repeat units) whereas traditional crystallinity does not. For this reason, it is necessary to keep the molecular weight of the PLA block below the critical point at which PDLA and PLLA form crystals with themselves, instead of forming stereocomplexes.[20]

2.5. Hydrophobic association

Hydrophobic association is one of the most common forms of physical crosslinking of polymers. Hydrophobic association occurs not because of attractive interaction among hydrophobic polymer chains, but because of repulsive interaction between the hydrophobic polymer chain and water. Thus, the hydrophobic association does not exist without water. For the hydrogels to form by hydrophobic association, polymer chains are usually made of two distinct segments, hydrophilic and hydrophobic domains, providing hydrogen bonding with water and hydrophobic association, respectively. Whether a block copolymer forms a gel or not depends on the temperature. At low temperature, hydrophobic association is weak and hydrogen bonding dominates, resulting in polymer dissolution in water. As temperature increases, however, hydrophobic association becomes stronger and hydrogen bonding becomes weaker. At a certain temperature, known as the lower critical solution temperature (LCST), a block copolymer undergoes phase transition from sol (i.e., solution phase) to gel (i.e., gel or solid phase).[21–24] this thermosensitive property, especially the gelling property at higher temperature, has been used to develop so-called "smart" hydrogels for drug delivery.

Hydrogels formed by hydrophobic association are based on either amphiphilic blocks or graft copolymers which contain distinct segments of hydrophobic and hydrophilic nature. Classic examples are di- and tri-block combinations of hydrophobic, biodegradable polyesters PLA, poly (lactic-co-glycolic acid) (PLGA), poly (e-caprolactone) (PCL), and poly(butylene terephthalate) (PBT) with PEG.[2,22,24] In an alternative method, hydrophobic moiety can be grafted to hydrophilic polymers, usually polysaccharides, such as chitosan, dextran, pullulan, cellulose, and carboxymethyl curdlan.[2,25] Hydrogels have also been generated based on non-degradable polymers which are derivatives of N-isopropylacrylamide (NIPAM), vinyl caprolactam (VCM), and N-(2-dimethylaminoethyl)methacrylamide (DMAEMA).[26–28] Block copolymers of poly(ethylene oxide) (PEO) and poly(propylene oxide) (PPO), PEO-PPO-PEO, have been commercially available under the trade name of Pluronic® or generic name of poloxamer.[29] Other hydrophobically crosslinked hydrogels include PEG-polyisobutylene, PEG-poly(γ-benzyl L-glutamate), poly(2-ethyl-2-oxazoline)-PCL, and poly(N-vinylpyrrolidinone-g-styrene).[2]

3. Chemically Crosslinked Hydrogels

All physically crosslinked hydrogels undergo gel-to-sol phase transition under certain conditions. For example, urea interferes with hydrogen bonding,[12] surfactants such as sodium dodecyl sulfate (SDS) interrupts hydrophobic interaction,[30] temperature disrupts stereocomplex domains,[20] and crystalline domains fall apart at higher temperatures.[3–5,10] On the other hand, chemically crosslinked hydrogels do not undergo sol-gel phase transition, unless the crosslinking agents are reversible. Chemical crosslinking can be achieved by a variety of bond types as long as the crosslinkers bridge at least two or more polymer chains together.[2] Chemically crosslinked hydrogels bring a level of strength which is usually not found with physical crosslinks, and this property allows various pharmaceutical and biomedical applications.[31–42]

Figure 6 shows examples of a variety of chemical crosslinks typically applied to make synthetic hydrogels. A detailed list of crosslinks can be found in a recent review.[2]

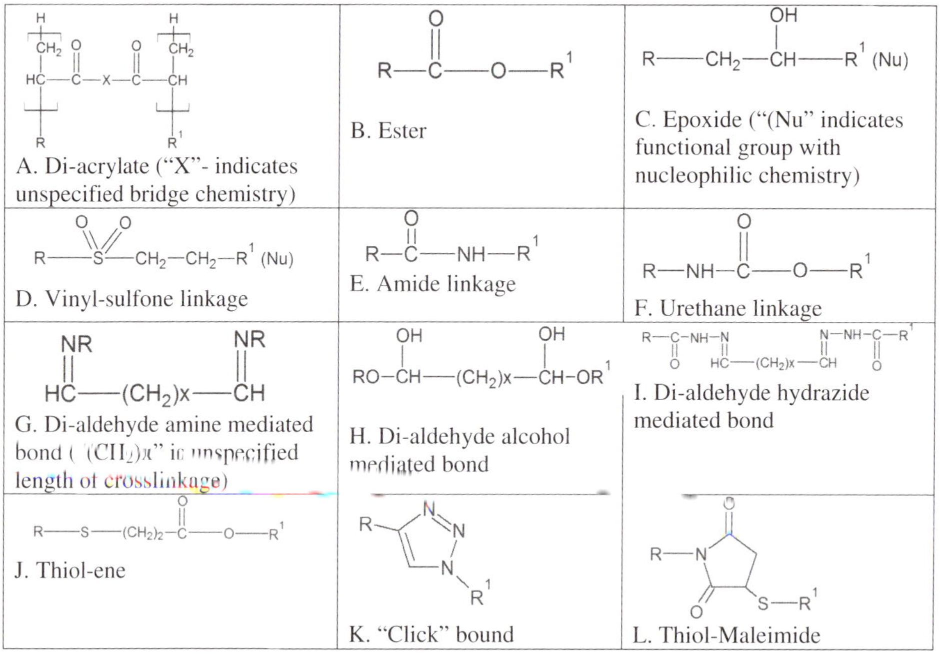

Fig. 6. Structures of chemical crosslinkers. ("R"/"R1" indicate different chains or branches of polymer). From Refs. 2, 43–45.

3.1. Diacrylate bonds

Chemically crosslinked hydrogels are commonly prepared by incorporating a bi-functional component which bridges two growing polymer chains during free radical polymerization. This method has found applications in drug delivery,[46] tissue engineering,[47] cell scaffolding,[48] anti-fouling surfaces for water treatment,[49] biosensor arrays,[50] heavy metal scavenging,[51] and fast swelling devices.[52]

The hydrogel properties are highly dependent on the nature of the crosslinker, in addition to the nature of the backbone structure. Strong, stiff hydrogels can be generated with high crosslinking density by having a relatively short crosslinker such as N, N′-methylenebisacrylamide (MBA)[53] or ethylene glycol dimethacrylate (EGDMAC).[51] alternatively, flexible hydrogels can be generated by utilizing a crosslinker which has a flexible PEG chain such as PEG diacrylate (PEGDA). PEGDA has tunable elasticity based on the PEG length.[54] Biodegradable hydrogels can be made by incorporating hydrolysable polyesters chains into the crosslinker. For instance PLA–PEG–PLGA can be modified to have acrylate groups on both endcaps and applied to generate a hydrogel that slowly increases in swelling until it dissolves (Fig. 7).[34]

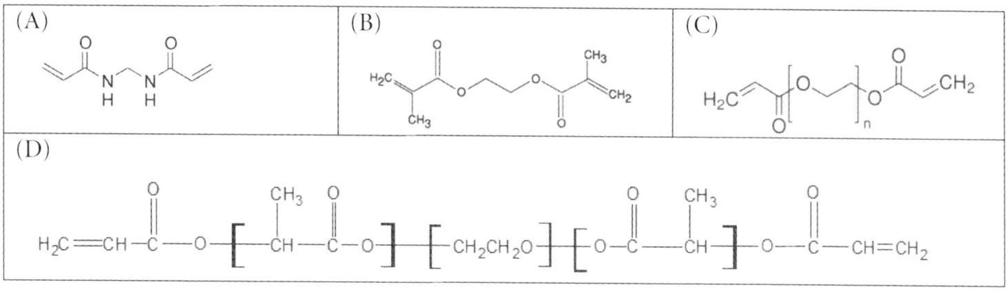

Fig. 7. Structure of di-acrylate crosslinkers. (A) N, N′-MBA, (B) EGDMAC, (C) PEGDA, and (D) PLA–PEG–PLGA.

More than two acrylates can be functionalized onto a molecule allowing for more than two chains to be crosslinked together. For example trimethylolpropane triacrylate (TMPTA) can be utilized to bridge three chains simultaneously. Superabsorbant hydrogels were formed using two crosslinkers, TMPTA and 1, 4-butanediol dimethacrylate (BDMA) for monomers of acrylamide (AM) and crotonic acid (CTA). These hydrogels can absorb water over 150 times of their own weight in.[55] Another example of a triacrylate is pentaerythritol triacrylate (PETA),[56] which, like TMPTA, drastically increases crosslinking density relative to its content by its capacity to conjugate multiple chains simultaneously.[56] Other multi-acrylates include acrylate functionalized natural compounds such as dextran.[57] In this situation, the number of acrylate groups on the dextran is controlled by stoichiometry. Because of the flexibility for its usage multi-acrylate crosslinking is widely applicable and popular in generating chemically crosslinked hydrogels.

3.2. Ester

Ester bonds are formed by dehydration reaction between an alcohol and a carboxylic acid. Because of this, ester units are ultimately susceptible to hydrolysis and fundamentally unstable in aqueous settings, such as swollen hydrogels. For this reason they are not commonly applied to hydrogel formation, but are utilized when degradation of the matrix is desirable. Often this form of crosslinking is combined with others to generate a matrix which has biodegradable and bioerodible components.[1]

3.3. Epoxide

Epoxide bonds form when a nucleophile attacks a carbon which forms part of an epoxide ring under aqueous conditions. Because of the ring-strain of an epoxide ring it is highly susceptible to this kind of attack, and this reaction proceeds quite easily

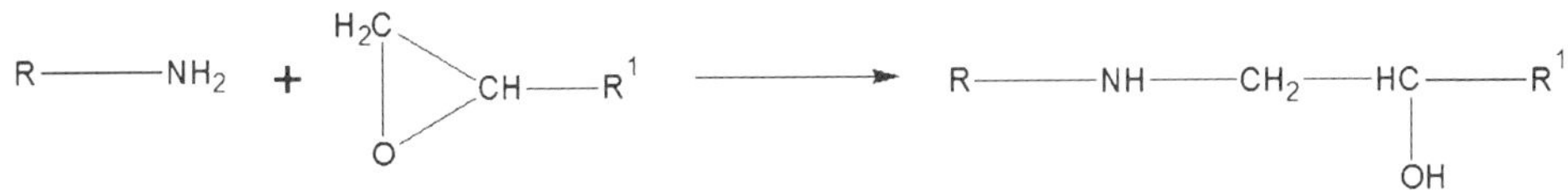

Fig. 8. General reaction between amine and epoxide.

even at room temperature without catalysts or initiators. Example of the reaction between amine and epoxide is shown in Fig. 8. Epoxide crosslinking has been applied to amine-bearing materials, such as polyethylenimine (PEI),[58] PAMAM dendrimers,[59] gelatin[60] and chitosan,[61] as well as alcohol bearing materials such as hyaluronic acid[62] and dextran.[63] Once formed the epoxide bond is permanent and non-degradable. PEG-diepoxide (or "PEG diglycidyl ether") has been widely used in making chemically crosslinked hydrogels,[59] an epoxide can be used to introduce vinyl groups for polymerization. Glycidyl methacrylate has been applied to effectively convert practically any soluble material with reactive nucleophilic functional groups into a vinyl monomer or crosslinker. This allows for natural components to be functionalized and subsequently crosslinked into synthetic hydrogels. Examples include hydrogels made from glycidyl methacrylated versions of cashew gum,[64] gallactomannan,[65] dextran,[66,67] and hyaluronic acid.[68]

3.4. Vinyl sulfone

Vinyl sulfone operates as a good Michael type reaction acceptor which reacts rapidly with thiols at low pH and alcohols and amines at a higher pH. Figure 9 shows a general reaction between vinyl sulfone and alcohol Reactions with thiols form stable thio-ether bonds and alcohols and amines to form respective bonds with these materials.[69] Although the reaction between vinyl sulfone and amines/alcohols does occur, the reaction rate with thiols is so much higher that this is considered a "selective towards thiols" reagent.[70] Similar to epoxides this reaction occurs readily in aqueous conditions at room temperature with no requirement for external catalysts or initiators. Classic application of this bond for forming hydrogels is the utilization of divinyl sulfone (DVS) to a wide array of materials including cellulose, hyaluronic acid, dextran, and proteins.[70,71] Vinyl sulfone endcapped PEGs and mulitarm PEGs were reacted with peptides[72,73] to generate hybrid synthetic-natural hydrogels with selective enzymatic degradability.

3.5. Amide

Amide linkages are generated by dehydration reaction between a carboxylic acid and an amine resulting in chemical bonding. Due to resonance stabilization, amides have

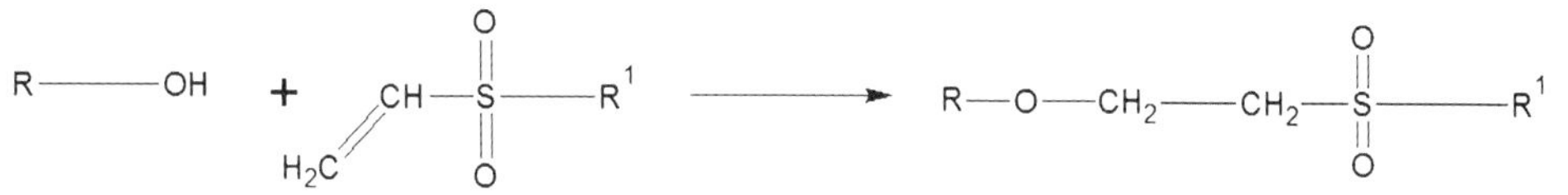

Fig. 9. Generalized vinyl-sulfone alcohol reaction.

much lower hydrolysis and are substantially more stable than closely related esters. This makes them functionally non-degradable, at the time scales that are commonly applied to degradable hydrogels, unless they are acted on by an external catalyst, reagent, or enzyme. Notably amide bonds are found in nature as the bond which holds amino acids together for form peptides and proteins.[74,75]

Synthetic amides require use of a strong dehydrating agent, most notably carbodiimide ($RN{=}C{=}NR^1$), to initiate the reaction between an amine and a carboxylic acid group.[76] Carbodiimide is converted to urea-type side products (which must be subsequently purified out) and not incorporated into the formed hydrogels, and thus, this is considered a "self-crosslinking" reaction within a hydrogel. This kind of reaction has been applied to a wide array of materials including gelatin, poly (L-glutamic acid),[77] collagen, chitosan,[78] alginate and carrageenan.[79] These hydrogels are highly stable and degradation proceeds primarily via enzymatic degradation which offers a level of biodegradation flexibility relative to ester bonds.

3.6. Urethane linkage

Isocyanates are a general class of reactive chemicals which terminate in "–N=C=O" functional group that is highly reactive with nucleophiles (alcohols and amines) and water (which creates CO_2, a blowing agent) (Fig. 10). Isocyanates commonly used for polymer synthesis are di-functionalized derivatives of alkanes or phenyls, such as methylene diphenyl diisocyanate (MDI), toluene diisocyanate (TDI), hexamethylene diisocyanate (HDI), ethyl lysine diisocyanate (LDI), and isophorone diisocyanate (IPDI). Since isocyanate can react with water, it is preferential for isocyanate crosslinkers to be hydrophobic. This popular chemistry has been applied to generate polyurethanes films and foams which are usually not hydrogels. Isocyanates are capable of reacting with hydrophilic materials, thus forming hydrogels.[80–84] Urethane-based hydrogels have been used in vaginal inserts for drug delivery. Cervidil® is formed by reacting PEG-diol with diisocyanate and a trifunctional alcohol. Reacting PEG-diol with diisocyanate alone does not create a crosslinked hydrogel, but rather just an extremely high molecular weight polymer. For this reason, a trifunctional alcohol crosslinker (such as 1, 2, 6 hexanetriol) must be incorporated to form crosslinked hydrogels.[85,86]

Fig. 10. Generalized isocyanate reaction to form urethane linkage.

Urethane chemistry has recently been applied to natural polymers such as gelatin to make hydrogels with controlled chemistry through reaction with HDI or LDI in dimethylsulfoxide, followed by transfer of the reactive mix to water. In this case no additional trifunctional linker is necessary, since gelatin presents a wide array of functional groups along its backbone.[87] Urethane linkages have also been applied to creating crosslinked hydrogels out of PEG, chitosan, alcohol-terminated poly (dimethyl siloxane) (PDMS),[88] tropoelastin/elastin,[89] HEMA/hydroxyethyl-cellulose,[90] collagen,[91] and PVA.[92]

3.7. Di-aldehyde crosslinking

Aldehydes are terminal carbonyl units that are highly reactive with amines, alcohols, and hydrazides, and participate in a wide variety of reactions such as condensation, oxidation, and reduction. Typically, dialdehydes are applied to generate crosslinking including glyoxal, malondialdehyde, succindialdehyde, glutaraldehyde, PEG-dialdehyde, and phthaldehyde (Fig. 11).[93–97] Di-aldehyde crosslinking is a rapid and spontaneous reaction at room temperature allowing for simple one step reactions. Di-aldehydes has been applied to synthesis of hydrogels with tropoelastin/elastin,[89] chitosan,[97] and alginate.[93]

3.8. Other crosslinking reactions

In addition to the common crosslinking reactions described above, there have been other approaches for crosslinking. Potta *et al.* created mixed polymer system based on polyphosphazene containing both functional thiols and acrylated portions. This thermosensitive polymer system can be directly injectable at low temperature to form into a gel upon injection at the body temperature, with further stiffening due

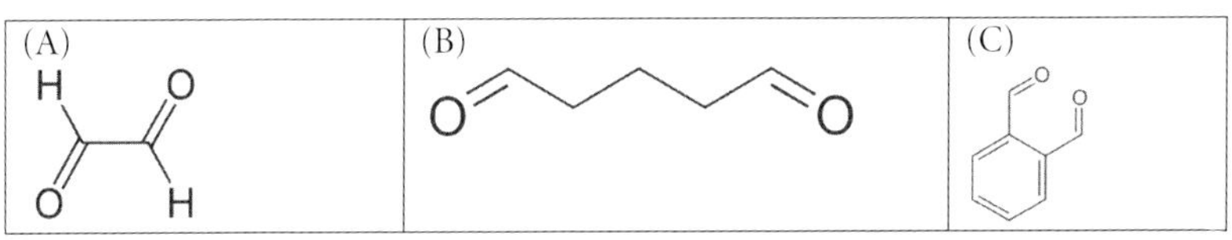

Fig. 11. Example of dialdehydes including (A) glyoxal, (B) glutaraldehyde, and (C) phthalaldehyde.

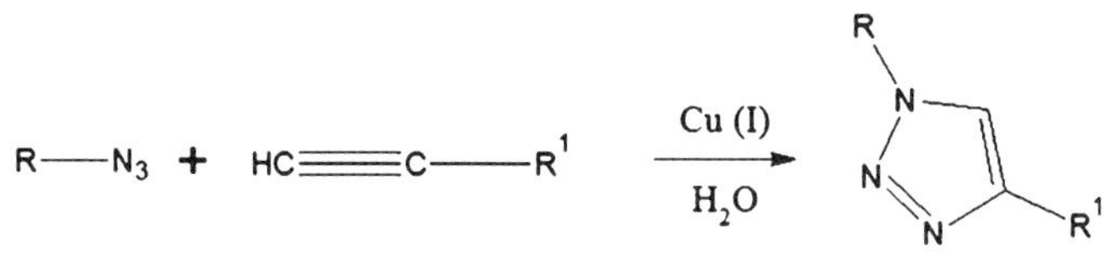

Fig. 12. Click chemistry for cycloaddition.

to chemical bonding through the Michael addition reaction between the thiol and acrylate units.[43] The Michaels type addition reactions between PEG-maleimide and PEG-thiol have also been applied to make *in-situ* forming hydrogels that react under physiological conditions.[45]

Other chemistries, such as "click" binding, are applied to making highly organized or micropatterned hydrogels. "Click chemistry" is a general term introduced by K. B. Sharpless in 2001 to describe reactions that are high yield, are easy to purify (without chromatography), are stereospecific, and can be conducted in easily removable or benign solvents.[98] This term is more specifically applied to the copper catalyzed reaction between alkynes and azides leading to cycloaddition (Fig. 12). Recently, this technique has been applied by reacting 4-arm alkyne terminated PEGs with azide functionalized plasma polymer. This reaction was converted to be UV sensitive by incorporating non-catalyzing Cu(II) and Irgacure 2595, commercially available free radical-forming UV initiator. Upon UV exposure through a mask the free radicals formed by Irgacure oxidize copper to catylitic Cu(I) which catalyzes the reaction between alkyne and azide. This led to the generation of a nanopatterned surface which could direct the growth of fibroblast cells onto the non-PEGylated surfaces.[44]

3.9. High energy irradiation

Crosslinking can occur between polymer chains by high energy (e.g., gamma or electron beam) radiation. This can occur in water-soluble polymers with or with introduction of vinyl groups. High energy radiation leads to homolytic scission of C–H bonds and formation of hydroxyl radicals by radiation of the water which can lead to the formation of macro-radicals. Crosslinking is normally performed in inert atmosphere, since oxygen reacts out these macroradicals. This method has been applied to PVA, PEG, PAA, poly (methyl vinyl ether), and polypeptides.[2] In some situations, UV can be used for direct crosslinking of unmodified gelatin.[99] Because this is random activation of various chains *in situ*, the exact nature and form of the bonds formed by this reaction cannot be controlled. The ill-defined crosslinking and other unexpected chemical reactions are undesired results of gamma sterilization process.[100–103]

4. Smart Hydrogels

Entering a search term "smart hydrogel" into Google scholar results in 1,740, 5,320, and 6,100 articles for the periods of 2000–2005, 2006–2010, and 2011–2013 respectively. This simple search shows dramatic increase in the publication of articles related to smart hydrogels. The term "smart hydrogel" is used to indicate that a hydrogel has an additional function as compared with the traditional, or normal, hydrogel which has only one function of absorbing water and swelling in the presence of a plenty of water regardless of the environmental condition. Smart hydrogels, on the other hand, swell or de-swell depending on minute changes in the environmental condition, including pH, temperature, electric signal, light, and specific molecules such as glucose. In a sense, it makes more sense to call "smart" hydrogels "responsive" hydrogels.

4.1. PH-responsive hydrogels

Hydrogels containing ionizable groups, such as carboxylic acids or amines, change their swelling behavior depending on the solution pH. When the ionizable groups are ionized, hydrogels swell due to increased interaction with water. Polymers containing acid groups (e.g., PAA) become ionized at high pH, and thus swell more. On the other hand, polymers with base groups (e.g., poly (N, N'-diethylaminoethyl methacrylate) or PDEAMA) become ionized at a low pH.

For weak acids, the dissociation of hydrogen ion is described as follows.

$$HA + H_2O \rightleftarrows H_3O^+ + A^-,$$

$$k = \frac{[\mathrm{H_3O^+}][\mathrm{A^-}]}{[\mathrm{HA}][\mathrm{H_2O}]}.$$

Since the concentration of water, $[H_2O]$, is 55.3 moles/L, which is essentially constant, the above dissociation constant can be rewritten as:

$$K_a = \frac{[\mathrm{H_3O^-}][\mathrm{A^-}]}{[\mathrm{HA}]} = \frac{[\mathrm{H^+}][\mathrm{A^-}]}{[\mathrm{HA}]},$$

where K_a is the acidity constant. When the hydrogen concentration, $[H^+]$, is high, the concentration of the ionized form, $[A^-]$, is low. Thus, at low pH, the acid exists mainly in the protonated form, i.e., unionized form. As pH increases, $[A^-]$ also increases, and the equal amount of protonated and ionized forms exist when pH is equal to pK_a. Table 1 lists several common ionizable monomers and their pK_a's.

Table 1. pK_a values of some monomers.

Monomer/residue	pK_a	References
	Acids	
Acrylic acid	4.35	104
Methacrylic acid	4.65	105
Glutamic acid	4.07	106
Vinyl sulfonic acid	Strong acid (<1)	107
Vinyl phosphonic acid	2 (first hydrogen), 8 (second hydrogen)	108
Aspartic acid	3.86	106
	Bases	
Histidine	6.10	106
Tyrosine	10.07	106
Lysine	10.53	106
arginine	12.48	106
2-(Dimethylamino)ethyl methacrylate	7.5	109
N,N′-diethylaminoethyl methacrylate	7.3	110
2-Aminoethyl methacrylate	8.8	111

The table includes information on several amino acids which have been used to make poly (amino acids). pK_a of a weak acid or a weak base can be shifted in the polymer form due to the changes in dissociation constant depending on the polymer molecular weight.

Changes in pH in the different parts of the body have been exploited for drug delivery. The pH of the cancer cells is known to be around 6.5–7.0,[112,113] lower than 7.4 of normal cells, and polymers made of histidine have been used to deliver a drug selectively to the cancer cells.[114–116] The pH change between the stomach and the intestine has also been used for localized drug delivery to a certain regions in the gastrointestinal tract.

4.2. Temperature-responsive hydrogels

There are two types of temperature-responsive hydrogels. The first is a "normal" type response in which a physical hydrogel melts upon heating due to reduction of chain-to-chain bonds/entanglements and an improvement in overall polymer solubility. A classic example of this type of interaction is gelatin which melts upon warming and other natural hydrogels such as mixtures of xanthan gum and locust bean gums.[117,118] the second type of response is an "inverse" response in which a physical hydrogel

Table 2. LCST values of selected polymers.[119]

Polymer	LCST (°C)
Poly (N-vinylcaprolactam), PNVC	30
Poly (NIPAM)	32
Poly (silamine)	37
Poly(vinyl methyl ether), PVME	40
Poly (propylene glycol), PPG	50
Poly (vinyl methyl oxazolidone), PVMO	65
PMA, PMAA	75
Methylcellulose, MC	80

transforms from solution to gel upon temperature increase. Polymers with LCST have the inverse thermo-sensitivity (Table 2).

Recently, polyurethane chemistry has been applied to synthesize temperature-responsive hydrogels. Reactions among PEO–PPO–PEO (poloxamer), succinic/citric acid, and ethyl ester L-lysine diisocyanate have been performed to synthesize polyurethanes with sol-gel transition at 40–60°C.[120] Polyurethane chemistry has also been applied to join two (mPEG–PLA–OH) diblocks to each other to form thermo-sensitive mPEG–PLA–PEGm using HDI.[121] Thermogels have been formed by reacting segmented polyurethanes (formed from PCL, LDI, and 1,4-butanediamine) and NIPAM, AA, and butyl methacrylate to form semi-interpenetrating networks of thermally sensitive gels.[122] It has been established that these phase transitions can occur under 1 minute.[123]

4.3. Electric signal-responsive hydrogels

When a hydrogel is in aqueous solution and mobile ions (such as Na^+ or Cl^-) are available, it can easily conduct electricity from a cathode to anode. Conducting electricity in aqueous solution requires the motion of ions, and this causes a change in the interaction of the hydrogel with the ions surrounding it. The motion of ions through the hydrogel is a directional stimulus in that positive ions flow towards the cathode and negative ions flow towards the anode. The uniform, directional change can lead to hydrogel warping in one direction.[124,125]

Hydrogels with ionic charge and hydrogen bonding capability can swell/deswell or bend under a low electric field. A hydrogel made of an interpenetrating network of PVA and PAA was prepared. The PVA and PAA chains in the hydrogel are also held together through hydrogen bonding between the acid/alcohol units. Because the hydrogen bonding is an electromagnetic force the hydrogel could be controlled by the application of a weak electric field.[8] When a hydrogel made of the sodium salt of PAA and polyacrylamide is placed in acetone/water solution with very little electrolyte, it shrinks markedly under a light electric charge. Hydrogels made of PMA and PAA also shrink under electric field as well. Notably poly (ethyloxazoline)–PMA complex has been shown to disintegrate completely under applied electric field by disruption of hydrogen bonding holding the gel together.[126]

4.4. Light-sensitive hydrogels

Light sensitive hydrogels are generated by incorporating a light-absorbing moiety which undergoes a transition to an ionized state upon exposure to either UV or visible light. Bis (4-(dimethylamino) phenyl) (4-vinylphenyl) methylleucocyanide converts to an ionized state upon exposure to UV light. Hydrogels sensitive to visible light can be generated by incorporating trisodium copper chlorophyllin into a thermogel. Exposure to light generates localized heating which triggers the thermosensitivity.[126] recently, new light sensitive monomers have been developed. 4-(4-((4-ethoxyphenyl) diazenyl) phenoxy)-N-(2-(methacryloyloxy)ethyl)-N, N-dimethylbutan-1-aminium bromide undergoes a rapid trans-cis photoisomerization with light exposure. When it was co-reacted with NIPAM, the formed hydrogel is dually sensitive to light and heat.[127] another recent strategy to generate photosensitivity is to incorporate light absorbing graphene oxide into thermo-gelling PNIPAM. In this case the highly light absorbing graphene oxide generates localized heat upon light exposure. The resultant color and phase transition can be controlled by the graphene oxide content and use of an infrared laser allows for the light-sensitive thermogel to undergo solidification remotely.[128] similarly solutions of graphene oxide and Pluronic (poloxamer) thermogel have also shown the same results.[129]

4.5. Glucose-sensitive hydrogels

Glucose-sensitive hydrogels have been the focus of extensive research for its potential to deliver insulin as a function of the blood glucose level. Glucose-sensitive hydrogels can be made by incorporating glucose-sensitive moieties, such as concanavalin A (Con A) or glucose oxidase. Each Con A molecule has four glucose binding sites, and thus, it can effectively function as a crosslinker for polymer chains containing pendent glucose molecules. A mixture of glucose-containing copolymer (e.g., vinylpyrrolidinone-allylglucose, VP-AG) and Con A forms a gel which undergoes phase transition in the presence of free glucose.[130] by adjusting the AG content and the VP-AG polymer concentration, the hydrogel can be tailor-made to respond to fluctuations in the glucose concentration normally found in blood. Hydrogels containing glucose oxidase respond to the changes in glucose concentrations by controlling the amount of acid generated by the enzyme. Glucose oxidase converts glucose into gluconic acid, and the level of gluconic acid controls the swelling of the pH-sensitive hydrogels, and thus, controlling the amount of released insulin.[126]

There are a few critical factors to consider in developing glucose-sensitive hydrogels. First, glucose-sensitivity has to occur in small changes in the glucose concentration, e.g., from < 100 mg/dL to 180 mg/dL). Second, the change has to be rapid to release insulin rapidly. The response time is most critical, as slow or delayed release of insulin will not be useful. Third, once the glucose level in blood is reduced to a normal level, the insulin release has to stop fast. Currently, there are no hydrogels that meet all these requirements. Developing clinically useful insulin delivery systems is one of the holy grails in the drug delivery field.

5. Biodegradable Hydrogels

For certain applications it is highly desirable to make hydrogels biodegradable. There are three primary requirements to consider for biodegradable hydrogels: biocompatibility, mechanical stability during degradation, and sterilizability. Biodegradable hydrogels designed to be used inside the human body must be biocompatible and generate non-toxic products. As biodegradation proceeds the gel structure will begin breaking down, weakening the mechanical properties. The degradation needs to be controlled to maintain the structural integrity necessary for the intended function. For clinical applications, all hydrogels must be sterilized, and quite often the sterilization process affects the properties of the hydrogels. Steam-autoclave can cause chemical damage to most degradable gels,[131] and gamma sterilization can also cause issues of self-crosslinking and other undesirable reactions.[132]

5.1. Hydrolysable polyesters

Ester bonds have the capacity to hydrolyze. Commonly these include polymers/copolymers of lactide, glycolide, caprolactone, p-dioxanone, trimethylene carbonate, 3-hydroxybutyrate, 3-hydroxyvalerate, valerolactone, tartonic acid, and malonic acid.[17,22,23,119,133] In all cases described here the monomer residue of these polyesters contains a carboxylic acid at one terminus and an alcohol at the other. Chemical structures of selected polyesters are shown in Fig. 13.

Polyesters can generally be synthesized at low molecular weights in an uncontrolled manner simply by polycondensation. In this process dehydrating conditions (high heat, vacuum, or gas purge) are applied to encourage dehydration reaction between carboxylic acid and the alcohol unit. Obtaining higher molecular weight

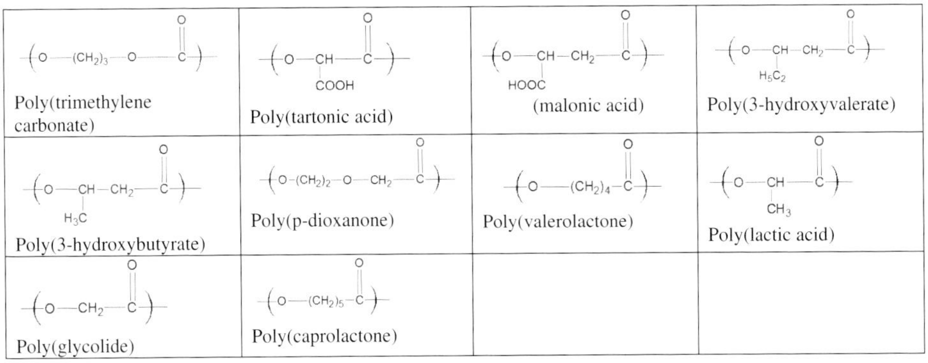

Fig. 13. Chemical structures of polyesters.

polymers requires ring-opening polymerization from either cyclic monomers (e.g., caprolactone and valerolactone) or cyclic dimers (e.g., lactide and glycolide). The initiating moiety can be an alcohol unit or even water, and thus, it requires high monomer purity, anhydrous conditions, and catalysts such as stannous octoate.[133] Water causes hydrolysis at the ester bond, breaking it into the respective carboxylic acid and alcohol units. This reaction can be catalyzed by either acid or base.

Degradation of polyesters is limited by the access of water to the ester unit. Thus, the degradation rate depends on the hydrophobicity and crystallinity of polymers. Significant differences in the degradation rates are observed between similar polymers, such as crystalline PLLA and non-crystalline PDLLA which degrades much more rapidly. Polycaprolactone degrades at a substantially slower rate due to the relatively lower number of available ester units and also higher hydrophobicity of the chain as a whole.[133] these factors primarily apply to solid polymer forms, but the trends continue into hydrogels.[134–136]

6. Conclusion

Synthetic hydrogels have been used widely in pharmaceutical and biomedical applications. These hydrogels can be physically or chemically crosslinked depending on the desired application. Physically crosslinked hydrogels have a unique property of undergoing phase transition between the solution and the solid states. This phase transition in physical hydrogels corresponds to transition between swelling and deswelling. Smart hydrogels possess the ability to respond to changes in environmental conditions, such as pH, temperature, electric signal, light or glucose. Hydrogels can also be made biodegradable. Synthetic hydrogels can be custom-tailored to possess specific properties for wide array of applications.

References

1. A. S. Hoffman, Hydrogels for biomedical applications. *Adv. Drug Deliver. Rev.*, **64**, 18–23 (2012).
2. W. E. Hennink and C. F. van Nostrum, Novel cross-linking methods to design hydrogels. *Adv. Drug Deliver. Rev.*, **64**, 223–236 (2012).
3. Y. Liu, L. M. Geever, J. E. Kennedy, C. L. Higginbotham, P. A. Cahill, and G. B. McGuinness, Thermal behavior and mechanical properties of physically cross-linked PVA/Gelatin hydrogels. *J. Mech. Behav. Biomed. Mater.*, **3**(2), 203–209 (2010).
4. Y. Liu, N. E. Vrana, P. A. Cahill, and G. B. McGuinness, Physically cross-linked composite hydrogels of PVA with natural macromolecules: Structure, mechanical properties, and endothelial cell compatibility. *J. Biomed. Mater. Res. A*, **90B**(2), 492–502 (2009).
5. E. Fathi, N. Atyabi, M. Imani, and Z. Alinejad, Physically cross-linked polyvinyl alcohol-dextran blend xerogels: Morphology and thermal behavior. *Carbohyd. Polym.*, **84**(1), 145–152 (2011).
6. L. Wei, C. Cai, J. Lin, and T. Chen, Dual-drug delivery system based on hydrogel/micelle composites. *Biomaterials*, **30**(13), 2606–2613 (2009).
7. S. K. Agrawal, N. Sanabria-DeLong, S. K. Bhatia, G. N. Tew, and S. R. Bhatia, Energetics of association in PLA-based hydrogels with crystalline and nanoparticle polymer junctions. *Langmuir*, **26**(22), 17330–17338 (2010).
8. S. Y. Kim and Y. M. Lee, Drug release behavior of electrical responsive poly (vinyl alcohol)/poly (acrylic acid) IPN hydrogels under an electric stimulus. *J. Appl. Polym. Sci.*, **74**(7), 1752–1761 (1999).
9. J. Yun, J. S. Im, Y.-S. Lee, S. J. Yoo, and H.-I. Kim, Sustained release behavior of pH-responsive poly (vinyl alcohol)/poly (acrylic acid) hydrogels containing activated carbon fibers. *J. Appl. Polym. Sci.*, **120**(2), 1050–1056 (2010).
10. X.-Y. Wu, S.-W. Huang, J.-T. Zhang, and R.-X. Zhuo, Preparation and characterization of novel physically cross-linked hydrogels composed of poly (vinyl alcohol) and amine-terminated PAMAM dendrimer. *Macromol. Biosci.*, **4**(2), 71–75 (2004).
11. D. M. Devine and C. L. Higginbotham, The synthesis of a physically cross-linked NVP based hydrogel. *Polymer*, **44**(26), 7851–7860 (2003).
12. A. Phadke, C. Zhang, B. Arman, C. C. Hsu, R. A. Mashelkar, A. K. Lele, M. J. Tauber, G. Arya, and S. Varghese, Rapid self-healing hydrogels. *P. Natl. Acad. Sci.*, **109**(12), 4383–4388 (2012).
13. N. A. Peppas, J. Z. Hilt, A. Khademhosseini, and R. Langer, Hydrogels in biology and medicine: From molecular principles to bionanotechnology. *Adv. Mater.*, **18**(11), 1345–1360 (2006).
14. C. K. Kuo and P. X. Ma, Ionically crosslinked alginate hydrogels as scaffolds for tissue engineering: Part 1. Structure, gelation rate and mechanical properties. *Biomaterials*, **22**(6), 511–521 (2001).
15. P. Sun, P. Li, Y. M. Li, Q. Wei, and L. H. Tian, A pH sensitive chitosan-tripolyphosphate hydrogel beads for controlled glipizide delivery. *J. Biomed. Mater. Res. A*, **97**(1), 175–183 (2011).

16. G. Laurent and D. Piat, Efficiency of swimming microrobots using ionic polymer metal composite actuators. *Robotics and Automation, 2001. Proceedings 2001 ICRA. IEEE International Conference on*, Vol. 4, IEEE (2001).
17. S. Li and M. Vert, Synthesis, characterization, and stereocomplex-induced gelation of block copolymers prepared by ring-opening polymerization of l(d)-lactide in the presence of PEG. *Macromolecules*, **36**(21), 8008–8014 (2003).
18. G. W. Bos, W. E. Hennink, L. A. Brouwer, W. den Otter, T. F. J. Veldhuis, C. F. van Nostrum, and M. J. A. van Luyn, Tissue reactions of *in situ* formed dextran hydrogels cross-linked by stereocomplex formation after subcutaneous implantation in rats. *Biomaterials*, **26**(18), 3901–3909 (2005).
19. S. J. de Jong, S. C. De Smedt, M. W. C. Wahls, J. Demeester, J. J. Kettenes-van den Bosch, and W. E. Hennink, Novel self-assembled hydrogels by stereocomplex formation in aqueous solution of enantiomeric lactic acid oligomers grafted to dextran. *Macromolecules*, **33**(10), 3680–3686 (2000).
20. S. J. de Jong, S. C. De Smedt, J. Demeester, C. F. van Nostrum, J. J. Kettenes-van den Bosch, and W. E. Hennink, Biodegradable hydrogels based on stereocomplex formation between lactic acid oligomers grafted to dextran. *J. Control. Release*, **72**(1–3), 47–56 (2001).
21. N. Idota, A. Kikuchi, J. Kobayashi, K. Sakai, and T. Okano, Modulation of graft architectures for enhancing hydrophobic interaction of biomolecules with thermoresponsive polymer-grafted surfaces. *Colloid Surface B*, **99**(0), 95–101 (2012).
22. S. J. Bae, M. K. Joo, Y. Jeong, S. W. Kim, W. K. Lee, Y. S. Sohn, and B. Jeong, Gelation behavior of PEG and polycaprolactone triblock and multiblock copolymer aqueous solutions. *Macromolecules*, **39**(14), 4873–4879 (2006).
23. B. Jeong, S. W. Kim, and Y. H. Bae, Thermosensitive sol–gel reversible hydrogels. *Adv. Drug Deliver. Rev.*, **64**, 154–162 (2012).
24. H. J. Moon, M. H. Park, M. K. Joo, and B. Jeong, Temperature-responsive compounds as *in situ* gelling biomedical materials. *Chem. Soc. Rev.*, **41**(14), 4860–4883 (2012).
25. S. C. Lee, Y. W. Cho, and K. Park, Control of thermogelation properties of hydrophobically-modified methylcellulose. *J. Bioact. Compat. Polym.*, **20**(1), 5–13 (2005).
26. B. Wang, X.-D. Xu, Z.-C. Wang, S.-X. Cheng, X.-Z. Zhang, and R.-X. Zhuo, Synthesis and properties of pH and temperature sensitive P(NIPAAm-co-DMAEMA) hydrogels. *Colloid. Surface. B*, **64**(1), 34–41 (2008).
27. E. A. Markvicheva, S. V. Kuptsova, T. Y. Mareeva, A. A. Vikhrov, T. N. Dugina, S. M. Strukova, Y. N. Belokon, K. A. Kochetkov, E. N. Baranova, and V. P. Zubov, Immobilized enzymes and cells in poly (N-vinyl caprolactam)-based hydrogels. *Appl. Biochem. Biotechnol.*, **88**(1), 145–157 (2000).
28. R. P. Washington and O. Steinbock, Frontal polymerization synthesis of temperature-sensitive hydrogels. *J. Am. Chem. Soc.*, **123**(32), 7933–7934 (2001).
29. A. V. Kabanov and V. Y. Alakhov, Pluronic block copolymers in drug delivery: From micellar nanocontainers to biological response modifiers. *Crit. Rev. Ther. Drug*, **19**(1), 1–73 (2002).
30. R. Pelton, Poly (N-isopropylacrylamide) (PNIPAM) is never hydrophobic. *J. Colloid Interface Sci.*, **348**(2), 673–674 (2010).

31. M. C. Swan, D. G. Bucknall, T. E. E. Goodacre, and J. T. Czernuszka, Synthesis and properties of a novel anisotropic self-inflating hydrogel tissue expander. *Acta Biomater.*, **7**(3), 1126–1132 (2010).
32. S. Bottcher-Haberzeth, S. Kapoor, M. Meuli, K. Neuhaus, T. Biedermann, E. Reichmann, and C. Schiestl, Osmotic expanders in children: No filling — no control — no problem? *Eur. J. Pediatr. Surg.*, **21**(3), 163–167 (2011).
33. A. Bacskulin, M. Vogel, K. G. Wiese, K. Gundlach, V. Hingst, and R. Guthoff, New osmotically active hydrogel expander for enlargement of the contracted anophthalmic socket. *Graefe. Arch. Clin. Exp.*, **238**(1), 24–27 (2000).
34. T. H. Tran, J. Garner, Y. Fu, K. Park, and K. M. Huh, in *Handbook of Biodegradable Polymers*, Eds. A. Lendlein and A. Sisson, New York: Wiley-VCH Verlag GmbH & Co. KGaA, pp. 217–236 (2011).
35. K. G. Wiese, D. E. Heinemann, D. Ostermeier, and J. H. Peters, Biomaterial properties and biocompatibility in cell culture of a novel self-inflating hydrogel tissue expander. *J. Biomed. Mater. Res.*, **54**(2), 179–188 (2001).
36. D. Kaner and A. Friedmann, Soft tissue expansion with self-filling osmotic tissue expanders before vertical ridge augmentation: A proof of principle study. *J. Clin. Periodontol.*, **38**(1), 95–101 (2011).
37. K. F. Kobus, Cleft palate repair with the use of osmotic expanders: A preliminary report. *J. Plast. Reconstr. Aes.*, **60**, 414–421 (2007).
38. M. P. Schittkowski, K. K. Gundlach, and R. F. Guthoff, Treatment of congenital clinical anophthalmos with high hydrophilic hydrogel expanders. *Ophthalmologe*, **100**(7), 525–534 (2003).
39. S. J. Berge, K. G. Wiese, J. J. von Lindern, B. Niederhagen, T. Appel, and R. H. Reich, Tissue expansion using osmotically active hydrogel systems for direct closure of the donor defect of the radial forearm flap. *Plast. Reconstr. Surg.*, **108**(1), 1–5, discussion 6–7 (2001).
40. J. Fan and J. Wang, The "silicone suture" for tissue expansion without an expander: A new device for repair of soft-tissue defects after burns. *Plast. Reconstr. Surg.*, **114**(2), 484–488, discussion 489–490 (2004).
41. M. A. Ronert, H. Hofheinz, E. Manassa, H. Asgarouladi, and R. R. Olbrisch, The beginning of a new era in tissue expansion: Self-filling osmotic tissue expander — four-year clinical experience. *Plast. Reconstr. Surg.*, **114**(5), 1025–1031 (2004).
42. M. A. Ronert, H. Hofheinz, and R. R. Olbrisch, The beginning of a new era: Self-filling tissue expander for defect coverage in a 3-year-old boy with a retroauricular nevus. *Plast. Reconstr. Surg.*, **112**(1), 189–191 (2003).
43. T. Potta, C. Chun, and S.-C. Song, Injectable, dual cross-linkable polyphosphazene blend hydrogels. *Biomaterials*, **31**(32), 8107–8120 (2010).
44. R. T. Chen, S. Marchesan, R. A. Evans, K. E. Styan, G. K. Such, A. Postma, K. M. McLean, B. W. Muir, and F. Caruso, Photoinitiated alkyne-Azide click and radical cross-linking reactions for the patterning of PEG hydrogels. *Biomacromolecules*, **13**(3), 889–895 (2012).

45. Y. Fu and W. J. Kao, *In situ* forming PEG-based hydrogels via thiol-maleimide Michael-type addition. *J. Biomed. Mater. Res. Part A*, **98A**(2), 201–211 (2011).
46. M. Hamidi, A. Azadi, and P. Rafiei, Hydrogel nanoparticles in drug delivery. *Adv. Drug Deliver. Rev.*, **60**(15), 1638–1649 (2008).
47. J. L. Drury and D. J. Mooney, Hydrogels for tissue engineering: Scaffold design variables and applications. *Biomaterials*, **24**(24), 4337–4351 (2003).
48. F. Yang, C. G. Williams, D. Wang, H. Lee, P. N. Manson, and J. Elisseeff, The effect of incorporating RGD adhesive peptide in PEG diacrylate hydrogel on osteogenesis of bone marrow stromal cells. *Biomaterials*, **26**(30), 5991–5998 (2005).
49. H. Ju, B. D. McCloskey, A. C. Sagle, V. A. Kusuma, and B. D. Freeman, Preparation and characterization of cross-linked PEG diacrylate hydrogels as fouling-resistant membrane coating materials. *J. Membrane Sci.*, **330**(1–2), 180–188 (2009).
50. J. E. Meiring, M. J. Schmid, S. M. Grayson, B. M. Rathsack, D. M. Johnson, R. Kirby, R. Kannappan, K. Manthiram, B. Hsia, and Z. L. Hogan, Hydrogel biosensor array platform indexed by shape. *Chem. Mater.*, **16**(26), 5574–5580 (2004).
51. A. Kara, L. Uzun, N. Berli, and A. Denizli, Poly (EGDMAC-n-vinyl imidazole) beads for heavy metal removal. *J. Hazard. Mater.*, **106**(2), 93–99 (2004).
52. J. Chen, W. E. Blevins, H. Park, and K. Park, Gastric retention properties of superporous hydrogel composites. *J. Control. Release*, **64**(1–3), 39–51 (2000).
53. J. P. Gong, Y. Katsuyama, T. Kurokawa, and Y. Osada, Double network hydrogels with extremely high mechanical strength. *Adv. Mater.*, **15**(14), 1155–1158 (2003).
54. S. Nemir, H. N. Hayenga, and J. L. West, PEGDA hydrogels with patterned elasticity: Novel tools for the study of cell response to substrate rigidity. *Biotechnol. bioeng.*, **105**(3), 636–644 (2010).
55. E. Karada and D. Saraydan, Swelling studies of super water retainer AM/CTA hydrogels cross-linked by trimethylolpropane triacrylate and 1,4-butanediol dimethacrylate. *Polym. Bull.*, **48**(3), 299–307 (2002).
56. M. B. Mellott, K. Searcy, and M. V. Pishko, Release of protein from highly cross-linked hydrogels of PEG diacrylate fabricated by UV polymerization. *Biomaterials*, **22**(9), 929–941 (2001).
57. L. Ferreira, A. Rafael, M. Lamghari, M. A. Barbosa, M. H. Gil, A. M. S. Cabrita, and J. S. Dordick, Biocompatibility of chemoenzymatically derived dextran-acrylate hydrogels. *J. Biomed. Mater. Res. Part A*, **68A**(3), 584–596 (2004).
58. S. V. Vinogradov, T. K. Bronich, and A. V. Kabanov, Nanosized cationic hydrogels for drug delivery: Preparation, properties and interactions with cells. *Adv. Drug Deliver. Rev.*, **54**(1), 135–147 (2002).
59. B. Unal and R. C. Hedden, Gelation and swelling behavior of end-linked hydrogels prepared from linear PEG and poly (amidoamine) dendrimers. *Polymer*, **47**(24), 8173–8182 (2006).
60. H. W. Sung, D. M. Huang, W. H. Chang, R. N. Huang, and J. C. Hsu, Evaluation of gelatin hydrogel cross-linked with various cross-linking agents as bioadhesives: *In vitro* study. *J. Biomed. Mater. Res.*, **46**(4), 520–530 (1999).

61. W. Wan Ngah, C. Endud, and R. Mayanar, Removal of copper (II) ions from aqueous solution onto chitosan and cross-linked chitosan beads. *React. Funct. Polym.*, **50**(2), 181–190 (2002).
62. M. N. Collins and C. Birkinshaw, Investigation of the swelling behavior of cross-linked hyaluronic acid films and hydrogels produced using homogeneous reactions. *J. Appl. Polym. Sci.*, **109**(2), 923–931 (2008).
63. A. Durand, Synthesis of amphiphilic polysaccharides by micellar catalysis. *J. Mol. Catal. A Chem.*, **256**(1), 284–289 (2006).
64. M. R. Guilherme, A. V. Reis, S. H. Takahashi, A.F. Rubira, J. Feitosa, and E.C. Muniz, Synthesis of a novel superabsorbent hydrogel by copolymerization of AM and cashew gum modified with glycidyl methacrylate. *Carbohyd. Polym.*, **61**(4), 464–471 (2005).
65. A. V. Reis, O. A. Cavalcanti, A. F. Rubira, and E. C. Muniz, Synthesis and characterization of hydrogels formed from a glycidyl methacrylate derivative of galactomannan. *Int. J. Pharm.*, **267**(1), 13–25 (2003).
66. W. Hennink, H. Talsma, J. Borchert, S. De Smedt, and J. Demeester, Controlled release of proteins from dextran hydrogels. *J. Control. Release*, **39**(1), 47–55 (1996).
67. S. De Smedt, A. Lauwers, J. Demeester, M. Van Steenbergen, W. Hennink, and S. Roefs, Characterization of the network structure of dextran glycidyl methacrylate hydrogels by studying the rheological and swelling behavior. *Macromolecules*, **28**(14), 5082–5088 (1995).
68. J. B. Leach, K. A. Bivens, C. N. Collins, and C. E. Schmidt, Development of photo-cross-linkable hyaluronic acid PEG peptide composite hydrogels for soft tissue engineering. *J. Biomed. Mater. Res. Part A*, **70**(1), 74–82 (2004).
69. G. Hermanson, *Bioconjugate Techniques*, London: Elsevier Inc., (2008).
70. D. Seliktar, A. Zisch, M. Lutolf, J. Wrana, and J. Hubbell, MMP-2 sensitive, VEGF-bearing bioactive hydrogels for promotion of vascular healing. *J. Biomed. Mater. Res. Part A*, **68**(4), 704–716 (2004).
71. A. Sannino, M. Madaghiele, F. Conversano, G. Mele, A. Maffezzoli, P. Netti, L. Ambrosio, and L. Nicolais, Cellulose derivative-hyaluronic acid-based microporous hydrogels cross-linked through DVS to modulate equilibrium sorption capacity and network stability. *Biomacromolecules*, **5**(1), 92–96 (2004).
72. M. P. Lutolf and J. A. Hubbell, Synthesis and physicochemical characterization of end-linked PEG-co-peptide hydrogels formed by michael-type addition. *Biomacromolecules*, **4**(3), 713–722 (2003).
73. S. C. Rizzi, M. Ehrbar, S. Halstenberg, G. P. Raeber, H. G. Schmoekel, H. Hagenmaler, R. Maller, F. E. Weber, and J. A. Hubbell, Recombinant protein-co-PEG networks as cell-adhesive and proteolytically degradable hydrogel matrixes. Part II: Biofunctional characteristics. *Biomacromolecules*, **7**(11), 3019–3029 (2006).
74. A. E. Tonelli, Stability of cis and trans amide bond conformations in polypeptides. *J. Am. Chem. Soc.*, **93**(26), 7153–7155 (1971).
75. C. A. Montalbetti and V. Falque, Amide bond formation and peptide coupling. *Tetrahedron*, **61**(46), 10827–10852 (2005).

76. N. Nakajima and Y. Ikada, Mechanism of amide formation by carbodiimide for bioconjugation in aqueous media. *Bioconjugate Chem.*, **6**(1), 123–130 (1995).
77. Y. Otani, Y. Tabata, and Y. Ikada, Hemostatic capability of rapidly curable glues from gelatin, poly (L-glutamic acid), and carbodiimide. *Biomaterials*, **19**(22), 2091–2098 (1998).
78. M. Rafat, F. Li, P. Fagerholm, N. S. Lagali, M. A. Watsky, R. Munger, T. Matsuura, and M. Griffith, PEG-stabilized carbodiimide cross-linked collagen-chitosan hydrogels for corneal tissue engineering. *Biomaterials*, **29**(29), 3960–3972 (2008).
79. J. Xu, J. Bartley, and R. Johnson, Preparation and characterization of alginate carrageenan hydrogel films cross-linked using a water-soluble carbodiimide (WSC). *J. Membrane Sci.*, **218**(1), 131–146 (2003).
80. S. Gogolewski, Selected topics in biomedical polyurethanes. A review. *Colloid Polym. Sci.*, **267**(9), 757–785 (1989).
81. L. Pinchuk, A review of the biostability and carcinogenicity of polyurethanes in medicine and the new generation of 'biostable' polyurethanes. *J. Biomat. Sci. Polym. E.*, **6**(3), 225–267 (1995).
82. D. Yuan, C. Ju, S. Ding, X. Jing, and C. Zhang, Synthesis of 1-octadecanol-modified water-swelling polyurethane hydrogels as vaginal drug-delivery vehicle. *J. Biomat. Sci. Polym. E.*, **21**(4), 493–505 (2010).
83. S. V. Levchik and E. D. Weil, Thermal decomposition, combustion and fire retardancy of polyurethanes a review of the recent literature. *Polym. Int.*, **53**(11), 1585–1610 (2004).
84. B. K. Kim and J. C. Lee, Polyurethane ionomer dispersions from poly (neopentylene phthalate) glycol and IPDI. *Polymer*, **37**(3), 469–475 (1996).
85. N. Graham, PEG gels and drug delivery. In *PEG Chemistry: Biotechnical and Biomedical Applications*, New York: Springer, pp. 263–281 (1992).
86. N. Graham and M. Zulfiqar, Interaction of poly (ethylene oxide) with solvents: 3. Synthesis and swelling in water of cross-linked PEG urethane networks. *Polymer*, **30**(11), 2130–2135 (1989).
87. G. Tronci, A. T. Neffe, B. F. Pierce, and A. Lendlein, An entropy elastic gelatin-based hydrogel system. *J. Mater. Chem.*, **20**(40), 8875–8884 (2010).
88. N. Rodkate, U. Wichai, B. Boontha, and M. Rutnakornpituk, Semi-interpenetrating polymer network hydrogels between polydimethylsiloxane/PEG and chitosan. *Carbohyd. Polym.*, **81**(3), 617–625 (2010).
89. N. Annabi, S. M. Mithieux, A. S. Weiss, and F. Dehghani, Cross-linked open-pore elastic hydrogels based on tropoelastin, elastin and high pressure CO_2. *Biomaterials*, **31**(7), 1655–1665 (2010).
90. Z. Peng and F. Chen, Synthesis and properties of temperature-sensitive hydrogel based on hydroxyethyl cellulose. *Int. J. Polym. Mater.*, **59**(6), 450–461 (2010).
91. G. Tronci, A. Doyle, S. J. Russell, and D. J. Wood, Structure-property-function relationships in triple helical collagen hydrogels. Preprint, arXiv: 1212.2206 (2012).
92. S. Bonakdar, S. H. Emami, M. A. Shokrgozar, A. Farhadi, S. A. H. Ahmadi, and A. Amanzadeh, Preparation and characterization of polyvinyl alcohol hydrogels

cross-linked by biodegradable polyurethane for tissue engineering of cartilage. *Mater. Sci. Eng. C*, **30**(4), 636–643 (2010).
93. A. R. Kulkarni, K. S. Soppimath, T. M. Aminabhavi, A. M. Dave, and M. H. Mehta, Glutaraldehyde cross-linked sodium alginate beads containing liquid pesticide for soil application. *J. Control. Release*, **63**(1), 97–105 (2000).
94. L. Wang and J. P. Stegemann, Glyoxal cross-linking of cell-seeded chitosan/collagen hydrogels for bone regeneration. *Acta Biomater.*, **7**(6), 2410–2417 (2011).
95. R. A. Muzzarelli, Chitins and chitosans for the repair of wounded skin, nerve, cartilage and bone. *Carbohyd. Polym.*, **76**(2), 167–182 (2009).
96. G. W. Yeager, Cross-linked polyimide and method of making them (US7339009 B2), 16 Decembe (2008).
97. S. Hirano and M. Takeuji, Structural analysis of the reaction products of chitosan with o-, m- and p-phthalaldehydes. *Int. J. Biol. Macromol.*, **5**(6), 373–376 (1983).
98. H. C. Kolb, M. Finn, and K. B. Sharpless, Click chemistry: Diverse chemical function from a few good reactions. *Angew. Chem. Int. Edit.*, **40**(11), 2004–2021 (2001).
99. S. Matsuda, N. Se, H. Iwata, and Y. Ikada, Evaluation of the antiadhesion potential of UV cross-linked gelatin films in a rat abdominal model. *Biomaterials*, **23**(14), 2901–2908 (2002).
100. V. Premnath, W. Harris, M. Jasty, and E. Merrill, Gamma sterilization of UHMWPE articular implants: An analysis of the oxidation problem. *Biomaterials*, 17(18), 1741–1753 (1996).
101. S. D. Bruck, Sterilization problems of synthetic biocompatible materials. *J. Biomed. Mater. Res.*, **5**(3), 139–158 (1971).
102. C. A. Rockwood and M. A. Wirth, Observation on retrieved hylamer glenoids in shoulder arthroplasty: Problems associated with sterilization by gamma irradiation in air. *J. Shoulder Elb. Surg*, **11**(2), 191–197 (2002).
103. T. von Woedtke, W.-D. Jalich, V. Hartmann, M. Stieber, and P. Abel, Sterilization of enzyme glucose sensors: Problems and concepts. *Biosens. Bioelectron.*, **17**(5), 373–382 (2002).
104. J. Dippy, S. Hughes, and A. Rozanski, 498. The dissociation constants of some symmetrically disubstituted succinic acids. *J. Chem. Soc. (Resumed)*, 2492–2498 (1959).
105. J. Delaire, M. Rodgers, and S. Webber, Quenching of fluorescence in water-soluble copolymers of methacrylic acid and vinyldiphenylanthracene. *J. Phys. Chem.*, **88**(25), 6219–6227 (1984).
106. A. Parrill, Amino Acid Structures. Michigan State University, (1997). Available at http://www.cem.msu.edu/~cem252/sp97/ch24/ch24aa.html.
107. H. Akikaze, Process for producing vinylsulfonic acid. EP Patent 2,128,131 (2009).
108. A. D. Wilson and J. Ellis, Poly-vinylphosphonic acid and metal oxide or cermet or glass ionomer cement. EP Patent 0,340,016, (1993).
109. Y.-L. Su and C. Li, The reorientation of poly (2-dimethylamino ethyl methacrylate) after environment stimuli improves hydrophilicity and resistance of protein adsorption. *J. Colloid Interface Sci.*, **316**(2), 344–349 (2007).

110. R. Palaniswamy, S. Dai, M. K. Tam, and L. H. Gan, Novel pH responsive amphiphilic diblock copolymers with reversible micellization properties, *Langmuir*, **19**(12), 5175–5177 (2004).
111. K. L. Thompson, E. S. Read, and S. P. Armes, Chemical degradation of poly (2-aminoethyl methacrylate). *Polym. Degrad. Stabil.*, **93**(8), 1460–1466 (2008).
112. X. Gao, Y. Cui, R. M. Levenson, L. W. Chung, and S. Nie, *In vivo* cancer targeting and imaging with semiconductor quantum dots. *Nat. biotechnol.*, **22**(8), 969–976 (2004).
113. Y. Urano, D. Asanuma, Y. Hama, Y. Koyama, T. Barrett, M. Kamiya, T. Nagano, T. Watanabe, A. Hasegawa, and P.L. Choyke, Selective molecular imaging of viable cancer cells with pH-activatable fluorescence probes. *Nat. Med.*, **15**(1), 104–109 (2008).
114. G. M. Kim, Y. H. Bae, and W. H. Jo, pH-induced micelle formation of poly (histidine-co-phenylalanine)-block-PEG in aqueous media. *Macromol. Bioscience*, **5**(11), 1118–1124 (2005).
115. E. S. Lee, H. J. Shin, K. Na, and Y. H. Bae, Poly (l-histidine)-PEG block copolymer micelles and pH-induced destabilization. *J. Control. Release*, **90**(3), 363–374 (2003).
116. Y.-F. Zeng, S. J. Tseng, I. M. Kempson, S.-F. Peng, W.-T. Wu, and J.-R. Liu, Controlled delivery of recombinant adeno-associated virus serotype 2 using pH-sensitive PEG-poly-l-histidine hydrogels. *Biomaterials*, **33**(36), 9239–9245 (2012).
117. G. Acharya, C. S. Shin, M. McDermott, H. Mishra, H. Park, I. C. Kwon, and K. Park, The hydrogel template method for fabrication of homogeneous nano/microparticles. *J. Control. Release*, **141**(3), 314–319 (2010).
118. M. Carafa, C. Marianecci, L. Di Marzio, F. Rinaldi, C. Di Meo, P. Matricardi, F. Alhaique, and T. Coviello, A new vesicle-loaded hydrogel system suitable for topical applications: Preparation and characterization. *J. Pharm. Pharm. Sci.*, **14**(3), 336–346 (2011).
119. B. Jeong, S. W. Kim, and Y. H. Bae, Thermosensitive sol-gel reversible hydrogels. *Adv. Drug Deliver. Rev.*, **54**(1), 37–51 (2002).
120. L. M. Gradinaru, C. Ciobanu, S. Vlad, M. Bercea, and M. Popa, Synthesis and rheology of thermoreversible polyurethane hydrogels. *Cent. Eur. J. Chem.*, 1–8 (2012).
121. B. Jeong, S. W. Kim, and Y. H. Bae, Thermosensitive sol-gel reversible hydrogels. *Adv. Drug Deliver. Rev.*, **64**, 154–162 (2012).
122. T. Thimma Reddy and A. Takahara, Simultaneous and sequential micro-porous semi-interpenetrating polymer network hydrogel films for drug delivery and wound dressing applications. *Polymer*, **50**(15), 3537–3546 (2009).
123. M. C. Hacker, L. Klouda, B. B. Ma, J. D. Kretlow, and A. G. Mikos, Synthesis and characterization of injectable, thermally and chemically gelable, amphiphilic PNIPAM-based macromers. *Biomacromolecules*, **9**(6), 1558–1570 (2008).
124. S. B. Lin, C. H. Yuan, A. R. Ke, Y. L. Li, and N. Ouyang, Electrical sensitivity and mechanical properties of fast responsive PAMPS-PAA-PVA T-IPN hydrogels. *Adv. Polym. Technol.*, **32**(S1), E20–E31 (2011).
125. S. J. Kim, S. G. Yoon, S. M. Lee, S. H. Lee, and S. I. Kim, Electrical sensitivity behavior of a hydrogel composed of polymethacrylic acid/PVA. *J. Appl. Polym. Sci.*, **91**(6), 3613–3617 (2004).

126. Y. Qiu and K. Park, Environment-sensitive hydrogels for drug delivery. *Adv. Drug Deliver. Rev.*, **53**(3), 321–339 (2001).
127. L. X. Li, X. D. Xing, Z. L. Liu, H. T. Fan, and M. Hu, Synthesis and properties of a thermo-/light-sensitive hydrogel. *Adv. Mater. Res.*, **557**, 1556–1562 (2012).
128. C. H. Zhu, Y. Lu, J. Peng, J. F. Chen, and S. H. Yu, Photothermally sensitive PNIPAM/graphene oxide nanocomposite hydrogels as remote light-controlled liquid microvalves. *Adv. Funct. Mater.*, **22**(19), 4017–4022 (2012).
129. A. Sahu, W. I. Choi, and G. Tae, Stimuli (temperature/light/pH)-sensitive injectable graphene oxide composite hydrogel. *Chem. Commun.*, **48**, 5820–5822 (2012).
130. S. J. Lee and K. Park, Synthesis and characterization of sol-gel phase-reversible hydrogels sensitive to glucose. *J. Mol. Recognit.*, **9**(5–6), 549–557 (1996).
131. E. Lopez-Montero, J. -F. R. dos Santos, J. J. Torres-Labandeira, A. Concheiro, and C. Alvarez-Lorenzo, Sertaconazole-loaded cyclodextrin polysaccharide hydrogels as antifungal devices. *Open Drug Deliver. J.*, **3**, 1–9 (2009).
132. R. Barbucci, S. Lamponi, A. Borzacchiello, L. Ambrosio, M. Fini, P. Torricelli, and R. Giardino, Hyaluronic acid hydrogel in the treatment of osteoarthritis. *Biomaterials*, **23**(23), 4503–4513 (2002).
133. P. A. Gunatillake and R. Adhikari, Biodegradable synthetic polymers for tissue engineering. *Eur. Cell. Mater.*, **5**(1), 1–16 (2003).
134. M. A. Rice, J. Sanchez-Adams, and K. S. Anseth, Exogenously triggered, enzymatic degradation of photopolymerized hydrogels with polycaprolactone subunits: Experimental observation and modeling of mass loss behavior. *Biomacromolecules*, **7**(6), 1968–1975 (2006).
135. S. Li, A. El Ghzaoui, and E. Dewinck, Rheology and drug release properties of bioresorbable hydrogels prepared from polylactide/PEG block copolymers. *Macromol. Symp.*, **222**, 23–36 (2005).
136. B. Jeong, Y. H. Bae, and S. W. Kim, Drug release from biodegradable injectable thermosensitive hydrogel of PEG-PLGA-PEG triblock copolymers. *J. Control. Release*, **63**(1), 155–163 (2000).

Chapter 3

Computational Nanomechanics of Hydrogels

Hossein Salahshoor and Nima Rahbar
Department of Civil and Environmental Engineering, Worcester Polytechnic Institute, Worcester, MA

1. Part I: All-Atom (AA) Molecular Dynamics (MD) Simulation

1.1. Introduction

Hydrogels are three-dimensionally crosslinked polymer networks that can absorb and retain large amount of water, even up to thousands of theirs dry wights.[1,2] They do not dissolve in water due to the presence of covalent bonds in the crosslinks zones. Among different physical properties of hydrogels, we are interested in the mechanical properties such as toughness[15] and strength at small scale that are required for many functional applications of hydrogels.

MD simulations have been employed to study various properties of hydrogels including the equilibrated structure, mechanical properties, diffusivity of water and ions.[20–22, 25–27] Jang *et al.*[17] have studied mechanical properties of double network (DN) hydrogels. They obtained stress–strain curves for DN hydrogels by applying uniaxial deformation up to 300%. Lee *et al.*[18,19] have studied the structure and mechanical properties of crosslinked hydrogels in both blocky and random hydrogels. Chiessi *et al.*[16] have studied dynamics of polymer and water in hydrogels. Swelling of hydrogels is one of the most characteristic properties of hydrogels which occurs in an aqueous solution by absorbing the solvent. This process is influenced by many factors. Walter *et al.*[28] have studied swelling behavior of hydrogels by proposing a realistic MD model of hydrogels obtained by the experiments on freeze-dried hydrogel. Also, Wu *et al.*[29] focused on the diffusivity of water and ions in hydrogels. They have shown in their studies that by increasing the crosslinking density, the diffusion coefficients decrease.

In this study, a novel computational method is applied to model the crosslinking process and studying mechanical properties of hydrogels using MD simulations. Stiffness matrices and elastic moduli are calculated by applying a uniaxial strain to the system. The simulation details are presented in the next section.

2. MD Simulation

2.1. Model construction

The epoxy and curing agent used for this study are Polyethylene glycol diglycidyl ether (PEGDGE) and the Jeffamine that is poly-oxy-alkylene-amines, respectively (see Fig. 1). The chemical structure of the PEGDGE and Jeffamine are built separately, and the end hydrogen atoms are removed to provide reactive atom sites at the end groups, where the crosslinks will form. The two polymer molecules are then packed into an amorphous unit cell which is constructed using self-avoiding random walk method of Theodorou and Suter.[3] The unit cell is built with a PEGDGE:Jeffamine ratio of 1 to 4, having a density of 1.086 g/cm^3. Also, the water molecule is packed into the system to reach different values for volume percent of water. Five different systems are modeled containing 0, 20, 40, 60, and 80 wt.%.

2.2. Crosslinking process

Conventional MD is not capable of modeling the crosslinking process that involves formation and breaking of bonds. On the other hand, with the present computational resources, sophisticated electronic structure calculation methods, such as *ab initio* method, are costly and impractical, if not impossible, for macromolecules (e.g., polymers) and large systems. New statistical methods have therefore been developed that allow for such calculations in a more tractable way. The method developed by Wu and Xu,[4] is an example of such methods. The main simplifying hypothesis in this technique is that it considers same reactivity for all the end groups. The charge

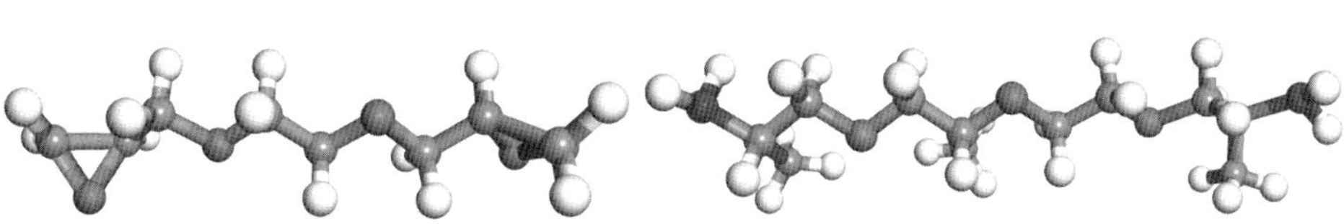

(A) (B)

Fig. 1. Chemical structure of epoxy and curing agent with oxygen, nitrogen, carbon and hydrogen as red, blue, grey and white respectively: (A) PEGDGE; (B) polyoxyalkyleneamine (Jeffamine).

distribution is calculated using QEq method.[5] The process is modeled through cyclic canonical (NVT) and isothermal-isobaric (NPT) ensembles. First a geometry optimization and energy minimization is performed in the room temperature (298 K). Next, the system's temperature is raised to 358 K. The system is then cooled down step by step at a rate of 10 K/50 ps. In each step, after the completion of NVT and NPT simulations, the proximity of reactive sites are examined and if they are within a radius of 2 Å from each other, bonds are created. This process is repeated until the system reaches the initial temperature. Nose-Hoover and Andersen algorithms are used as thermostat and barostat, respectively.

2.3. Force field and simulation parameters

A crucial point in atomistic simulations is choosing a force field that result in an accurate enough approximation of the potential energy hypersurface in which the nuclei moves. The potential energy can be described as follows:

$$E_{\text{total}} = E_{\text{valence}} + E_{\text{cross-term}} + E_{\text{non-bonded}}. \tag{1}$$

The valence energy consists of the bond-stretching term, bending energy and the four body terms including a dihedral bond-torsion angle term and an inversion (out-of-plane interaction) term

$$E_{\text{valence}} = E_{\text{stretching}} + E_{\text{bendeing}} + E_{\text{dihedral torsion}} + E_{\text{inversion}}. \tag{2}$$

The cross-term accounts for the energy changes induced by the change in the bond length and the angle changes in the surrounding atoms as illustrated in the Eq. (3):

$$\begin{aligned} E_{\text{cross-term}} = {} & E_{\text{bond-bond}} + E_{\text{angle–angle}} + E_{\text{bond–angle}} + E_{\text{end\_bond–torsion}} \\ & + E_{\text{middle\_bond–torsion}} + E_{\text{angle–torsion}} + E_{\text{angle–angle–torsion}}. \end{aligned} \tag{3}$$

The last term in the Eq. (1) (the non-bonded term) consists of inter- and intramolecular interactions, including hydrogen bonds (H-bonds), van der Waals interactions which are the induced dipole–dipole interactions (also named as London forces) and finally, the Coulomb interactions which account for electrostatic interactions.

$$E_{\text{non-bonded}} = E_{\text{vdW}} + E_{\text{Coulomb}} + E_{\text{H-bond}}. \tag{4}$$

The condensed-phased optimized molecular potential (COMPASS) that has proved to be a promising force field for organic and inorganic systems, is used in this study.[6–8] It is well parametrized for non-bonded interactions which makes it a good fit for long chain molecules like biomaterials or polymers and systems where the vdW is the dominant interaction.[9–11] The COMPASS force field uses the following expressions for various components of the potential energy:

$$E_{\text{bond}} = \sum_b [K_2(b-b_0)^2 + K_3(b-b_0)^3 + K_4(b-b_0)^4], \tag{5}$$

$$E_{\text{angle}} = \sum_\theta [H_2(\theta-\theta_0)^2 + H_3(\theta-\theta_0)^3 + H_4(\theta-\theta_0)^4], \tag{6}$$

$$E_{\text{torsion}} = \sum_\phi [V_1[1-\cos(\phi-\phi_1^0)] + V_2[1-\cos(2\phi-\phi_2^0) + V_3[1-\cos(3\phi-\phi_3^0)]], \tag{7}$$

$$E_{\text{oop}} = \sum_x K_x \chi^2, \tag{8}$$

$$E_{\text{bond-bond}} = \sum_b \sum_b F_{bb}(b-b_0)(b'-b'_0), \tag{9}$$

$$E_{\text{angle-angle}} = \sum_\theta \sum_\theta F_{\theta\theta}'(\theta-\theta_0)(\theta'-\theta'_0), \tag{10}$$

$$E_{\text{bond-angle}} = \sum_b \sum_\theta F_{b\theta}(b-b_0)(\theta-\theta_0), \tag{11}$$

$$E_{\text{end\_bond-torsion}} = \sum_b \sum_\phi F_{b\phi}(b-b_0)[V_1\cos\phi + V_2\cos 2\phi + V_3\cos 3\phi], \tag{12}$$

$$E_{\text{middle\_bond-torsion}} = \sum_b \sum_\phi F_{b\phi}(b'-b'_0)[F_1\cos\phi + F_2\cos 2\phi + F_3\cos 3\phi], \tag{13}$$

$$E_{\text{angle-torsion}} = \sum_\theta \sum_\phi F_{\theta\phi}(\theta-\theta_0)\times[V_1\cos\phi + V_2\cos 2\phi + V_3\cos 3\phi], \tag{14}$$

$$E_{\text{angle-angle-torsion}} = \sum_\phi \sum_\theta \sum_\theta K_{\phi\theta\theta}'\cos\phi(\theta-\theta_0)(\theta'-\theta'_0), \tag{15}$$

$$E_{\text{Coulumb}} = \sum_{i>j} \frac{q_i q_j}{\varepsilon r_{ij}}, \tag{16}$$

$$E_{\text{vdW}} = \sum_{i>j}\left[\frac{A_{ij}}{r_{ij}^9} - \frac{B_{ij}}{r_{ij}^6}\right], \tag{17}$$

where b, θ, Φ and χ are the bond length, bond-angle, dihedral torsion angle and the inversion or out of plane angle respectively. Also, q is the atomic charge, ε is dielectric constant and r_{ij} is the interatomic distance between the atoms i and j. Finally, b_0, K_i $(i = 2-4)$, θ_0, H_i $(i = 2-4)$, Φ_i^0 $(i = 1-3)$, V_i $(i = 1-3)$, $F_{bb'}$, b_0, $F_{\theta\theta'}$, θ_0, $F_{b\theta}$, F_{bf}, $F_{bf'}$, $Fi(I = 1-3)$, $F_{\theta f}$, $K_{f\theta\theta'}$, A_{ij}, and B_{ij} are the system dependent parameters implemented in the Material Studio 6.0 software package, which is used in this study.

3. Results and Discussion

3.1. Crosslinking process

As mentioned earlier, the crosslinking process is performed by creating reactive sites and cyclic NVT and NPT dynamic simulations.[11] To this end, H-atoms are removed from N_{Jeff} (end nitrogen atoms in the Jeffamine) and C_{PEGDGE} (end carbon atoms in the PEGDGE). These are shown in solid and grey in Fig. 1. Figure 2 shows the hydrogel structure before and after crosslinking. In order to mimic the natural crosslinking process, a probability of 70% is imposed when creating bonds. In other words, about 70% of crosslinks are created. This is clearly seen in the Fig. 2(B), where some N_{Jeff} atoms are still not connected to any carbon atoms of PEGDGE.

The distribution of N_{Jeff} and C_{PEGDGE} atoms before and after the crosslinking provides a better insight into the process. This is analyzed by radial distribution function (RDF). $g_{A-B}(r)$ is the probability density of finding atoms A and B at a distance r averaged over the equilibrium trajectory, so that:

$$g_{A-B}(r) = \frac{\left(\dfrac{n_B}{4\pi r^2 dr}\right)}{\left(\dfrac{N_B}{V}\right)}, \tag{18}$$

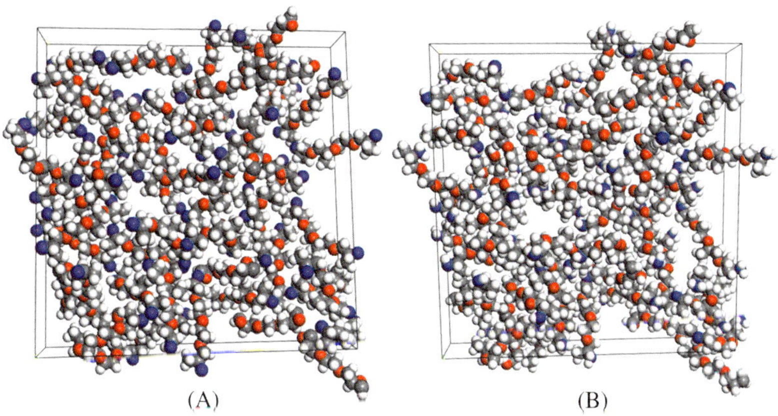

(A) (B)

Fig. 2. The hydrogel initial model without water: (A) before crosslinking; (B) after crosslinking.

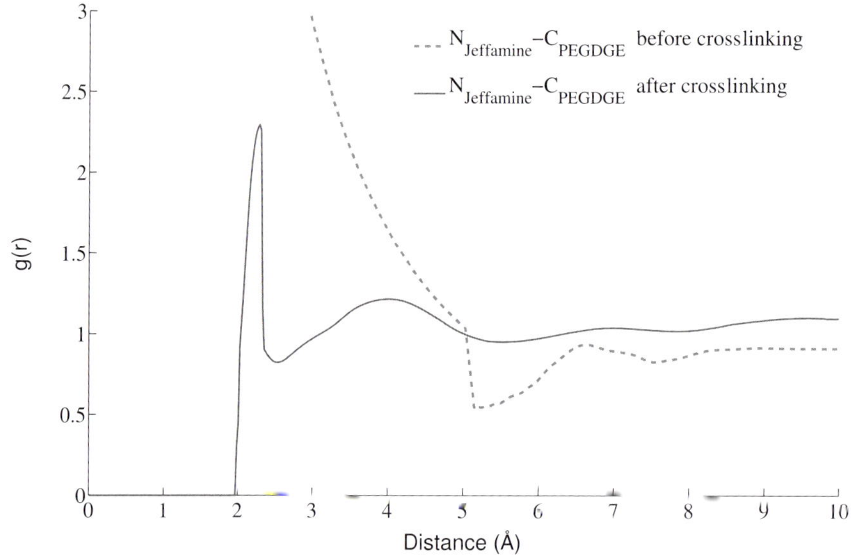

Fig. 3. Radial Distribution Function of N_{Jeff}–C_{PEGDGE} pair for the initial model: (A) before crosslinking; (B) after crosslinking.

where n_B is the number of *B* particles located at a distance *r* in a shell of thickness *dr* from A particle, N_B is the total number of *B* particles in the system, and *V* is the total volume of the system. $g_{N_{Jeff}-C_{PEGDGE}}$ characterizes the relative configuration of *N* and *C* atoms in the curing agent and epoxy quantitatively. Figure 3 shows the RDF of the system before and after the crosslinking simulations. Basically, the two RDFs are for a pair of atoms: case I) in two difference molecules. case II) In a continuous polymer system packed in a unit cell. The graph demonstrates a discontinuous RDF for the system before crosslinking and a smooth, continuous curve after the crosslinking, which is due to the created crosslinks. The graph is a quantitative proof for bond creations between the Jeffamine and PEGDGE molecules.

3.2. Equilibrated structure and the role of water

The structure of hydrogel is equilibrated and studied for 20, 40, 60, and 80 volume percent of water content. For each system, the crosslinking process is performed. Also, an energy minimization is performed on the final crosslinked structure to reach the minimum energy configuration of the system. This is done via NVT simulation on the system at the room temperature with a time step of 1 fs and for a duration of 50 ps. The final equilibrated structures before and after the crosslinking with various water percentages are presented in Fig. 4.

The system evolves through the dynamic simulations to reach its minimum energy configuration. The effect of water content on the distances between

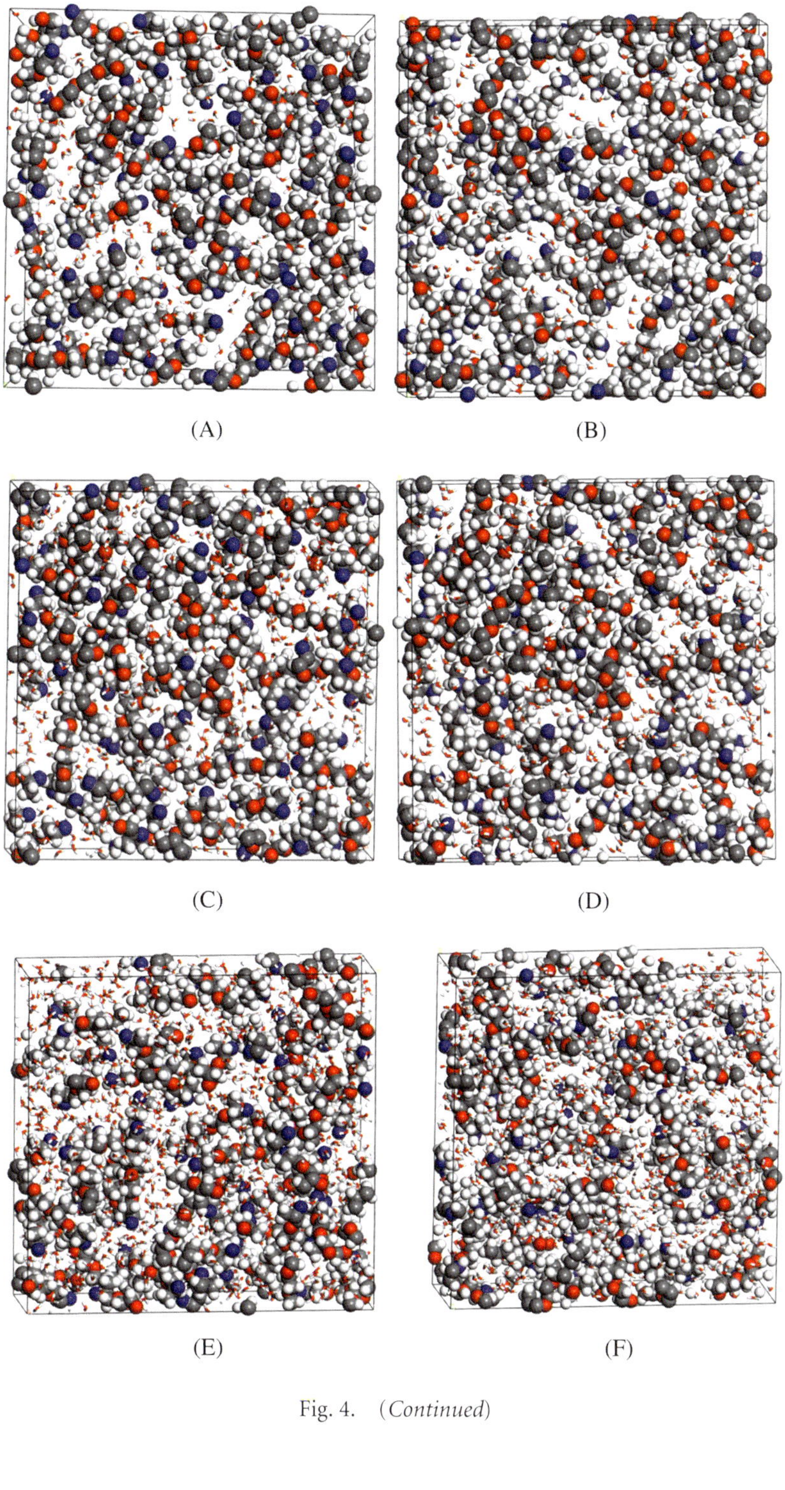

(A) (B) (C) (D) (E) (F)

Fig. 4. (*Continued*)

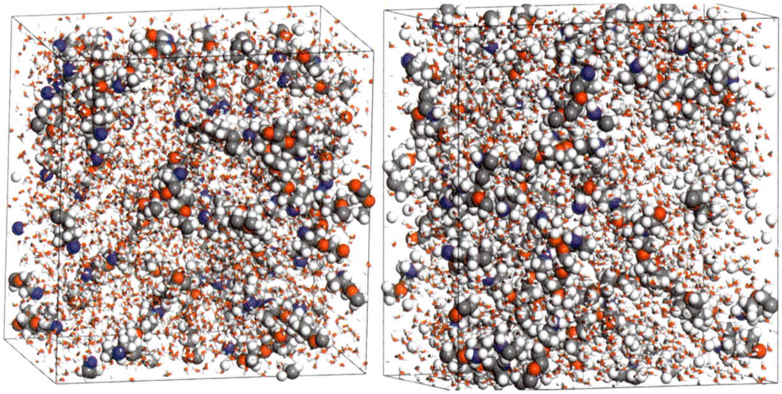

(G) (H)

Fig. 4. Equilibrated hydrogel structures: (A) 20 wt.% before crosslinking; (B) 20 wt.% after crosslinking; (C) 40 wt.% before crosslinking; (D) 40 wt.% after crosslinking; (E) 60 wt.% before crosslinking; (F) 60 wt.% after crosslinking; (G) 80 wt.% before crosslinking; (H) 80 wt.% after crosslinking.

different atoms in the final and evolved structures is studied using RDFs (see Fig. 5). In order to directly compare the intensities, the product of RDF and the number density $rg(r)$ is used instead of $g(r)$. Figure 5 depicts $rg_{Oxygen-O(Water)}(r)$, $rg_{Nitrogen-O(Water)}(r)$ and $rg_{Carbon-O(Water)}(r)$, and for different water contents. These results show that the intensity of $rg(r)$ increases with the increase in water content. The Nitrogen and Oxygen atoms of the crosslinked hydrogel contain negative charges, while the Carbon atoms have positive charge. As water content increases, the electrostatic interactions dominate more, thus the probability of finding a carbon atom near the water molecules increases. Since the N atoms are only present in Jeffamine molecule, they are the zones where the crosslinks are built (N_{Jeff}). Analysis of RDFs proves that the water molecules are closer to the crosslink zones.

3.3. Effect of crosslinking on diffusion coefficients

Based on the MD simulations, the coefficients of the effective diffusion D (D in equilibrium diffusion) is computed for the water molecules in the hydrogel with different water contents using the Mean-Square Displacement (MSD) formula.[2] According to the following equation, the MSD of water molecules are computed before and after the crosslinking process:

$$\mathrm{MSD} = \frac{1}{NM}\sum_{i}^{N}\sum_{k}^{M}\left\langle \left| r_i(t_k+\Delta t) - r_i(t_k) \right| \right\rangle^2, \tag{19}$$

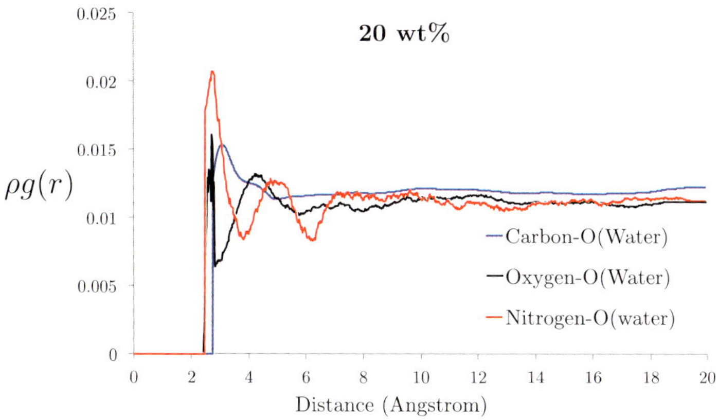

(A)

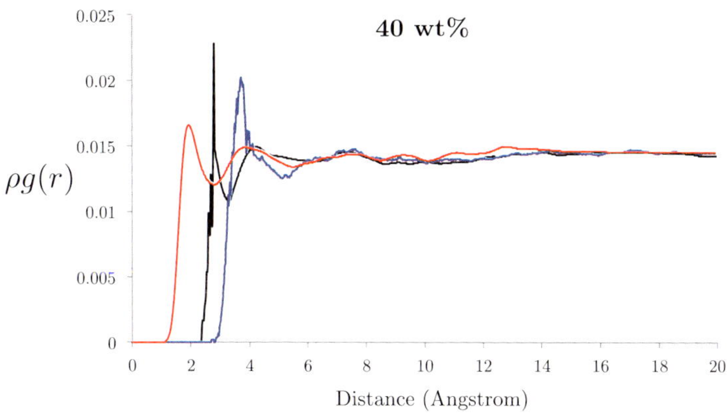

(B)

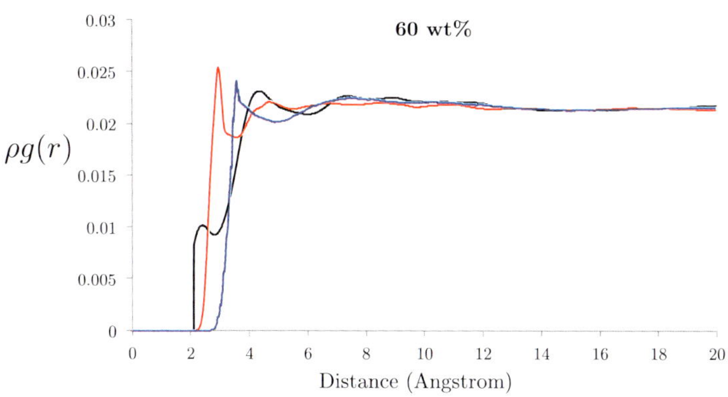

(C)

Fig. 5. (*Continued*)

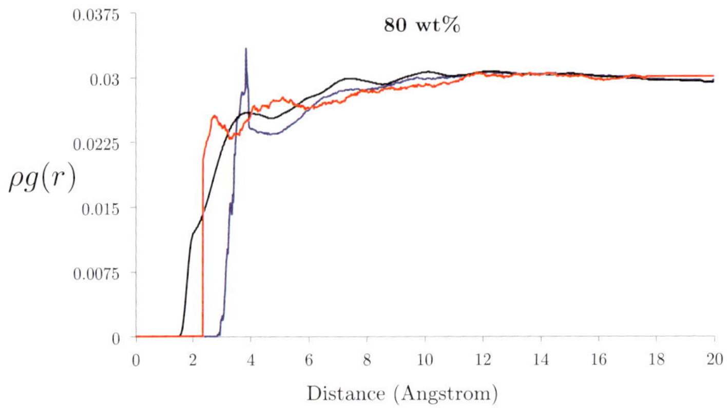

D

Fig. 5. Radial Distribution Function for Oxygen–O (Water, Nitrogen–O (Water) and Carbon–O (Water) pairs for different water contents: (A) 20 wt.%; (B) 40 wt.%; (C) 60 wt.%; (D) 80 wt.%.

N: Number of particles (in here, water molecules),
M: Number of Time Series,
r_i: Location of particle,
t_k: Starting time of the *k*th time series.

After computing the MSD, determination of diffusion coefficient *D*, is performed using the Einstein's equation as follows:

$$D = \lim_{t \to \infty} \frac{1}{6t} \text{MSD}. \tag{20}$$

Instead of using an infinitely long running time as indicated in the equation, the 500 ps simulations time for the evaluation stage was found to be long enough to reach to linear portion of MSD, indicating the equilibrium diffusion stage of water molecules in the MD simulations.

Figure 6 demonstrates the effect of crosslinking on the diffusion coefficients. It is clearly seen that crosslinking decreases the diffusion coefficients and thus decreasing the mobility of water molecules. Also, by increasing the water content, the diffusion coefficients increase. The results are consistent with the prescribed hydrophilicity of the crosslink zones.

3.4. Elastic properties of hydrogels

Mechanical properties of hydrogel were studied by applying a predefined strain to unit cell. For a uniaxial testing, a total strain amplitude of 0.003 was applied to the simulation box which was enforced equally at each simulation step (every 1 fs). The stress was calculated from the uniaxial test in the x-direction using the virial relation:

$$\sigma_{ij} = \frac{1}{2\Omega^i} \sum_{j(\neq i)} r_{ij} \otimes f_{ij}, \tag{21}$$

where Ω^i is a small volume around an atom i. The interatomic force f_{ij} applied on atom i by atom j is:

$$f_{ij} = \frac{\partial E(r_{ij})}{\partial r_{ij}} \frac{r_{ij}}{\left\| r_{ij} \right\|}. \tag{22}$$

This procedure was performed for the systems with different water contents. After computing σ_{xx}, σ_{yy}, σ_{zz} independently for the simulation box, the three stress values were averaged to compute the elastic modulus. Finally, the 6 × 6 stiffness matrices were also computed, by applying a unit displacement in each degree of freedom, for different water contents:

$$0\text{wt.\%} \Rightarrow C_{ij} = \begin{pmatrix} 6.7650 & 3.0836 & 4.6568 & -0.5538 & -0.6347 & 0.4578 \\ 3.0836 & 9.6250 & 4.6229 & -0.1655 & -0.0066 & 1.2009 \\ 4.6568 & 4.6229 & 11.9052 & -0.5518 & -0.8331 & 0.5603 \\ -0.5538 & -0.1655 & -0.5518 & 1.7093 & -0.5200 & -0.0709 \\ -0.6347 & -0.0066 & -0.8331 & -0.5200 & 1.6852 & 0.3397 \\ 0.4578 & 1.2009 & 0.5603 & -0.0709 & 0.3397 & 2.1630 \end{pmatrix},$$

$$20\text{wt.\%} \Rightarrow C_{ij} = \begin{pmatrix} 10.0473 & 2.9468 & 3.6788 & -0.0066 & 0.3673 & 0.6654 \\ 2.9768 & 7.7488 & 4.1584 & 0.5323 & 0.3339 & 0.2095 \\ 3.6788 & 4.1584 & 9.1498 & -0.1284 & -0.1745 & -0.0464 \\ -0.0066 & 0.5323 & -0.1284 & 1.6645 & 0.3879 & -0.1146 \\ -0.3676 & 0.3339 & -0.1745 & 0.3897 & 2.3715 & -0.7634 \\ 0.6654 & 0.2095 & -0.0464 & -0.1146 & -0.7634 & 1.4606 \end{pmatrix},$$

$$40\text{wt.\%} \Rightarrow C_{ij} = \begin{pmatrix} 6.5619 & 3.3001 & 4.0905 & -0.2213 & -0.0032 & -0.3711 \\ 3.3001 & 7.7734 & 4.2747 & -0.1413 & 0.0666 & -0.5896 \\ 4.0905 & 4.2747 & 7.1310 & -0.0827 & 0.5737 & -0.6408 \\ -0.2213 & -0.1413 & -0.0827 & 2.6061 & -0.1855 & 0.1544 \\ -0.0032 & 0.0666 & 0.5737 & -0.1855 & 1.7400 & -0.4800 \\ -0.3711 & -0.5896 & -0.6408 & 0.1544 & 0.4800 & 0.9157 \end{pmatrix},$$

$$60\text{wt.\%} \Leftrightarrow C_{ij} = \begin{pmatrix} 5.7631 & 3.4711 & 3.3436 & -0.0054 & -0.1865 & -0.1339 \\ 3.4711 & 4.7573 & 3.8203 & -0.0708 & -0.4171 & -0.3931 \\ 3.3436 & 3.8206 & 6.9301 & -0.2693 & 0.0132 & -0.1272 \\ -0.0054 & -0.0708 & 0.2693 & 1.5602 & -0.2298 & 0.1333 \\ -0.1865 & -0.4171 & 0.0132 & -0.2298 & 1.8788 & -0.3903 \\ -0.1339 & -0.3931 & -0.1272 & 0.1333 & -0.3903 & 2.4970 \end{pmatrix},$$

$$80\text{wt.\%} \Rightarrow C_{ij} = \begin{pmatrix} 4.9663 & 4.5360 & 3.3063 & 0.3025 & 0.6299 & -0.1029 \\ 4.5360 & 6.5612 & 4.6907 & -0.6374 & 0.1067 & -0.2596 \\ 3.3063 & 4.6907 & 5.7067 & -0.0107 & 0.6878 & 0.6421 \\ 0.3025 & -0.6374 & 0.0107 & 1.6099 & 0.4820 & 0.2120 \\ 0.6299 & 0.1067 & 0.6078 & 0.4820 & 0.7627 & -0.9780 \\ -0.1029 & -0.2596 & 0.6521 & 0.2120 & -0.9780 & 0.5030 \end{pmatrix}.$$

Elastic moduli were calculated after energy minimizations in different water contents. Figure 6 illustrates elastic modules for 20, 40, 60, and 80 wt.%. Water molecules act as lubricators allowing more deformation in the hydrogel under a specific stress. Therefore, the stiffness of hydrogel decreases with the increase in water content.

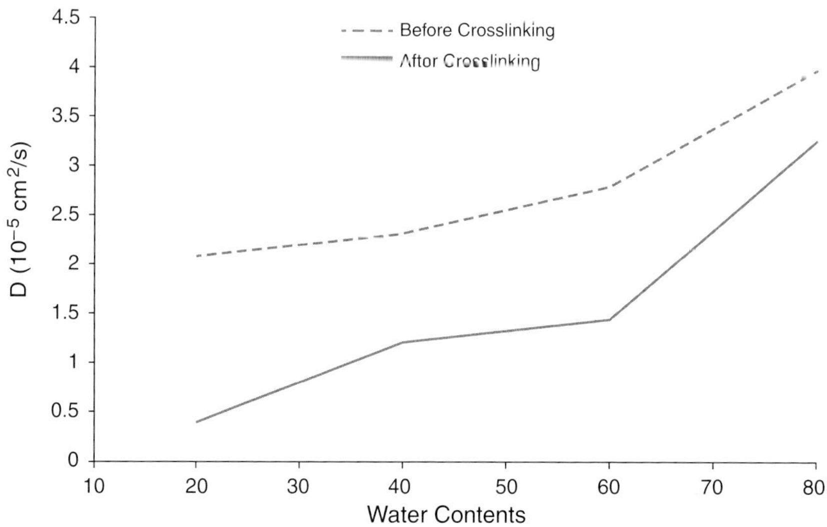

Fig. 6. Diffusion coefficients for water molecules in different water contents, both before and after crosslinking.

4. Part II: Coarse-Grained (CG) Model of Hydrogel

4.1. Introduction

The use of CG models in a variety of simulation techniques has proven to be an effective tool to probe the time and length scales of systems beyond what is feasible with traditional AA models. Using AA methods, long simulations are costly and even close to impossible. They also limit us to small length and especially time scales. A promising strategy to overcome these limitations is to decrease number of degrees of freedom by grouping atoms into pseudoatoms (or particles) referred to as beads.[13] This represents the basis of the so-called CG approach, where, starting at the nanoscale, it is possible to derive parameters for higher hierarchical levels, up to the macroscale by systematically feeding information from smaller, more accurate to larger, coarser levels. Coarse-graining models were initiated for modeling huge biomolecules.[14]

Among different CG models, MARTINI CG model, developed by Marrink and co-workers is used in this study. The MARTINI model provides suitable level of CG, as it retains information about the chemistry. In the following section, the details of MARTINI approach for the CG modeling are described.[24]

4.2 MARTINI Model

4.2.1. *Interaction sites*

The general mapping rule is that four heavy atoms (non-hydrogen atoms) are grouped together into one bead, i.e., on average four heavy atoms are represented by a single interaction center. For ring structures a different mapping mechanism is introduced, as will be explained below. In order to keep the model simple, we still consider only four main types of interaction sites: polar (P), non-polar (N), apolar (C), and charged (Q). Each particle type has a number of subtypes, which allow for a more accurate representation of the chemical nature of the underlying atomic structure. Within a main type, subtypes are either distinguished by a letter denoting the hydrogen-bonding capabilities (d = donor, a = acceptor, da = both, 0 = none), or by a number indicating the degree of polarity (from 1, low polarity, to 5, high polarity).

4.2.2. *Bonded and non-bonded interactions*

The form of the non-bonded interactions is the Lennard–Jones (LJ) 12–6 potential energy function. In addition to the LJ interaction, charged groups bear a full charge $q_{i,j}$ interacting via a shifted Coulombic potential energy function:

$$U_{el}(r) = \frac{q_i q_j}{4\pi\varepsilon_0\varepsilon_r r}, \tag{23}$$

with relative dielectric constant $\varepsilon_r = 15$ for explicit screening.

Among bonded interactions, the bond stretch form is weak harmonic potential with an equilibrium distance $R_{bond} = \sigma = 0.47$ nm and a force constant of $K_{bond} = 1250$ kJ mol^{-1} nm^{-2}. The LJ interaction is excluded from bonded particles, because they are on average somewhat closer to each other than neighboring non-bonded particles.

Also, weak harmonic potential of the cosine type is used for bending potential. Again, a set of parameters are defined for this form. Also for most of linear chain-like molecules, a standard force constant of $K_{angle} = 25$ kJ mol^{-1} with an equilibrium bond angle $\theta_0 = 180°$ is the best initial choice.

Basically, the coarse graining recipe consists of three steps:

1. Mapping onto CG representation: The first step is to divide the molecule into small chemical building blocks, ideally of four heavy atoms each. Because most molecules cannot be entirely mapped onto groups of four heavy atoms, however, some groups will represent a smaller or larger number of atoms. There are different strategies for modulation of building blocks, especially for certain compounds like those having ring structures, described in Marrink *et al.*[14]
2. Selecting bonded interactions: For most molecules the use of a standard bond length (0.47 nm) and force constant of $K_{bond} = 1250$ kJ mol^{-1}nm^{-2} seems to work well. Ring structures needs additional adjusting. Also, the values defined before for the bending parameters work quite well for most molecules.
3. Optimization: Since coarse graining procedure does not lead to a unique assignment of particle types and bonded interactions, the structure should be optimized. Hence, validating the results with the AA model is also popular.

4.3. CG Model for the Hydrogel

CG models of the PEGDGE and Jeffamine were built according to the MARTINI model. Figure 8 presents the bead assignments to the AA model. According to the crosslinking protocol prescribed earlier in Section 3.1, the end groups of the two molecules are assigned as charged groups, one as Q_a (Charged, acceptor) and the other one as Q_d (Charged donor). The CG model of the Jeffamine and PEGDGE are shown in the Fig. 9. Also, the water molecules were assigned as one bead. Since, water is a highly polar molecule, it was assigned as type P4 (very polar).

The CG model for the Jeffamine, PEGDGE and water were constructed by packing them in an amorphous cell, using the random walk method developed by Theodorou and Suter. The total density for the unit cell is 1.3096 g/cc^3. Periodic Boundary Conditions were applied for the system and the initial unit cell dimensions is 5 × 5 × 5 nm. Four different models were created containing 20, 40, 60 and 80% water content. The same crosslinking protocol was applied to the coarse grained system. The main focus in here was to study the mechanical properties of hydrogel and the effect of water content on the elastic properties. The results are validated with the available experimental data.

4.4. Results and Discussion

The first step after constructing the unit cells of the hydrogel is energy minization. For this purpose, for each of the systems, 5,000 steps of geometry optimization is performed. Then two dynamic simulations of NVT and NPT are performed sequentially. The time length for each dynamic simulation is 5 ns with the time step of 1 fs. Through these dynamic simulations, the system finds its minimum energy and the desired volume and pressure. Table 1 shows the final dimensions of the unit cells in different water contents after the initial minimization.

Figure 10 shows the final structure after the initial minimization for different water contents.

Transport properties of water molecules were studied in the CG model. For this purpose, MSD was calculated (as discussed in the previous section). Diffusion coefficients of water molecules were calculated using the random walk formula. The results of the CG model were validated with the AA model. As shown in Fig. 11, the results show a good compatibility among the two models, certifying the CG model in capturing the transport properties. This also verifies the CG algorithm and the bead assignment procedure.

After the optimization and minimization steps, shear strain is applied to the system. The shear is applied to the system step by step with a rate of 1e–5, through

Table 1. Cell dimensions, before and after the initial 10 ns minimization.

Water content (%)	Initial dimension (Å)	Final dimension after the minimizations (Å)
20	50 × 50 × 50	63.99 × 63.99 × 63.99
40	50 × 50 × 50	68.58 × 68.58 × 68.58
60	50 × 50 × 50	72.54 × 72.54 × 72.54
80	50 × 50 × 50	76.61 × 76.61 × 76.61

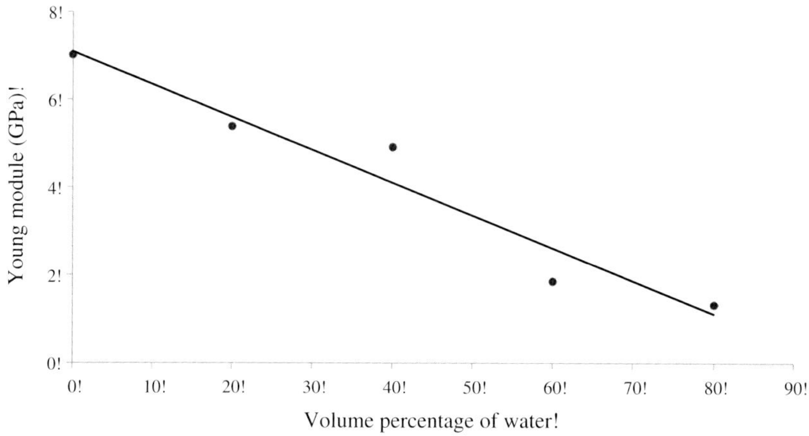

Fig. 7. Variation of elastic modulus as a function of water content.

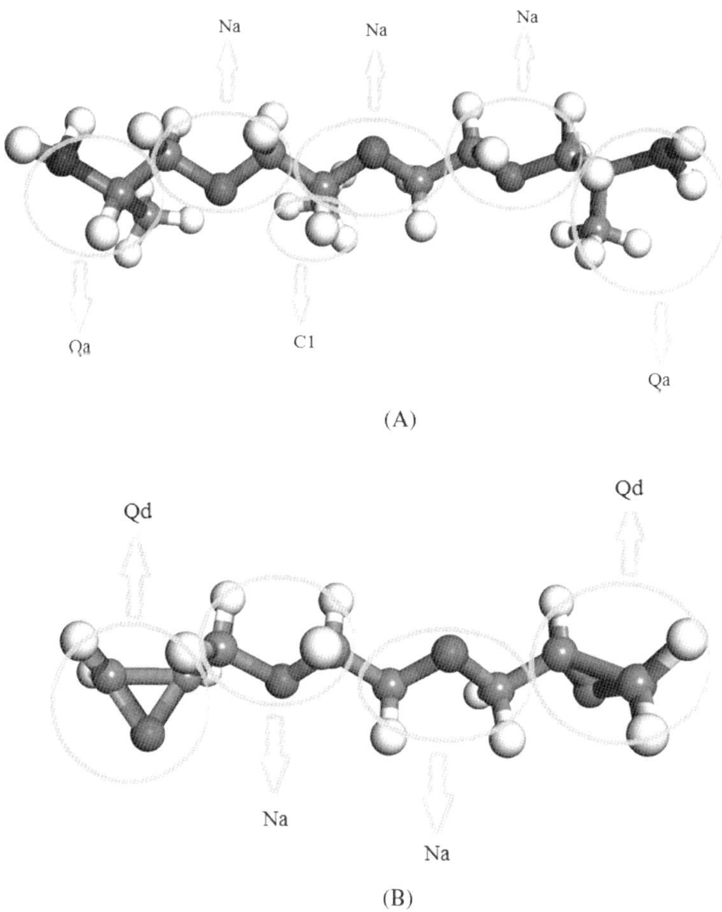

Fig. 8. AA model for: (A) Jeffamine; (B) PEGDGE. The Nitrogen, Oxygen, Carbon and Hydrogen atoms are shown in blue, red, grey and white, respectively.

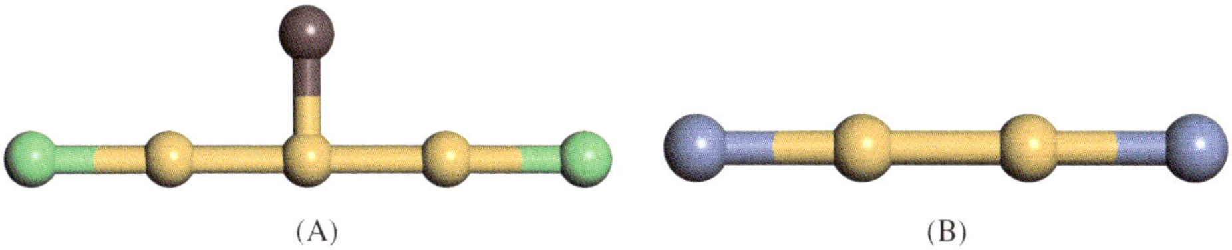

Fig. 9. CG model for the: (A) Jeffamine; (B) PEGDGE.

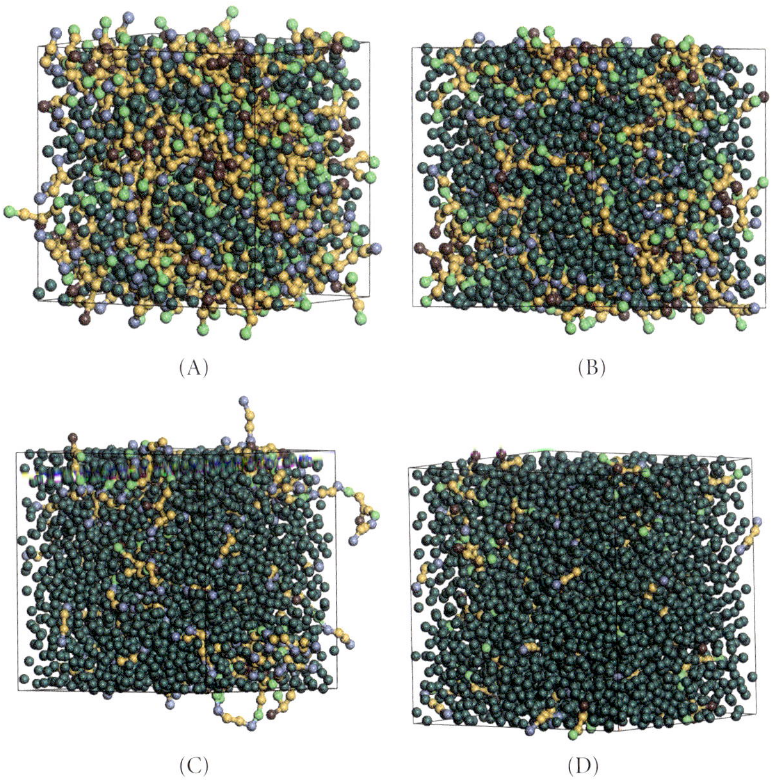

Fig. 10. The structure after minimizations: (A) 20 wt.%, (B) 40 wt.%, (C) 60 wt.%, (D) 80 wt.%.

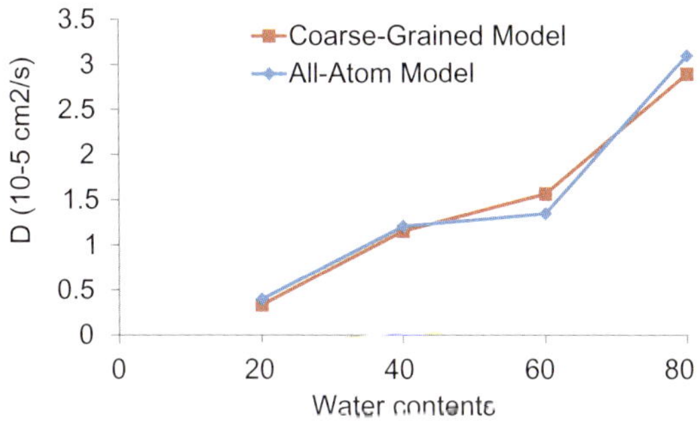

Fig. 11. Diffusion coefficients of water molecules: CG model and AA model.

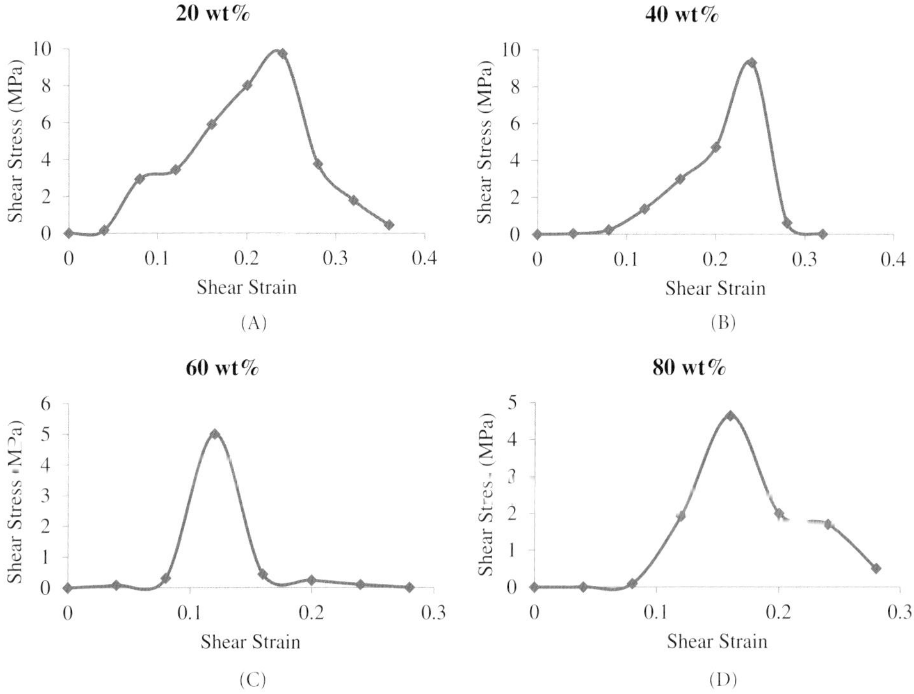

Fig. 12. Stress–Strain curves for the CG-Hydrogel containing different water percentages.

NPT dynamic simulations. Each NPT simulation (applying shear) is performed within 4 ns with the time step of 10 fs. The Berendsen algorithm is chosen for the thermostat and barostat. In order to optimize and stabilize the pressure, each shear simulation is followed by a 1 ns dynamic NVT simulation.

The shear simulations are performed for the systems with several water contents, from 20 to 80 wt.%. Figure 12 shows the stress–strain curves for the unit cells, demonstrating the role of water on the mechanical properties.[24] The results illustrate that by increasing the water content, the shear strength decreases, while this drop occurs significantly after the 40 wt.%. Thus we can conclude around 40% water content, is the optimized amount for the mechanical performance of hydrogels.

5. Summary

In this chapter, molecular dynamic simulation was used to study the effect of water content on the equilibrated structure and mechanical properties of crosslinked hydrogel at Atomistic scales. The hydrogel consisted of PEGDGE as epoxy and the Jeffamine, poly-oxy-alkylene-amines, as curing agent. Different water contents (from 0 to 80 wt.%) were examined. COMPASS forcefield was employed for the atomistic simulations. Radial distribution functions, calculated for systems with various water contents, indicate that the crosslinks are more hydrophilic within the hydrogel structure. Mechanical properties were also studied by applying strain to the system and the stiffness matrices and elastic moduli were calculated for different water percentages. The results of the all-atom simulations show that the elastic modulus decreases by increasing the water content. CG simulations using MARTINI force field were used to simulate the mechanical and transport properties. This method results in a realistic representation of the stiffness of the hydrogel at larger scale. The variation of the stiffness of the hydrogel as a function of the water content also shows that 40% water content is the optimal value for hydrogel mechanical performance of hydrogels.

References

1. A. M. Lowman, N. A. Peppas and E. Mathiowitz, *"Hydrogels" Encyclopedia of Controlled Drug Delivery*. New York: John Wiley & Sons (1999).
2. A. S. Hoffman, Hydrogels for biomedical applications. *Adv. Drug Deliver. Rev.*, **64**, 18–23 (2012).
3. D. N. Theodorou and U. W. Suter, Detailed molecular structure of a vinyl polymer glass. *Macromolecules*, **18**, 1467 (1985).
4. C. Wu and W. Xu, Atomistic molecular modeling of crosslinked epoxy resin. *Polymer*, **47**, 6004–6009 (2006).
5. A. K. Rappe and W. A. Goddard, Charge equilibration for MD Simulations. *The J. Phys. Chem.*, **95**, 3358 (1991).
6. H. Sun, COMPASS: An *ab initio* force field optimized for condensed-phase applications overview with details on alkane and benzene compounds. *Phys. Chem. B*, **102**, 7338 (1998).
7. H. Sun, P. Ren, and J. R. Fried, The COMPASS force field: parameterization and validation for phosphazens. *Comput. Theor. Polym. S*, **8**(1/2), 229 (1998).
8. M. Grujicic, Y. P. Sun, and K. L. Koudela, The effect of covalent functionalization of carbon nanotube reinforcements on the atomic-level mechanical properties of poly-vinyl-ester-epoxy. *Appl. Surf. Sci.*, **253**, 3009 (2007).
9. Z. Lu and M. L. Dunn, van der Waals adhesion of graphene membranes. *J. Appl. Phys.*, **107**, 044301 (2010).
10. H. Salahshoor, and N. Rahbar, Nano-scale fracture toughness and behavior of graphene/epoxy interface. *J. Appl. Phys.*, **112**, 023510-1–6 (2012).

11. Salahshoor, Hossein, Mazdak Tootkaboni, and Nima Rahbar. "Nanoscale structure and mechanical properties of cross-linked hydrogels." *Journal of Nanomechanics and Micromechanics*, 5.2, A4014007. (2014).
12. M. P. Allen and D. J. Tildesley, *Computer Simulation of Liquids*. New York: Oxford University Press (1987).
13. A. Gautieri, A. Russo, S. Vesentini, A. Redaelli, and M. J. Buhler, Coarse-Grained model of collagen molecules using an extended MARTINI force field. *J. Chem. Theor. Comput.*, **6**, 1210–1218 (2010).
14. S. J. Marrink, H. J. Risselada, S. Yefimov, D. P. Tieleman, and A. H. de Vries, The MARTINI force field: Coarse grained model for biomolecular simulations. *J. Phys. Chem. B*, **111**, 7812–7824 (2007).
15. P. Calvert, Hydrogels for soft machines. *Adv. Mater.*, 743–756, (2009.)
16. E. Chiessi, F. Cavalieri, and G. Paradossi, Water and polymer dynamics in chemically cross-linked hydrogels of poly(vinyl alchohol): A MD simulation study. *J. Phys. Chem. B*, **111**, 2820–2827 (2007).
17. S. S. Jang, W. A. Goddard, and M. Y. S. Kalani, Mechanical and transport properties of the poly(ethylene oxide)-poly(acrylic acid) DN hydrogel from molecular dynamic simulations. *J. Phys. Chem. B*, **111**, 1729–1737 (2007).
18. S. G. Lee, G. F. Brunello, S. S. Jang, and D. G. Bucknall, Molecular dynamics simulation study of P(VP-co-HEMA) hydrogels: Effect of water content on equilibrium structures and mechanical properties. *Biomaterials*, **30**, 6130–6141 (2009).
19. S. G. Lee, Structure-property relationship of hydrogel: Molecular dynamics simulation approach, PhD Dissertation, Georgia Institute of Technology (2011).
20. S Dumitriu (ed.), *Polymeric Biomaterials, Revised and Expanded*. Boca Raton, US: CRC Press (2001).
21. C. Oldiges, T. Tonsing, and K. Wittler, Molecular dynamics simulation of structural, mobility effects between dilute aqueous CH3CN solution and crosslinked PAA — Part 2. Dynamics. *Phys. Chem. Ch. Ph.*, **4**, 5135–5141 (2002).
22. C. Oldiges, K. Wittler, T. Tonsing, and A. Alijah, MD calculated structural properties of clusters in liquid acetonitrile/water mixtures with various contents of acetonitrile. *J. Phys. Chem. A*, **106**, 7147–7154 (2002).
23. N. A. Peppas, Hydrogels and drug delivery. *Curr. Opin. Colloid In*, **2**, 531–537 (1997).
24. Hossein Salahshoor and Nima Rahbar. "Multi-scale mechanical and transport properties of a hydrogel." Journal of the Mechanical Behavior of Biomedical Materials, **37**, 299–306 (2014).
25. Y. Tamai, H. Tanaka, and K. Nakanishi, MD study of polymer–water interaction in hydrogels. 2. Hydrogen-bond dynamics. *Macromolecules*, **29**, 6761–6769 (1996).
26. Y. Tamai and H. Tanaka, Effects of polymer chains on structure and dynamics of supercooled water in poly(vinyl alcohol). *Phys. Rev. E*, **59**, 5647–5654 (1999).
27. Y. Tamai and H. Tanaka, Structure and dynamics of poly(vinyl alcohol) hydrogel. *Molecular Simulation*, **21**, 283–301 (1999).

28. J. Walter, V. Ermatchkov, J. Vrabec, and H. Hasse, MD and experimental study of conformation change of poly (N-isopropylacylamide) hydrogels in water. *Fluid Phase Equilibria,* **296**, 164–172 (2010).
29. Y. Wu, S. Joseph, and N. R. Aluru, Effect of cross-linking on the diffusion of water, ions, and small molecules in hydrogels. *J. Phys. Chem. B*, **113**, 3512–3520 (2009).

Chapter 4

Mechanical Properties of Hydrogels

Anne S. van Oosten, Peter A. Galie and Paul A. Janmey
Institute for Medicine and Engineering,
University of Pennsylvania,
1010 Vagelos Laboratories, 3340 Smith Walk,
Philadelphia, PA 19104, USA

1. Introduction

Networks composed of water soluble biopolymers such as polysaccharides, proteins, nucleic acids, and a large variety of synthetic polymers form viscoelastic solids with a very wide range of rheological properties when assembled in aqueous media. In some cases, such as hydrogels formed by flexible polymers attached by covalent linkages, these networks can be nearly perfectly linearly elastic, with the magnitudes of their shear and Young's moduli well described by theories developed for flexible polymer melts and modified to account for the dilution of these elastomers by the solvent. In other cases in which the polymer strands are more rigid, the crosslinks more pliable, or where volume changes due to solvent flowing through the network mesh, the static shear and Young's moduli can depart strongly from predictions for either perfectly flexible or rigid fibrous networks. Additionally, the rheology can become highly nonlinear, and the time dependence of elastic and viscous moduli become complicated, with the result that shear and Young's moduli are no longer simply related. In this chapter we summarize experimental and theoretical studies of viscoelasticity to illustrate the enormous range of rheologic responses observed from different common classes of biological and non-biological hydrogels.

2. Flexible Polymer Networks

Most commonly used hydrogels are formed by flexible linear polymers crosslinked by covalent interactions between two networks strands. These gels include alginate, gelatin, polyethylene oxide (PEG), and hyaluronic acid (HA) or other polysaccharides or glycosaminoglycans. In some cases, hydrogels have also been formed by star polymers or dendrimers with more complex geometries.[1] One of the simplest and most thoroughly characterized hydrogel systems is the one formed by crosslinked polyacrylamide. These gels are made by mixing acrylamide monomers with bis-acrylamide crosslinkers and initiating polymerization by addition of the free radical, ammonium persulfate. In this reaction, linear polymers of acrylamide occasionally incorporate bis-acrylamide monomer within them, and the tetra-functional bis-acrylamide crosslinks the linear polyacrylamide chains. Water is a good solvent for polyacrylamide, but the chains are still so flexible that there is a vast excess of contour length of the polymer chain compared to the typical distance between bis-acrylamide mediated crosslinks. Viscoelastic solids from polyacrylamide can be made with polymer concentrations from below 1% to approximately 30% and the gels that are formed remain optically clear to the eye. The elastic moduli of the gels can be varied both by changing the polymer mass concentration and the concentration of this acrylamide crosslinker. Figure 1 demonstrates the linear elasticity of these gels and how well they conform to the predictions of rubberlike elasticity appropriate for networks of flexible polymers. Figure 1(A) shows that the shear storage modulus G' is more than two orders of magnitude greater than the loss modulus G'', and both moduli are remarkably independent of shear strain magnitude up to at least 50%. These moduli are also nearly independent of frequency over a range from 0.01 to 200 Hz, approximately spanning timescales appropriate for biological and other applications.[2] Figure 1(B) illustrates that the shear storage modulus is proportional to the crosslinker concentration but also depends on the total polymer mass density. Figure 1(C) shows that the elastic modulus is also proportional to the absolute temperature, at least in the physiologically relevant range of 275° to 360°. Other studies have shown similar results when polyacrylamide gels are deformed uniaxially in either extension or compression. The measured Young's modulus is approximately three times the shear modulus, consistent with an isotropic, linear elastic material of Poisson's ratio close to 0.5, assuming that solvent flow through centimeter-sized polyacrylamide gels occurs too slowly to allow for volume change under typical conditions of rheological measurements. The simple elasticity, optical clarity, and chemical stability of polyacrylamide gels have driven an enormous range of applications, in both biological and non-biological settings.

3. Controlled Morphological Changes in Hydrogels

Contributing to the simple mechanical properties of polyacrylamide gels is the fact that the strongly hydrophilic polymer strands are uncharged (Fig. 2). Classic work

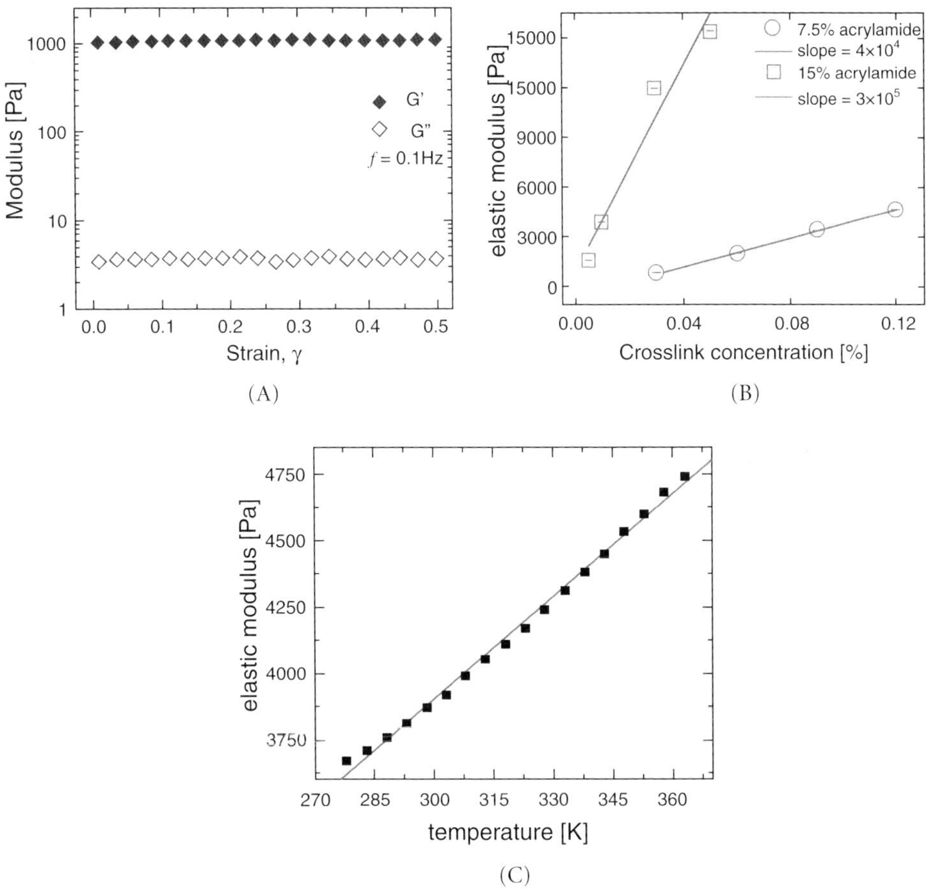

Fig. 1. Rheology of polyacrylamide gels. (A) Dependence of shear storage modulus G' and loss modulus G'' at different frequencies; (B) Shear storage modulus as functions of total acrylamide concentration and crosslinker concentration than 2% of the mean elastic moduli. The solid lines indicate linear fits to the data; (C) Shear modulus as a function of temperature. From Ref. 21.

from Tanaka and others since the 1980s showed the dramatic effect of incorporating a fixed electrostatic charge within these aqueous networks, for example by polymerizing polyacrylamide with acrylic acid. The presence of the charged monomer groups did not by itself alter the rheology of these networks dramatically, at least in the range where electrostatic repulsions did not strongly alter the persistence length of the polymer. However the fixed charge makes these flexible polymer gels highly dependent on the concentration and valence of counterions within the hydrogel system, the dielectric constant of the solvent, and the solubility of the polymer in the solvent. As a result, substituting divalent for monovalent counter ions can strongly decrease the volume of hydrogels containing fixed charged groups and increasing ionic strength can increase polyelectrolyte gel elastic moduli.[3] Decreasing the dielectric constant of the solvent by substituting methanol for water can strongly swell the hydrogels.[4] The dynamics by which these gels change their volume reveal important aspects of the polymer physics of flexible polymer gels yet significant issues still remain to be understood.

Phase changes leading to changes in volume, shape, or stiffness of hydrogels can be triggered by altering pH,[5] counterion concentrations,[3] hydrogen bonding,[6] temperature, solvent quality for the polymer, or by addition of specific ligands for sites on the polymer,[7] substrates for enzymes immobilized on the polymer[8] or by application of light,[9] electric[10–12] or magnetic[13] fields. The chemical free energy of such phase transformations can be coupled to mechanical work, and this capability has led to numerous strategies to produce artificial muscles or other self-propelling soft materials.[12,14]

The relatively simple rheology of polyacrylamide shown in Fig. 1 is also approximated by other crosslinked networks formed by flexible hydrophilic polymers such as polysaccharides, poly(ethylene glycol) or the protein polymers elastin and gelatin.[15,16] The common feature of these networks is that the elastic response is primarily entropic and due to the change in configurational entropy when the end-to-end distance of polymer strands between crosslinks is altered by strain away from its resting distance. Theories derived to account for the elasticity of pure rubber-like elastomers can also account for hydrogel rheology with modifications due to the somewhat expanded configuration of hydrogel polymer chains, since water is generally a good solvent for the polymers forming the hydrogel. A key feature of flexible polymer networks is that the elastic response, and equivalently the force-extension relation of the polymer chain are symmetric to elongation and compression.

4. Hydrogels Formed by Semi-flexible or Rigid Polymers

4.1. Consequences of filament stiffness in biopolymer hydrogels

Rather than arising primarily from entropic effects related to the displacing the ends of flexible polymers, the elastic response from crosslinked networks of stiffer polymers depends on contributions from both entropic effects and enthalpic effects related to bending and stretching of the polymer contours. Very approximately, the purely entropic shear modulus G of covalently crosslinked flexible polymer hydrogels can be calculated from the relation

$$G = nRT,$$

where n is the number density of crosslinks, R is the gas constant, and T is temperature. When filaments with bending stiffness κ are stiff enough not to be modeled as random coil polymers, as is appropriate for cytoskeletal, extracellular matrix (ECM), and other biopolymers, an expression appropriate for small strains is

$$G = \frac{\kappa^2}{k_B T \xi^2 l^3},$$

where l is the distance between crosslinks, and ξ is the mesh size of the network.[17]

This expression assumes rigid and stable crosslinks, both of which assumptions are questionable for biological hydrogels where the crosslinks are formed by non-covalent interaction between linear polymers and crosslinking proteins that are often flexible. The consequences of crosslink dynamics[18] and flexibility[19] have been addressed in several recent theoretical studies, and lead to important effects when such networks are deformed to large strains and long times.

The effect of filament stiffness in hydrogels has several major consequences. For example the elongated structure of rigid polymers such as cytoskeletal or ECM filaments means that they can be assembled into three-dimensional networks at much lower volume fractions than are required in order to form gels from more flexible polymers. Consequently a network with the same rigidity or elastic modulus as a 5% polyacrylamide gel can be made by crosslinked actin filaments with a concentration nearly two orders of magnitude lower. A second consequence of the length and rigidity of cytoskeletal polymers is that the elastic response of the depends strongly on the strain magnitude, in contrast with the strain-independent shear moduli of polyacrylamide gels seen in Fig. 1.

4.2. Non-affinity in stiff polymer hydrogels

A major assumption in theories of rubberlike elasticity is that the networks deform affinely, meaning that the microscopic strain of an originally isotropic material is equal everywhere within the sample and equal to that macroscopic strain. Affine strain, depicted schematically in Figs. 2 and 3 has been measured in polyacrylamide gels and other similar networks and verified to be a good approximation. Theoretical models predict some degree of non-affinity within even perfectly flexible polymer gels because of thermal fluctuations that occur as the linear strand become captured by the crosslinkers.[20] The magnitude of these non-affine effects are too small to visualize in common gels at the level of light microscopy, but larger non-affinities within even optically clear gels can arise from such effects as finite polymer length, aggregation of crosslinks, and differences in hydrophilicity of monomer and crosslinker units. Nevertheless, flexible polymer gels undergo largely affine deformations even at significant macroscopic stains.[21]

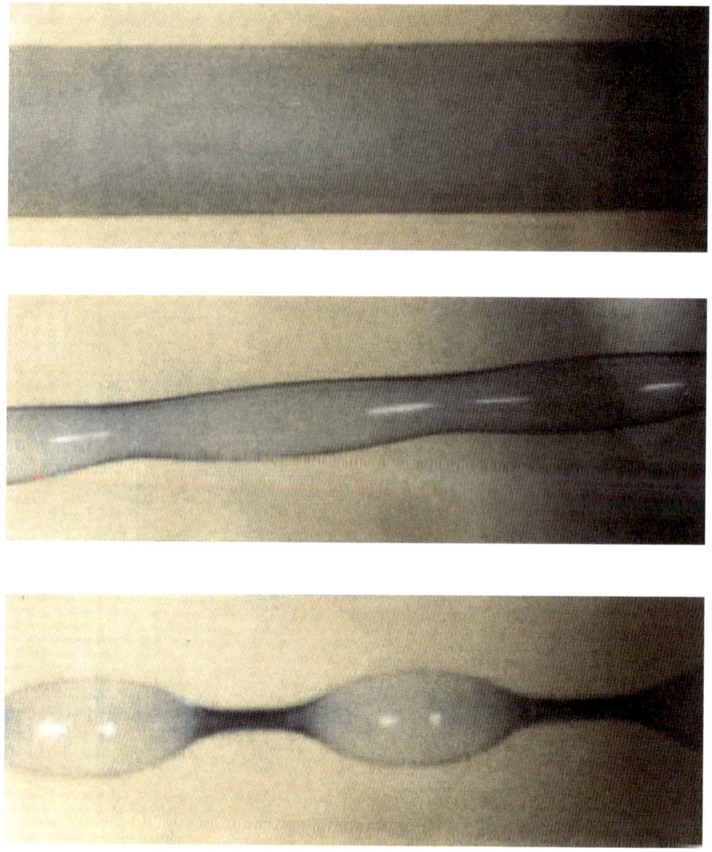

Fig. 2. Morphological change in an originally cylindrical polyacrylamide gel induced to shrink by transferring it to medium with increased acetone concentration. From Ref. 61.

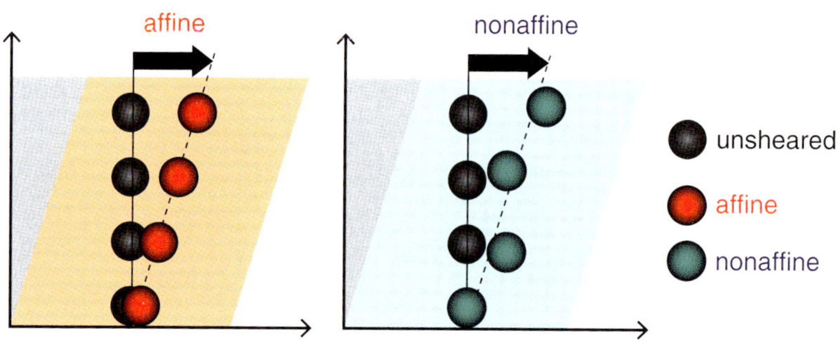

Fig. 3. Schematic depiction of affine (right) or non-affine shear deformation. From Ref. 2.

In contrast to flexible polymer networks, hydrogels formed by stiff polymers at low volume fraction exhibit a high degree of non-affinity, which depends on network geometry and strain magnitude, even if the network at rest is approximately isotropic.[22–26] As a result, imposed macroscopic stresses are non-uniformly carried by a subset of network strands, and the deformation of polymers shifts from softer bending modes to stiffer stretching modes as shear strains are increased. In addition, stiff biopolymer strands can buckle in compression and this effect contributes further to nonlinear elastic responses in such networks.[27]

4.3. Strain-stiffening in stiff polymer hydrogels

In contrast to the approximately linear elastic response of hydrogels formed by flexible polymers, gels made from semiflexible or rigid polymers, including those formed by the cytoskeletal polymers actin and vimentin or the ECM component collagen has a fundamentally different rheology. One example of this difference is shown in Fig. 4, where the shear storage moduli of polyacrylamide gels are compared with those of the cytoskeletal polymers actin and vimentin, and fibrin, the major extracellular component of blood clots.

The molecular mechanism for strain-stiffening in biopolymer gels has been the subject of extensive theoretical work. Depending on the filament stiffness, network deformation can be accommodated by bending, stretching, and reorientation of individual filaments. The strain-stiffening of semiflexible polymer networks can, within a limited range of strain, be accounted for by an entropic model that assumes that network deformation is uniform throughout the sample due to affine stretching of each semiflexible polymer. The elasticity comes from the resistance of each thermally

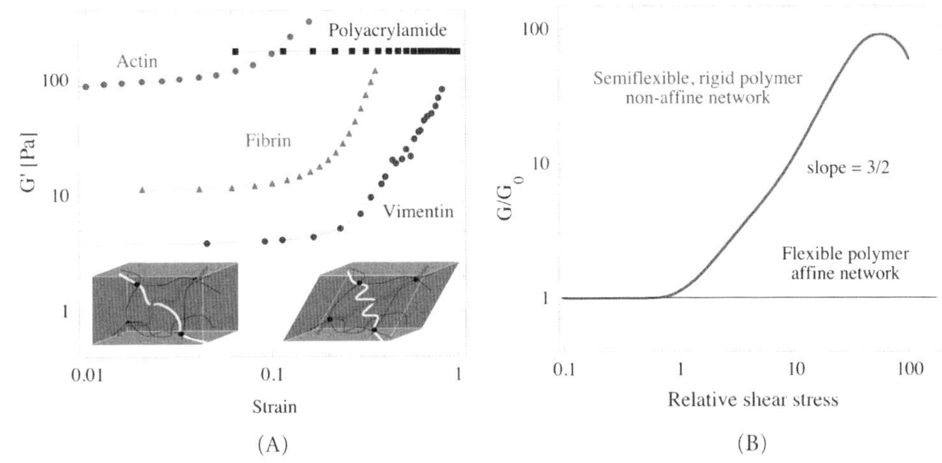

Fig. 4. Shear moduli of linear and strain-stiffening hydrogels at different strains (A) or stresses (B).

writhing polymer against the stretching, which effectively reduces the amplitude of thermal fluctuation and thus the thermal entropy of the filament.[28] In this model, strain stiffening arise because each network strand has an inherently asymmetric force-extension relation and is more resistant to elongation than to compression.[29–31]

An alternative explanation for strain-stiffening based on filament bending and enthalpic stretching has also been proposed for stiff filament networks[25,32,33] and can arise in networks formed by filaments that themselves are linearly elastic. In this model, because it is easier to bend stiff filaments than to stretch them, the filaments initially bend at small network deformations. With increasing strain, the bent filaments reorganize so that more and more filaments align along the direction of shear. The network deformation then comes mainly from the enthalpic stretching of the aligned stiff filaments. This transition from bending to stretching gives rise to strain-stiffening. The bending, buckling, and reorganization of filaments cause non-affine deformations in the network.[33] The network structure and filament stiffness determine the relative contributions of these two mechanisms: inherently nonlinear force-extension relations of single filaments and the network-level balance between filament bending and stretching.

The nonlinear mechanical properties of hydrogel formed by stiff biopolymers has motivated significant experimental and theoretical work, because the strong strain-dependence of elastic moduli suggest strategies by which internal stresses or alignment of these networks can change their mechanical properties without altering polymer mass, filament length, or crosslink density. The consequences and potential utility of nonlinear rheology in hydrogels formed by rigid biopolymers is evident in two examples of soft materials formed by the two most abundant ECM proteins, collagen and fibrin.

4.3.1. *Collagen*

Collagen is the most abundant protein in mammals and the main component of the ECM of connective tissues. Hydrogels of reconstituted collagen are used in a wide array of biomedical applications. The mechanical properties of collagen have been of much interest because collagen networks form an important component in load-bearing tissues. Here we will focus on the fibrillar collagen Type 1, which is the predominant type of collagen *in vivo* and the most common collagen used to create collagen hydrogels *in vitro*. The situation *in vivo* is much more complex because of the addition of other collagen Types[34,35] and other ECM components such as HA,[36] chondroitin sulfate,[35] fibronectin and laminin,[37] which alter the structure and mechanics of hydrogels based on collagen Type 1.

The mechanical behavior of collagen gels in the linear regime has been tested extensively, both in shear and uniaxial deformation. Generally, the variability of mechanical measurements of collagen hydrogels is rather large due to differences in the collagen source, hydrogel preparation and testing conditions.[38–40] For example the fibril diameter and striation is modified by fluctuations in polymerization temperature, pH, and ionic strength.[41–43] The isolation method of collagen also affects the mechanical properties of the networks; when acid-extraction is used the collagen telopeptides remain intact, whereas with pepsin digestion the telopeptides are cleaved, thereby eliminating important crosslinking sites.[38–40]

The shear storage modulus of collagen hydrogels in the concentration range of 0.5–10 mg/ml falls between 2 and 150 Pa and consistently approximately linearly with increasing collagen concentration under most assembly conditions, as shown in Fig. 5. The loss modulus is typically 10–20% of the elastic modulus. The shear moduli show little frequency dependency.[34,44]

In contrast to the relatively low magnitudes of shear storage moduli, tensile testing of 0.3–3 mg/mL collagen at fast loading rates or short times after deformation, reveals an elastic modulus between 1.5 and 24.3 kPa[45,46] and an equilibrium modulus between 0.5 and 5 kPa for gels ranging from 1 to 10 mg/mL.[47–49] The orders or magnitude difference between the tensile and shear moduli are striking, but a systematic direct comparison of identical samples in shear and uniaxial deformation has not yet been reported. In prolonged confined compression at large strains, collagen gels have been observed to have low moduli in the order of single Pascals; eventually collapsing when compression is continued.[40,50]

The nonlinear properties of collagen hydrogels in shear deformation are similar to those of many other networks of reconstituted biopolymers, showing strain-stiffening[31,38,51] and negative normal stress.[52] The critical strain for the onset of

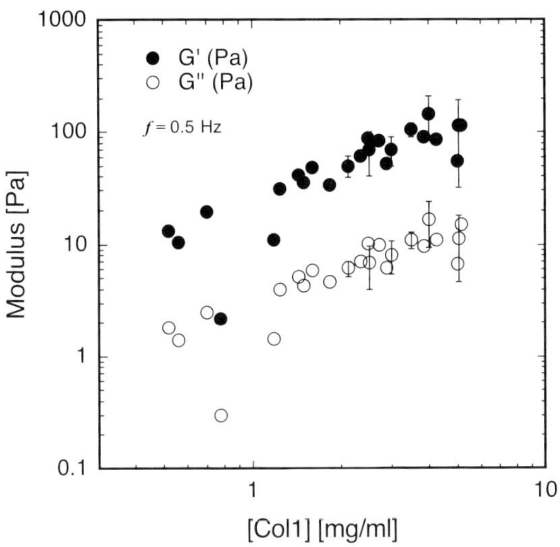

Fig. 5 Viscoelastic properties of collagen Type 1 gels over a concentration range between 0.5 and 5.5 mg/mL; measured at a frequency of 0.5 Hz at 0.5% shear strain. Graph adapted from Ref. 34.

nonlinear behavior starts between 5%–30% strain and shows dependence on concentration.[34,38,41,44]

Upon recurring large strains collagen networks show a shift of the critical strain; the nonlinear mechanical response starts occurring at higher strains.[51] However, strain-stiffening behavior is remarkably reversible unless rupture occurs, which is typically around 100% strain.[38,44]

4.3.2. *Fibrin*

Fibrin hydrogels, like collagen, are used extensively in both *in vivo* and *in vitro* applications.[53] Because of this prevalence, their mechanical properties are well-characterized. Fibrin forms from thrombin-activated monomers that assemble into protofibrils of approximately 10 nm diameter.[54] Depending on the pH and ionic strength of the solution, protofibrils aggregate laterally to create fibers of varying diameter and branching frequency, which affects the pore size of the mesh and consequently tunes the mechanical properties of the hydrogels. These fibers can reach 100 s of nm diameter, and span roughly the same size scale as collagen fibers. From a mechanical perspective, fibrin fibers are somewhat more flexible than collagen fibers of the same length and diameter. Like collagen gels, fibrin is strongly strain stiffening at strain magnitudes greater than 10% and can withstand strain as large as 100%.[55,56]

Fibrin, like most biomaterials, demonstrates a viscoelastic response to mechanical loading: its resistance to deformation depends on the rate at which it's deformed. In contrast to other protein hydrogels like collagen, the material behaves remarkably elastically at low strain rates when it is covalently reinforced by Factor XIIIa.[57] There is evidence that bending of the fibers causes this elastic behavior at low strain rates. Fibrin also exhibits the viscoelastic property of creep, meaning that the material undergoes plastic deformation to a constant load. Previous studies suggest that slippage between fibers is responsible for this property.[58]

The strain-stiffening of fibrin at strain magnitudes greater than 10%[56] is attributable at least in part to the mechanical properties of single fibrin fibers. Individual fibers are much stiffer in response to extensional loading compared to bending. At low strain magnitudes, the fibers primarily undergo bending, but, at high levels of strain, the fibers in the hydrogel begin to align in the direction of strain.[59] This alignment diminishes the ability of fibers to bend to perpetuate the global strain, and fiber extension takes over as the primary mode of deformation. Consequently, the gel becomes stiffer as the strain increases and augments fiber alignment.

The mechanical properties of fibrin gels have several physiological implications for blood clotting, since clots are composed primarily of fibrin. Blood clots are exposed to a wide array of mechanical forces within the body, including both solid stress from tensile and compressive deformation and fluid shear stress from blood flow.[60] The elastic properties of fibrin at low strain magnitudes allow clots to exhibit a relatively constant stiffness in response to the varying shear rates of non-uniform blood flow. Moreover, strain stiffening protects clots from failure in response to excessive loading. These mechanical properties elucidate the importance of the relationship between structure and function in fibrin gels, and help to explain the behavior of fibrin *in vivo*.

5. Conclusion

The mechanical properties of hydrogels span a wide range of stiffness values, and differences in their viscoelastic relaxations and responses to large strains. These mechanical responses are fundamental to their practical applications or biological functions, and sometimes lead to striking changes in morphology. Hydrogels with flexible polymers like polyacrylamide conform well to predictions of rubberlike elasticity, but gels consisting of semi-rigid or stiff filaments exhibit both strain and time-dependent behavior that is not fully defined by theoretical models. Gels formed by cytoskeletal and ECM proteins are examples of the latter, and consequently display responses to mechanical loading that are more difficult to predict. For example, the shear and elastic moduli of some gels such as collagen are not related by the constant Poisson's ratio, as a simple isotropic continuum would be. Therefore, new models of the mechanics of these hydrogels are required. Understanding the mechanics of hydrogels formed by still polymers such as collagen and fibrin, is critical for gaining insight into soft tissue physiology.

References

1. Y. Wang, Q. Zhao, H. Zhang, S. Yang, and X. R. Jia, *Adv. Mater.*, **26**, 4163–4167 (2014).
2. Q. Wen, A. Basu, P. A. Janmey, and A. G. Yodh, *Soft Matter*, **8**, 8039–8049 (2012).
3. M. Rubinstein, R. H. Colby, A. V. Dobrynin, and J. F. Joanny, *Macromolecules*, **29**, 398–406 (1996).
4. T. Tanaka and M. Annaka, *Makromol. Chem. Macromol. Symp.*, **70–1**, 13–22 (1993).
5. S. Mafe, J. A. Manzanares, A. E. English, and T. Tanaka, *Phys. Rev. Lett.*, **79**, 3086–3089 (1997).
6. F. Ilmain, T. Tanaka, and E. Kokufuta, *Nature*, **349**, 400–401 (1991).
7. E. Kokufata, Y. Q. Zhang, and T. Tanaka, *Nature*, **351**, 302–304 (1991).
8. E. Kokufuta and T. Tanaka, *Macromolecules*, **24**, 1605–1607 (1991).
9. A. Suzuki and T. Tanaka, *Nature*, **346**, 345–347 (1990).
10. M. Bassil, J. Davenas, and M. El Tahchi, *Sensor Actuator. B Chem.*, **134**, 496–501 (2008).

11. P. J. Glazer, M. van Erp, A. Embrechts, S. G. Lemay, and E. Mendes, *Soft Matter*, **8**, 4421–4426 (2012).
12. E. A. Moschou, S. F. Peteu, L. G. Bachas, M. J. Madou, and S. Daunert, *Chem. Mater.*, **16**, 2499–2502 (2004).
13. J. K. Wu, X. L. Gong, Y. C. Fan, and H. S. Xia, *Soft Matter*, **7**, 6205–6212 (2011).
14. Y. Takashima, S. Hatanaka, M. Otsubo, M. Nakahata, T. Kakuta, A. Hashidzume, H. Yamaguchi, and A. Harada, *Nat. Commun.*, **3**, 1270 (2012).
15. J. Gosline, M. Lillie, E. Carrington, P. Guerette, C. Ortlepp, and K. Savage, *Philos. T. Roy. Soc. B.*, **357**, 121–132 (2002).
16. A. A. Braidot and J. A. Deiber, *Biorheology*, **36**, 267–284 (1999).
17. F. C. MacKintosh, J. Käs, and P. A. Janmey, *Phys. Rev. Lett.* **75**, 4425–4428 (1995).
18. L. Wolff, P. Fernandez, and K. Kroy, *PLoS one*, 7(7), e40063 (2012).
19. A. Sharma, M. Sheinman, K. M. Heidemann, and F. C. MacKintosh, *Phys. Rev. E*, **88**, 052705 (2013).
20. B. A. DiDonna and T. C. Lubensky, *Phys. Rev. E*, **72**, 066619 (2005).
21. A. Basu, Q. Wen, X. M. Mao, T. C. Lubensky, P. A. Janmey, and A. G. Yodh, *Macromolecules*, **44**, 1671–1679 (2011).
22. A. S. Abhilash, L. Zhang, J. Stiefel, P. K. Purohit, and S. P. Joshi, *Phys. Rev. E*, **89**, 022607 (2014).
23. M. Atakhorrami, G. H. Koenderink, J. F. Palierne, F. C. MacKintosh, and C. F. Schmidt, *Phys. Rev. Lett.*, **112**, 088101 (2014).
24. J. Liu, G. H. Koenderink, K. E. Kasza, F. C. MacKintosh, and D. A. Weitz, *Phys. Rev. Lett.*, **98**, 198304 (2007).
25. T. van Dillen, P. R. Onck, and E. Van der Giessen, *J. Mech. Phys. Solids*, **56**, 2240–2264 (2008).
26. Q. Wen, A. Basu, J. P. Winer, A. Yodh, and P. A. Janmey, *New J. Phys.*, **9**, 428 (2007).
27. E. Conti and F. C. MacKintosh, *Phys. Rev. Lett.*, **102**, 088102 (2009).
28. F. C. MacKintosh, J. Kas, and P. A. Janmey, *Phys. Rev. Lett.*, **75**, 4425–4428 (1995).
29. M. L. Gardel, J. H. Shin, F. C. MacKintosh, L. Mahadevan, P. Matsudaira, and D. A. Weitz, *Science*, **304**, 1301–1305 (2004).
30. J. S. Palmer and M. C. Boyce, *Acta Biomater.*, **4**, 597–612 (2008).
31. C. Storm, J. J. Pastore, F. C. MacKintosh, T. C. Lubensky, and P. A. Janmey, *Nature*, **435**, 191–194 (2005).
32. G. Zagar, P. R. Onck, and E. Van der Giessen, *Macromolecules*, **44**, 7026–7033 (2011).
33. P. R. Onck, T. Koeman, T. van Dillen, and E. van der Giessen, *Phys. Rev. Lett.*, **95**, 178102 (2005).
34. I. K. Piechocka, A. S. van Oosten, R. G. Breuls, and G. H. Koenderink, *Biomacromolecules*, **12**, 2797–2805 (2011).
35. K. Stuart and A. Panitch, *Biomacromolecules*, **10**, 25–31 (2008).
36. Y.-l. Yang, C. Sun, M. E. Wilhelm, L. J. Fox, J. Zhu, and L. J. Kaufman, *Biomaterials*, **32**, 7932–7940 (2011).
37. D. Guarnieri, S. Battista, A. Borzacchiello, L. Mayol, E. De Rosa, D. Keene, L. Muscariello, A. Barbarisi, and P. Netti, *J. Mater. Sci. Mater. M.*, **18**, 245–253 (2007).

38. S. Motte and L. J. Kaufman, *Biopolymers*, **99**, 35–46 (2013).
39. S. L. Wilson, M. Guilbert, J. Sulé-Suso, J. Torbet, P. Jeannesson, G. D. Sockalingum, and Y. Yang, *FASEB J.*, **28**, 14–25 (2014).
40. C.-C. Wu, S.-J. Ding, Y.-H. Wang, M.-J. Tang, and H.-C. Chang, *J. Biomat. Sci. Polym. E.*, **16**, 1261–1275 (2005).
41. D. Vader, A. Kabla, D. Weitz, and L. Mahadevan, *PloS one*, **4**, e5902 (2009).
42. D. Velegol and F. Lanni, *Biophys. J.*, **81**, 1786–1792 (2001).
43. Y. Yang and L. J. Kaufman, *Biophys. J.*, **96**, 1566–1585 (2009).
44. N. A. Kurniawan, L. H. Wong, and R. Rajagopalan, *Biomacromolecules*, **13**, 691–698 (2012).
45. M. Lopez-Garcia, D. Beebe, and W. Crone, *Biomed. Mater. Eng.*, **20**, 361–369 (2010).
46. B. A. Roeder, K. Kokini, J. E. Sturgis, J. P. Robinson, and S. L. Voytik-Harbin, *J. Biomech. Eng.*, **124**, 214–222 (2002).
47. B. Ozerdem and A. Tözeren, *J. Biomech. Eng.*, **117**, 397–401 (1995).
48. K. M. Pryse, A. Nekouzadeh, G. M. Genin, E. L. Elson, and G. I. Zahalak, *Ann. Biomed. Eng.*, **31**, 1287–1296 (2003).
49. M.-T. Sheu, J.-C. Huang, G.-C. Yeh, and H.-O. Ho, *Biomaterials*, **22**, 1713–1719 (2001).
50. D. M. Knapp, V. H. Barocas, A. G. Moon, K. Yoo, L. R. Petzold, and R. T. Tranquillo, *J. Rheol. (1978–present)*, **41**, 971–993 (1997).
51. S. Münster, L. M. Jawerth, B. A. Leslie, J. I. Weitz, B. Fabry, and D. A. Weitz, *P. Natl. Acad. Sci.*, **110**, 12197–12202 (2013).
52. P. A. Janmey, M. E. McCormick, S. Rammensee, J. L. Leight, P. C. Georges, and F. C. MacKintosh, *Nat. Mater.*, **6**, 48–51 (2006).
53. T. A. E. Ahmed, E. V. Dare, and M. Hincke, *Tissue Eng. Part B Rev.*, **14**, 199–215 (2008).
54. A. P. Laudano and R. F. Doolittle, *P. Natl. Acad. Sci. USA*, **75**, 3085–3089 (1978).
55. A. E. Brown, R. I. Litvinov, D. E. Discher, P. K. Purohit, and J. W. Weisel, *Science*, **325**, 741–744 (2009).
56. J. V. Shah and P. A. Janmey, *Rheol. Acta*, **36**, 262–268 (1997).
57. J. W. Weisel, *Biophys. Chem.*, **112**, 267–276 (2004).
58. E. A. Ryan, L. F. Mockros, J. W. Weisel, and L. Lorand, *Biophys. J.*, **77**, 2813–2826 (1999).
59. T. T. Tower, M. R. Neidert, and R. T. Tranquillo, *Ann. Biomed. Eng.*, **30**, 1221–1233 (2002).
60. M. Anand, K. Rajagopal, and K. R. Rajagopal, *J. Theor. Med.*, **5**, 183–218 (2003).
61. E. S. Matsuo and T. Tanaka, *Nature*, **358**, 482–485 (1992).

Chapter 5

Hydrogel Architecture

Fariba Dehghani and Ali Fathi
*School of Chemical and Biomolecular Engineering,
The University of Sydney, Sydney, NSW 2006, Australia*

1. Introduction

Tissue engineering holds a great promise for repair and reconstruction of defected tissues or organs.[1,2] This approach involves *in vitro* or *in vivo* culture of cells within a three-dimensional (3D) structure of a scaffold as a physical support for regeneration of a functional tissue.[3] Scaffolds are used as structural platforms for cells attachment, spreading, proliferation, and differentiation. Hydrogels are the material of choice as scaffolds to replace extracellular matrix (ECM) due to their superior water uptake properties and high permeability for nutrients, long chain molecules, proteins, and oxygen.[4–8] Hydrogels are hydrophilic networks of polymers that are chemically or physically crosslinked and can absorb substantial amount of water. Permeability of long chain molecules, cell migration, and proliferation within the 3D structure of hydrogels relies on the microarchitecture of hydrogels.

This chapter provides an insight for the microarchitecture of hydrogels for various biomedical applications. In the first part process driven approaches for the formation of porosity within the structure of hydrogels are discussed. Methods such as particle leaching, lyophilization, electrospinning, and gas foaming have been used for the fabrication of macro-constructs with dimensions in the range of 100 nm to few centimeters to regenerate functional tissues. In the second part an overview is provided for microtopography and microsize hydrogel fabrication techniques that have been developed to mimic ECM. Microhydrogels are assembled with bottom-up approaches to form biomaterial constructs, favorable for variety of tissue engineering applications.

2. Process Driven Methods

Porous structures in biomaterials are potentially useful for mimicking ECM of native tissues. Permeability of nutrients, diffusion of oxygen, migration, and proliferation of cells within the 3D structure of hydrogels relies on the microarchitecture of hydrogels. High degree of porosity and pore interconnectivity can promote the proliferation and viability of cells within the 3D structure of hydrogels and thus regeneration of functional tissues.[9–11] For instance, Fig. 1 shows the effect of porosity on hepatic cells viability and proliferation after day 5 within agarose hydrogels.[12] It is shown that hepatic cell viability was substantially higher in the porous hydrogels due to higher transfer rate of nutrients and oxygen to the cells.[12]

The optimal pore size in hydrogel structures for biomedical applications is tissue specific. For instance, it is reported that 5 μm pore diameters is favorable for neovascularization, 15 μm for fibroblast ingrowth, 20–125 μm for mammalian skin regeneration,[13] 100–300 μm for cartilage formation,[11] 40–100 μm for osteoid ingrowths,[13] 200 μm for hepatocyte proliferation and ingrowth,[14] 100–350 μm for bone regeneration[15] and above 500 μm for regeneration of fibro-vascular tissues.[16] In hydrogels with small pore size, cells are tending to proliferate without secreting ECM proteins.[11] This effect leads to regeneration of tissues with very low physical integrity.[11] Upon *in vivo* implantation, local angiogenesis occurs within hydrogel porosity to induce vascularization in the structure of newly formed tissues.[17–20] The architecture of individual and cluster of pores, therefore, affects many aspects of cellular orientation, function, and aggregation within the structure of hydrogels.[9,21]

Different process driven techniques including particle leaching, freeze drying, electrospinning, and gas foaming with chemical reaction and high pressure are used for the formation of porosity within the structure of hydrogels. Table 1 summarizes the limitations associated with each of these techniques. These process driven techniques are schematically shown in Fig. 2 and are described more in detail in this section.

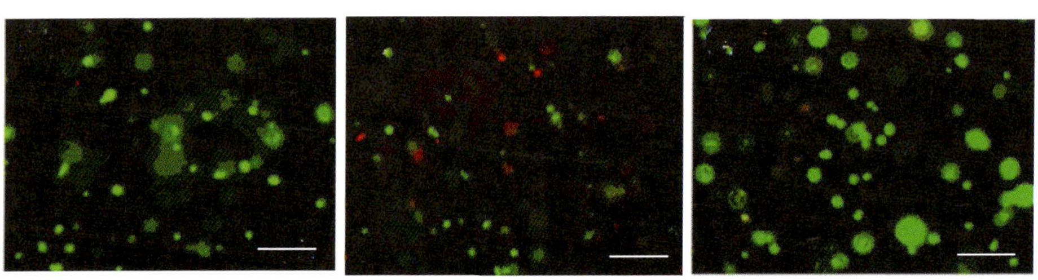

(A) (B) (C)

Fig. 1. The viability of hepatic cells at day 0 (A) and day 5 (B and C) on non-porous (B) and porous hydrogel (C), the scale bar is 200 μm and live cells stained green and dead cells red.[12]

Table 1. Microarchitectural specification of hydrogels fabricated with different process driven techniques.

Process	Porosity (%)	Pore size (μm)	Limiting factor
Salt leaching	40–70	15–700	• Thin layers of hydrogel to assure complete leaching of particles. • Lack of control on porosity and pore interconnectivity. • Applicable for cell-laden hydrogel.
Lyophilization	50–80	<150	• Formation of skin layer at top and bottom of hydrogels. • Decrease the mechanical stability of hydrogels. • Long processing time and energy intensive.
Electrospinning	~90	<10	• Very low average pore size. • Low proliferation of cells in 3D structure of hydrogels. • Applicable for cell-laden hydrogels.
Conventional gas foaming	60–90	10–1000	• Not applicable for hydrogel precursors with low crosslinking kinetic. • Required surfactants to stabilize the foam during the process.
Gas foaming by high pressure CO_2	60–90	~100	• Low solubility of CO_2 in hydrogels. • Not applicable for cell-laden approaches.

2.1. Particle leaching

In this technique porosity is formed by leaching out porogen particles after hydrogel formation.[22,23] Porogen particles are dispersed in polymer phase before or during the crosslinking reaction to achieve a homogenous distribution of particles within the structure of hydrogels, as shown schematically in Fig. 2(A). Salt,[24,25] sugars,[26] and gelatin[27] are commonly used as a porogen in this technique, which are all water soluble. Therefore, these porogens are suitable for systems in which the crosslinking of hydrogel occurs in polymer phase or in an organic solvent. Salt leaching is used for creation of porosity in polymers such as poly(ethylene glycol) diacrylate (PEGDA), poly(N-isopropylacrylamide) (PNIPAAm), and poly(2-hydroxyethyl methacrylate) (PHEMA). In addition to the nature of porogen, their geometry has important impact on microstructure of pores and overall porosity of fabricated hydrogels.[28] The effect of geometry of porogen particles on microarchitecture of pores was shown in Fig. 3, spherical porogen particles enhances the overall degree of pore

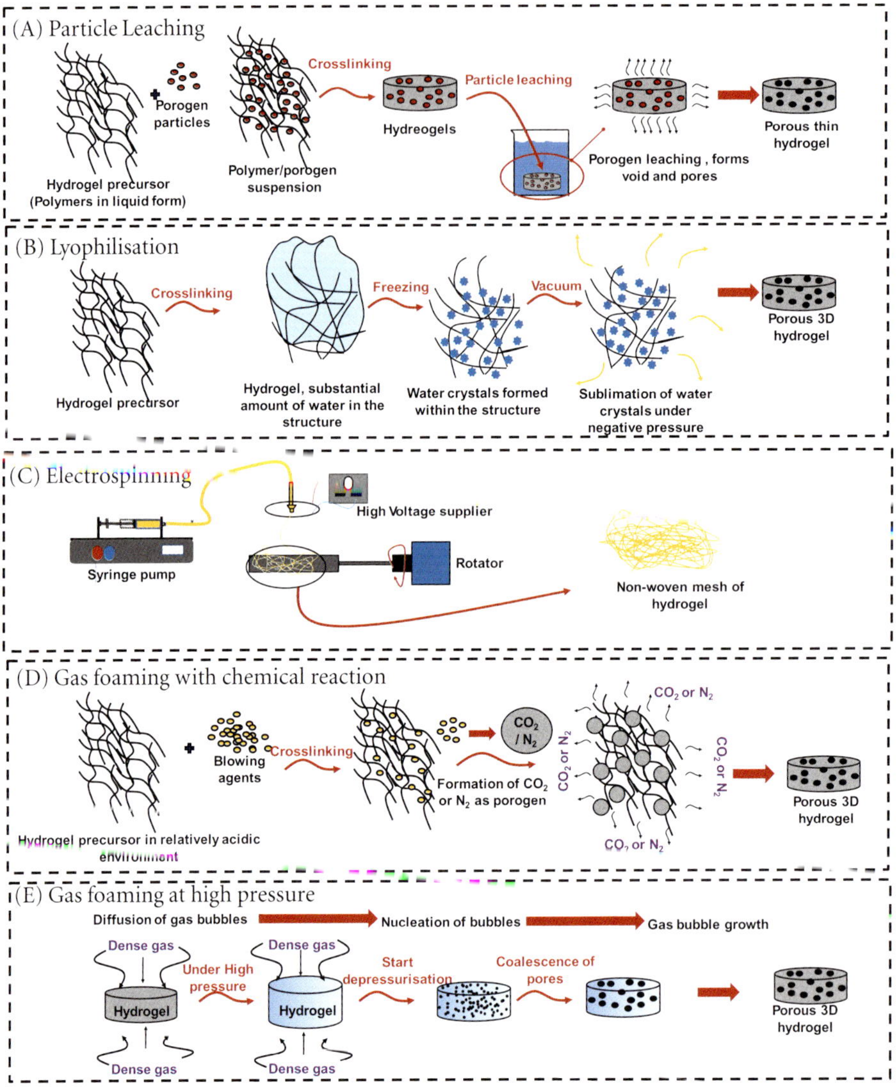

Fig. 2. Different process driven techniques for formation of porosity within the structure of hydrogels; (A) Particle leaching, (B) lyophilization, (C) electrospinning, (D) conventional gas foaming, and (E) gas foaming by high pressure CO_2.

interconnectivity within the hydrogel structures.[29] Channel-like pores are created within the structure of PHEMA hydrogel by using microfibers of ammonium sulfate as porogen (Fig. 3(A)). The shape of pores tends to be more random by using crystals of NaCl as porogen in oligo poly(ethylene glycol fumarate) (OPF) hydrogels as shown in Fig. 3(B).[30,31] Porous PHEMA hydrogels are fabricated by particle leaching technique, using NaCl or ammonium sulfate as porogen. HEMA monomers were

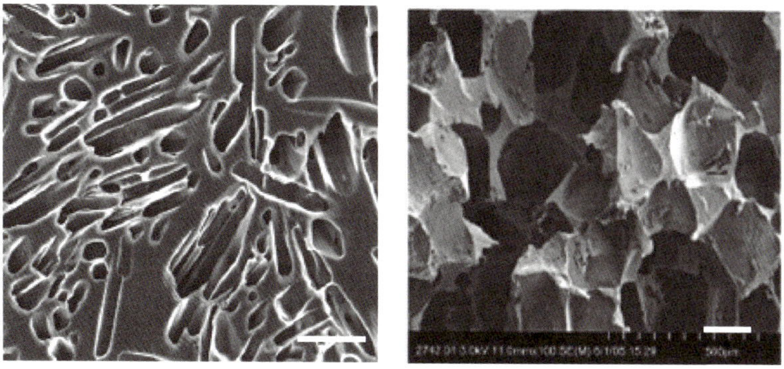

(A) (B)

Fig. 3. The effect of particle geometry on microarchitecture of hydrogels produced by leaching technique. Microstructure of PHEMA[29] hydrogels, (A, scale bar is 100 μm) fabricated with particle leaching technique and microfibers of ammonium sulfate, (B) as porogen and OPF hydrogels fabricated with NaCl particle leaching.[28]

crosslinked with 2 wt.% ethylene dimethacrylate and pores with an average size of 100 μm are produced by leaching porogen particles with a buffered solution.[26] In another study for promoting the biological properties of PHEMA, this polymer is modified with cholesterol methacrylate and laminin.[31] Rectangular shape particles of ammonium oxalate are used as porogen to create pores with dimensions of 100 μm × 10 μm during the hydrogel formation.[31] The results of their *in vitro* studies show that mesenchymal stem cells (MSCs) adhere and proliferate within these porous hydrogels.[31]

Conductive microporous hydrogels are also fabricated by particle leaching technique for nerve regeneration and cardiovascular tissue engineering.[33] Hybrid hydrogel of polyaniline/PEGDA is fabricated by *in situ* precipitation of polyaniline in PEGDA/NaCl solution, followed by photo-crosslinking of PEGDA. Pores with average size in the range of 50–130 μm are generated within the structure of these hydrogel by leaching out NaCl particles in aqueous solution.[33] These hybrid hydrogels exhibited electrical conductivity of $(1.1 \pm 0.5) \times 10^{-3}$ mS/cm. Microarchitectural and electrical conductivity of these polyaniline/PEGDA hydrogels is favorable for nerve regeneration.[33] Dadsetan *et al.* fabricated OPF hydrogels with different average pore sizes, using salt leaching technique to investigate the effect of pore size on the mechanical properties of constructs and MSCs' proliferation and growth. NaCl particles with different sizes are used as porogen and N-vinyl pyrrolidinone is used as a photo-crosslinking agent in the fabrication of oligo poly(ethylene glycol) hydrogels.[30] MSCs cultured within these oligo poly(ethylene glycol) porous hydrogels possessed osteogenic phenotype by exhibiting alkaline phosphatase activity.[30] The hydrogels with larger average pore size exhibited significantly higher alkaline phosphatase activity (a marker for osteogenic activity of cells) after 14 days of *in vitro* culture.[30] This result confirms the significance of microstructure of hydrogels in tissue engineering applications. It is crucial to use cell friendly porogen particles such as sucrose for fabrication of cell-laden hydrogels. This technique has been used for the preparation of 40% porosity in cell-laden agarose hydrogels.[12]

Water soluble particles cannot be used as porogen for the creation of porosity within the structure of hydrogels due to high solubility of these particles in aqueous solution. To address this problem, microparticle hydrogels are fabricated and used as porogen for the creation of porosity in other hydrogels. For instance, microparticle hydrogels of physically crosslinked gelatin are produced by decreasing the temperature of gelatin solution in PBS from 37°C to 4°C. These microparticles are dispersed within the structure of alginate hydrogels and leached out by increasing the temperature to 37°C to create pores with dimension in the range of 150 μm to 300 μm.[14] The pore size and overall porosity is controlled by adjusting size and concentration of gelatin particle, respectively.[14] These alginate porous hydrogels have been used for encapsulation of hepatocarcinoma cells. Proliferation and albumin secretion of the encapsulated cells are significantly promoted in the porous alginate hydrogels.[14] Additionally, microparticles of poly (ethylene glycol) sebacic acid diacrylate and gelatin hydrogels have been used as porogen with particle size ranged from 100 μm to 500 μm to create porosity within poly (ε-caprolactone fumarate) hydrogels.[34]

In summary, particle leaching is an efficient approach to create porosity in a class of hydrogels that are in liquid form prior to crosslinking reaction. This method is applicable for formation of porosity within the structure of cell laden hydrogels. In this method however, there is a limited control over the pore interconnectivity, the orientation of generated pores and overall degree of porosity. In addition, there is a limitation for the thickness of hydrogels to be less than 500 μm to remove the porogens efficiently from the hydrogel matrix.

2.2. Lyophilization

In this method, as shown schematically in Fig. 2(B), the rapid cooling of hydrogel system produces thermodynamic instability and subsequently results in phase separation within the structure of hydrogels. The water is then removed by sublimation under vacuum to generate pores within the hydrogel structure.[35] Lyophilization, also termed as freeze-drying, has been widely used for the formation of porous hydrogels of synthetic and naturally derived polymers.[36,37]

It has been demonstrated that in lyophilization temperature is one of the key factors that have significant impact on microarchitecture of hydrogels. For instance,

Wu *et al.* alter the lyophilization temperature to tune the microstructure of chitosan-collagen hydrogels. The pore interconnectivity in these hydrogels is enhanced by increasing lyophilization temperature from −196°C to the range of −80°C to −20°C.[38] The porous hydrogels fabricated with lyophilization temperature in the range of −80°C to −20°C is used for *in vitro* culture of pre-adipocytes cells.[38] High cell viability and proliferation rate are reported within the structure of these porous hydrogels due to their favorable microarchitecture for 3D cell growth.[38] Lyophilization has been used for the creation of porosity within the range of 70–80% in the composite hydrogels of β-chitin and hydroxyapetite (βCT-HA). *In vitro* cell studies showed high potential of these microporous hydrogels for variety of tissue engineering applications such as wound healing and bone regeneration.[39]

Uniaxial variation of temperature within a structure of a hydrogel can align the pores and generate a gradient of porosity in hydrogels.[40,41] For instance one side of an agarose hydrogel is kept in contact with dry ice, while the sample is immersed in a pool of liquid nitrogen to generate a temperature ramp within the agarose hydrogels. This temperature gradient leads to the formation of linear networks of pores, suitable for axonal regeneration in spinal cord injury.[40,41]

In summary, the orientation and interconnectivity of pores in natural and synthetic polymer hydrogels can be controlled by using lyophilization technique.[36,37,42–44] The microarchitecture of pores, however, cannot be finely controlled in this method. In addition, the thermal quenching of hydrogels decreases their mechanical stability and forms skin like layer at the hydrogel–air interface. This layer is generated due to the collapse of hydrogel structure as the result of solvent evaporation at the interface.[45] This effect might prevent migration of cells into the hydrogel structure and thus proliferation of cells into 3D structure. This method is also not applicable for formation of porosity in cell-laden hydrogels.

2.3. Electrospinning

The process of electrospinning has been commercially used in textile industry as a versatile technique for the fabrication of microfibers since early 20th century.[46] In the recent decade, it has been used for the fabrication of microfibers of various types of hydrophobic and hydrophilic biomaterials such as polymers, ceramics and their composites for biomedical applications.[47–50] As shown in Fig. 2(C), electrospinning apparatuses consist of three main components: (i) a high voltage power supply, (ii) a spraying system, and (iii) a collector.

In this technique, polymers are dissolved in a solvent at a concentration high enough for polymer chain entanglement to allow some degree of physical crosslinking. The polymer solution is fed through a capillary tube in which the solution is charged with high voltage. A Taylor cone is formed when the force created from the electric field is strong enough to compensate the surface tension of the solution at the capillary tip. This Taylor cone is then stretched till a jet of hydrogel is drawn and then attracted to the oppositely charged/grounded collecting target plate. This process is lauded for fabrication of non-woven meshes of micro or nanoscale fibers which can replicate physiochemical and microstructural properties of natural ECM. Rotational collecting plate is used for the fabrication of 3D scaffolds. This technique has also been used for fabrication of cell-laden hydrogels.[51]

Electrospinning has been used for the preparation of fibers with the diameters within the range of 50 nm to 10 μm.[46,52–55] Broad range of solvents including polar and non-polar have been used in electrospinning process for the fabrication of fibers.[49,50] The properties of solution and electrospin process parameters affect the microarchitecture of characteristics of fibers. The intrinsic properties of the solution such as polarity, viscosity, and electrical conductivity of the solution; the molecular weight, concentration, and conformation of the polymer chain are key parameters that affect the fiber formation. Additionally, process variables such as the voltage, the distance between the nozzle and collector, solution flow rate are other critical factors that can be used to tune the microarchitecture of fibers.

Increasing the viscosity of polymer solution by elevating the concentration and molecular weight of polymer, changing the solvent, and addition of surfactant results in the formation of fibers with larger diameter. This effect is due to higher surface tension at the capillary tip.[56,57] In addition, increasing the flow rate also elevates the diameter of fibers. High flow rate, however, prevents the evaporation of solvent in electrospinning process and thus substantially decreases the physical integrity of hydrogels. Enhancing the electrical conductivity of solution increases the electrical force applied on the polymer solution and thus decreases the average fiber diameter.[58]

Electrospinning technique is used for the formation of porous structure of polyvinyl alcohol (PVA) hydrogels, mixed with poly(ε-caprolactone) and multi-walled carbon nanotubes as a conductive scaffold for skeletal muscle tissue engineering.[59] Porous hybrid hydrogels of PVA and polyacrylic acid are also fabricated by using electrospinning technique. In this approach, solutions of PVA and polyacrylic acid with different ratios are extruded from a glass capillary with inner diameter of 400 μm. To compensate the effect of viscosity of solution with different concentration of PVA and polyacrylic acid, the capillary tubes are tilted downwards at the angle of 0–40° from vertical axis for the extrusion of hydrogel solution with higher viscosity. PVA/polyacrylic acid hydrogel with the microstructure composed of interconnected submicron fibers have been fabricated, which exhibits favorable microarchitecture for various tissue engineering applications.[60] PHEMA hydrogels are also fabricated by electrospinning to form fiber with diameters in the range of 270 nm to 3.6 μm. The diameter of fibers and overall porosity of PHEMA hydrogels is altered by changing the concentration and solution flow rate.[61] These fibrous hydrogels resist against non-specific protein adsorption, which makes them a potential candidate for wound dressing. Electrospun collagen hydrogels mimic structure and biological properties of natural collagenous ECM. Electrospun collagen-based hydrogels are fabricated with fiber diameter in the range 20 nm to 2 μm.[46,52,62–64] These electrospun hydrogels, however, possessed very low mechanical and structural stability upon hydration, which, might limit their application for tissue engineering purposes. To address this problem, collagen microfibers are crosslinked with glutaraldehyde vapors, formaldehyde, and epoxy compounds. *In vitro* cell studies on the chemically crosslinked hydrogels, however, reveals that the proliferation and growth of keratinocytes and fibroblasts are significantly decreased compared to physically crosslinked collagen hydrogels.[46] This effect is due to low pore interconnectivity in the chemically crosslinked collagen microfibrous hydrogel compared to physically crosslinked hydrogel.

Elastin has been increasingly used for various tissue engineering and biomedical applications as it naturally constitutes the walls of many tissues such as skin,[65] cartilage,[66] and smooth muscles.[67] Tropoelastin and α-elastin microfibrous hydrogels have been prepared by electrospinning using hexafluoroisopropanol as the solvent, forming flattened quasi-elastic wave-like patterns with diameters in the nano and microscale range. The surface evaporation of solvent in the distance between the tip of the capillary to the collecting plate in electrospinning apparatus is necessary for formation of fibrous hydrogels with high physical integrity. Low boiling point of hexafluoroisopropanol (~60°C) therefore, makes this solvent a favorable candidate for electrospinning of naturally derived polypeptides in comparison with water.[68] Chemically crosslinked electrospun tropoelastin hydrogels exhibits a ribbon like microarchitecture with diameters ranging from 0.9 μm to 2.7 μm.[69] Due to its suitable microstructure, this hydrogel supports the proliferation of human dermal fibroblast, human umbilical vein endothelial cells, and human coronary artery smooth muscle cells.[69]

Electrospinning technique is also used in combination with other process driven approaches such as salt leaching for the fabrication of interconnected porous hydrogels with higher average pore size. Microfibrous hydrogels of hyaluronic acid (HA) and collagen with nanoscale fibers have been produced by using electrospinning and salt leaching techniques.[70] NaCl particles were deposited onto the electrospun jets of hydrogel solution to induce inter-fiber porosity. This step is followed by chemical crosslinking and salt leaching process to produce interconnected microfibrous HA/collagen hydrogels. *In vitro* cell studies shows that these HA/collagen hydrogels could support adhesion and 3D proliferation of bovine chondrocytes.[71] In addition, cell-laden constructs are fabricated to promote the 3D proliferation of cells within the electrospun hydrogels.[71]

In summary, electrospinning can be used for the fabrication of fibrous hydrogels with high porosity. The porosity, diameter, and shape of fibers can be altered by tuning the process parameters such as voltage, flow rate, and the concentration of polymer. Solvents with low boiling point are favorable in this approach to assure surface evaporation from the fibers before reaching the collecting plate. Chemical crosslinking of polymers can promote the physical integrity and mechanical properties of hydrogels fabricated with this method. The overall degree of porosity, however, is substantially decreased by chemical crosslinking. Electrospinning can be used for fabrication of cell-laden constructs. Low average pore size in electrospun hydrogels is the main drawback associated with this technique.

2.4. Gas foaming

In gas foaming the porosity is generated by nucleation and growth of gas bubbles as an internal phase within the 3D structure of hydrogels. Gas bubbles can be generated *in situ* either via chemical reaction,[72–76] or by the addition of an inert gas to the hydrogel precursor at high pressure.[77–82]

2.4.1. *Gas foaming by chemical reaction*

The gas foaming by chemical reaction is schematically shown in Fig. 2(D). In this process, inert gases such as N_2 or CO_2 are generated and dispersed within the 3D structure of hydrogel as a result of a chemical decomposition of a blowing agent or reaction between two compounds.[83] These compounds are commonly added to the polymer solution during the crosslinking reaction that the viscosity of hydrogel solution gradually increases. The formation of porosity in a hydrogel in this technique relies on retention of the gas bubbles in the solution during the crosslinking reaction.[76,83,84] During the gas foaming process the hydrogel system is unstable due to significant differences between the density of polymer solution and gas bubbles. This effect may result in creation of gradient of pore sizes. For instance, in system that the viscosity or the rate of crosslinking of polymer solution is low, the gas phase is rapidly moved upward due to lower density leading to the formation of a low porosity at the bottom layers and a highly porous structures on top layers of hydrogels.[76,84]

The rate of crosslinking, the viscosity of solution, and the concentration of blowing agents are the key factors that governs the microarchitecture of hydrogels fabricated with gas foaming technique. In some studies a surfactant is added into the polymer solution to stabilize the foam and to prevent coalescence of pores.[75] Additionally, the nature and the molecular weight of polymer may have an impact on viscosity of solution, hence the pore characteristics. The average pore size and the geometry of pores are significantly changed when using different types of polymers. The average pore sizes in these hydrogels are changed from 10 μm to approximately 1 mm. In this technique, therefore, the pore size is tuned in a wide range by changing different processing parameters such as polymer concentration, crosslinking rate (by addition of catalyst) and addition of surfactants.

Sodium bicarbonate is the most commonly used blowing agent due to its ability to form CO_2 in a relatively low acidic and cell friendly environment.[77] Ammonium bicarbonate has also been used in many studies as a gas foaming agent. Gas foaming has been used for both natural and synthetic polymer that crosslink rapidly. For instance, sodium bicarbonate has been used as the gas foaming agent to create porosity in acrylic acid-acrylamide system. N,N′-methylenebisacrylamide crosslinks this hydrogel in less than 5 min. The average pore size in this hydrogel was varied in the range of 100 μm to 250 μm by changing the concentration of sodium bicarbonate.[85,87] Various vinyl monomers were also polymerized and gas foamed by using sodium bicarbonate as a blowing agent and N,N′-methylenebisacrylamide as the crosslinking compound to create porous hydrogels with a high swelling ratio.[86] In another study poly (propylene fumarate-co-ethylene glycol) is crosslinked with PEGDA and gas foamed by using sodium bicarbonate as the blowing agent. The average pore size in this hydrogel was varied between 50 μm and 200 μm by changing the concentration of sodium bicarbonate from 0.05 M to 0.1 M.[88] For bone regeneration, UV-crosslinkable PEGDA/arginine-glycine-aspartic acid (RGD) hydrogels has been fabricated and gas foamed by using sodium bicarbonate as the blowing agent. The average pore size in the PEGDA/RGD hydrogels is in the range of 100 μm to 600 μm, which is favorable for bone regeneration.[77] These porous PEGDA/RGD hydrogels facilitated the osteogenesis of MSCs when they are cultured with osteogenic medium. This result confirms the desirable microstructures produced by gas foaming in these hydrogels for bone regeneration.[77]

Gas foaming has been used for the formation of porosity in composite hydrogels. For instance, chitosan/hydroxyapatite hydrogel is fabricated by microwave irradiation, and glyoxal and sodium bicarbonate as the blowing agent.[89] In this study, microwave irradiation is used to increase the decomposition rate of sodium bicarbonate, which enhances the rate of gas bubble formation and accelerates the rate of crosslinking reactions to increase the viscosity of solution. As a result, interconnected and well-established macro-porous hydrogels are fabricated in less than one minute. The results of *in vitro* cell study on MC3T3-E1 pre-osteoblastic cells demonstrate that the presence of hydroxyapatite particles promotes the cellular proliferation and osteoblast differentiation within the 3D structure of this composite hydrogel.[89]

In gas foaming systems that uses ammonium bicarbonate as a blowing agent, produces CO_2, which subsequently can form interconnected pores in hydrogels. For instance, pores are generated in the structure of carboxymethylcellulose–sodium and poly(acrylamide) hydrogels, crosslinked with electron beam irradiation by using ammonium bicarbonate as the blowing agent.[90] The limiting factor in application of ammonium bicarbonate as a blowing agent is, the formation of NH_3 as the by-product, which might have negative impact on biocompatibility of hydrogels.

Different surfactants are used in gas foaming process to promote the stability of generated foams and to fabricate hydrogels with homogeneous porous structure. Barbetta *et al.* introduced sodium dodecyl sulfate and poly-Q as surfactants for the formation of porosity in gelatin hydrogels, while also using sulfamic acid and sodium nitrite as blowing agent to form N_2 gas as a porogen.[76] These gelatin hydrogel possesses homogenous porous structures composed of micropores (90 μm) and macropores (230 μm).[76] The presence of micropores in the structure enhances the interconnectivity. Porous alginate hydrogels have also fabricated by using sodium bicarbonate and tartaric acid in the presence of pluronic F-108 as a surfactant to stabilize hydrogel foam.[75] The alginate hydrogels in this study possess microarchitecture consisted of both, micropores in the range of 30–80 μm, and macropores varied from 100 μm to 300 μm. These alginate hydrogel might be used for the fabrication of absorbent microparticles for water purification and scaffold preparation for different tissue engineering applications.[75] The surfactants may have an impact on the physiochemical properties of hydrogels.[91–93] For instance, the addition of cation type surfactants enhances the water uptake properties of hydrogels. Additionally, the incorporation of anionic type surfactants (such as sodium dodecyl sulfate and sodium oleate) substantially increases the rheological properties of hydrogels that promote the uniform distribution of pores within the structure of hydrogels.[93]

Conventional gas foaming is a cost effective technique for fabrication of porous hydrogel with highly interconnected pores. The surfactant and gas foaming agent may have negative impact on the biocompatible properties of hydrogels. In biomedical application therefore, care must be taken in selection of these reagents. Additionally, it is important to control the concentration of gas foaming agents, rate of both gas bubble formation and the crosslinking reaction to fabricate desirable pore architecture during the hydrogel formation. It is more viable for systems that exhibit rapid crosslinking reaction to maintain gas bubbles within their structure. Crosslinking time of approximately 3 to 5 min is deemed to be the optimum to fabricate a hydrogel with uniform distribution of pores. It is suggested to add a catalyst to promote the kinetic of crosslinking reaction and thus increase the uniform distribution of pores within the structure of hydrogels.[94,95]

2.4.2. *Gas foaming by high pressure CO_2*

In this technique as it is shown in Fig. 2(E), a gas diffuses into the hydrogel matrix at high pressure and rapid depressurization of the system resulted in nucleation of gas bubbles and formation of pores in 3D structure of hydrogels.[96,97] CO_2 is the most commonly used gas due to its moderate critical point (73 bar at 31°C), non-flammability and low toxicity.[22,78] Due to solubility of CO_2 in hydrophobic and amorphous polymers at high pressures, it has been widely used for the fabrication of polymeric scaffolds. For example, porous scaffolds of poly (ε-caprolactone), poly (lactic acid), poly(lactic-co-glycolic acid) are fabricated for tissue engineering applications.[24,25,98] However, CO_2 has very low solubility in hydrophilic polymers, which consequently leads to creation of close-pores with very low average pore size in the structure of hydrogels. Different techniques such as "CO_2–water" emulsion templating[99–101] and use of co-solvent systems have been used to promote the diffusion of dense gas within the structure of hydrophilic polymers.

Emulsion templating technique involves foaming a curable polymer (external phase) and droplets (internal phase). The structure of external phase is then fixed by reaction-induced phase separation such as redox polymerization or free-radical polymerization.[102] The internal phase is then removed, which leads to the formation of highly porous structure of polymers. The main drawback associated with this technique is the need of organic solvent for the formation of internal phase, which might be difficult to remove. The residues of the organic solvents in the structure of hydrogels might have negative impact on the biocompatibility of hydrogels. To address this problem, CO_2–water emulsion technique has been developed in which supercritical CO_2 is used as the internal droplet phase and water as the external phase.[103] High pressure CO_2–water emulsion templating techniques have been used for the fabrication of highly porous hydrogels from many naturally derived and synthetic polymers.[99,104,105]

CO_2–water emulsion technique has been used for fabrication of porous alginate hydrogels.[105] In this study, CO_2 acts as internal phase for gas foaming process and also to decrease pH of the alginate solution. The acidity of solution triggers the release of calcium ions from their stable form and subsequently leads to crosslinking of alginate polymer chains. The alginate hydrogel fabricated in this study possesses an average pore size of 24–250 μm.[105] Porous polysaccharide dextran hydrogels have been fabricated using CO_2–water emulsion technique.[99] Perfluoropolyethers is used as a surfactant to stabilize the foam and potassium peroxydisulfate is added to initiate the crosslinking reaction for the preparation of dextran hydrogel. The dextran hydrogel fabricated in this study possesses the average pore size of 26 μm, which is not favorable for many tissue engineering applications.[99] It is shown that the porosity, pore morphology, and microarchitecture of hydrogels fabricated with CO_2–water emulsion technique can be altered by changing the volume fraction of CO_2 and the concentration of surfactant.[99,105]

Other CO_2 assisted methods such as CO_2-induced phase inversion[106] and solvent exchange/supercritical fluid drying[109] have been developed for the creation of porosity within the structure of hydrophilic polymer systems. The use of organic solvents and also the formation of small pores (less than 1 μm) are the main drawbacks associated with these techniques.[108] For instance, Ji *et al.* used a solvent exchange technique to create porosity in chitosan hydrogel. In this method as shown in Fig. 4, a chitosan film is first soaked in water and then gradually the solvent is exchanged from water to an organic solvent by using 80%, 60%, 40%, 20%, and pure solvent.[108] This sample is then kept at high pressure CO_2 to remove organic solvent and create porosity in hydrogel. A homogenous, highly interconnected submicron sized pores is created in chitosan at temperatures between 25°C and 60°C and pressures above 25 bar. These pore sizes may not be favorable for tissue engineering and cell proliferation, however, the dense gas solvent exchange method has been used for the impregnation of a drug within these chitosan hydrogels. Both griseofulvin and camptothecin were successfully impregnated into chitosan during the pore formation by dense gas solvent exchange technique. It is interesting to note that these drugs were impregnated as amorphous form due to the molecular interaction with chitosan. Amorphous form of drugs is not thermodynamically stable and converts to crystalline form. However, in this formulation prepared by dense gas solvent exchange griseofulvin and camptotechin were maintained in amorphous form for a period of six months and their dissolution rate were dramatically enhanced compared with their crystalline forms. The chitosan hydrogel produced by this method is desirable for oral administration and transdermal delivery. The enhancement of drug potency, coupled with the mucoadhesive properties of chitosan is favorable for administration of the formulation for sublingual or buccal delivery.[108]

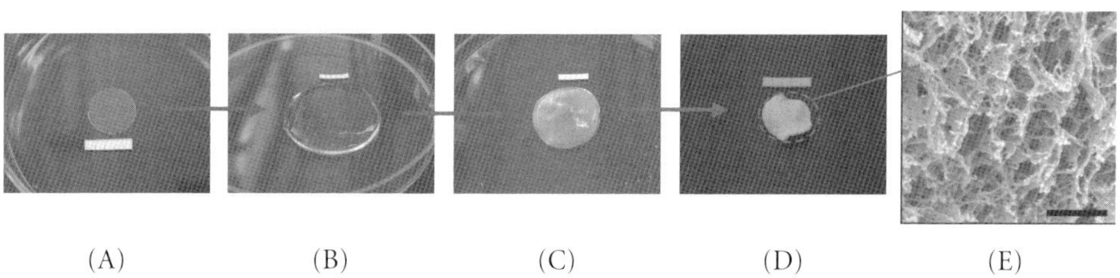

Fig. 4. Creation of porosity in chitosan hydrogels by dense gas solvent exchange process. (A, Step 1) Fabrication of chitosan film by solvent casting technique, (B, Step 2) swollen chitosan film in water, (C, Step 3) chitosan film after solvent exchange, (D, Step 4) chitosan film after dense gas process and (E, scale bar is 1 μm) microstructure of chitosan layer fabricated with dense gas solvent exchange process.[108]

Annabi *et al.* and Ji *et al.* have developed a new strategy for the creation of porosity in hydrogels that is comprised of producing gas bubbles in an aqueous solution from the depressurization and releasing the dissolved CO_2. In this technique high pressure CO_2 is first dissolved into a polymer solution during the crosslinking reaction. As shown in Fig. 5, at each temperature the solubility of CO_2 in water is substantially enhanced by increasing the pressure. After the solution is saturated with CO_2, the system is depressurized to create nuclei of gas bubbles within the hydrogel structure.[109] To fabricate porous hydrogel with uniform distribution of pores, it is critical to depressurize the system when the foam exhibits

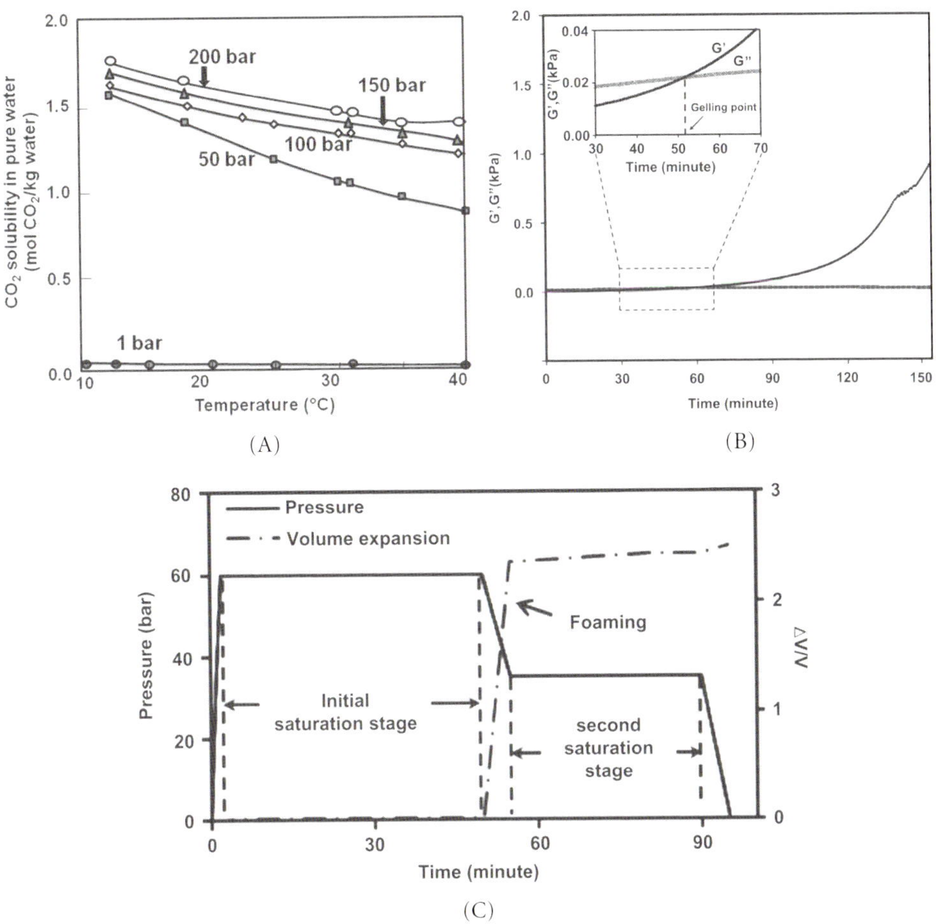

Fig. 5. Pore formation in hydrogel structures by dissolving high pressure CO_2 during the crosslinking reaction. (A) Solubility of CO_2 in water[109], (B) rheological behavior of chitosan hydrogel, and (C) tuning the depressurization phase of chitosan hydrogel gas foaming to enhance the microarchitecture of chitosan hydrogels.[91]

sufficient physical stability. The depressurization is therefore conducted after the gelling time of hydrogels. Ji *et al.* tune the microarchitecture of chitosan hydrogels by investigating the rheological behavior of chitosan solution and designing multiphase depressurization step as shown in Figs. 5(B) and 5(C) to fabricate highly porous chitosan hydrogel.[81]

Chitosan is crosslinked under high pressure CO_2 using different crosslinking reagent such as glutaraldehyde and genipin.[80,81] Pores with average size of 30–40 μm are produced in these chitosan hydrogels.[80] By implementing gradient depressurization strategy, the average pore size in the chitosan hydrogel is increased to 60 μm as shown in Fig. 6(A).[81] Average pore size in these hydrogels is further increased to 140 μm with the porosity of 87% by using acacia gum as a cytocompatible surfactant to stabilize the hydrogel foam during the process. On these chitosan hydrogels, fibroblast cells are able to penetrate up to 400 μm into the hydrogel structure due to high degree of porosity and presence of large pores within the structure of

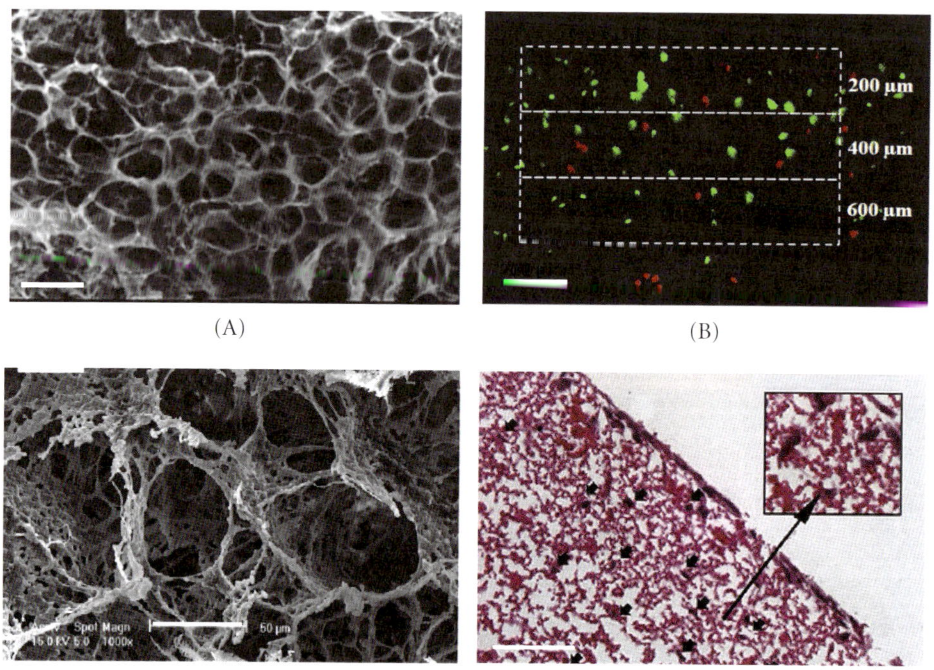

(A) (B) (C) (D)

Fig. 6. Microstructure and cell proliferation within the 3D structure of porous hydrogels fabricated by gas foaming : (A) SEM images of chitosan hydrogel, (B, live dead assay) proliferation of fibroblast cells within the 3D structure of chitosan hydrogels (live/dead staining of cells within the structure of chitosan hydrogels), (C) SEM image of tropoelastin hydrogel, and (D) histology tests from staining of tropoelastin hydrogels (arrows show fibroblast cells proliferated within the structure of hydrogel).[81,112]

chitosan hydrogels as shown in Fig. 6(B).[81] Same approach has been used for the fabrication of porosity in a protein-based hydrogels such as elastin and tropoelastin using CO_2 at 37°C and 60 bar.[110–112] The results of this study shows that high pressure CO_2 promotes the kinetic of crosslinking reaction by decreasing the gelling time from 24 h in atmospheric condition to less than 1 h under high pressure CO_2.[111] Figure 6(C) shows that the depressurization of the system induced large channels in the 3D structure of hydrogel with average pore size of approximately 80 μm.[112] The formation of these open channels within the structure of hydrogels promotes the migration of fibroblast cells into the deep layers of hydrogels as shown in Fig. 6(D).[112] Application of high pressure CO_2 during the crosslinking reaction therefore is deemed to be an efficient method for generation of open pores within the structure of hydrogels. The same technique has also been used for fabrication of porous silk fibroin hydrogels under high pressure CO_2 without using surfactants and organic solvent.[113] In this approach, silk protein gelation is considerably expedited under high pressure CO_2 by formation of β-sheet structures ad very stable hydrogels. The gelation time in this process was decreased from 10 h in atmospheric condition to less than 2 h at 100 bar. The silk fibroin hydrogel fabricated under high pressure CO_2 possess highly porous microstructure with average pore size of approximately 10 μm.[113]

Gas foaming technique provides a mean for processing of hydrogels at low temperature which prevents the denaturation of biopolymers and preserves bioactivity of growth factors if they are directly incorporated with the hydrogel structures. High pressure CO_2 has been used for impregnation, micronization, and fabrication of hydrogels from wide range of proteins and polypeptides such as recombinant human deoxyribonuclease,[114] elastin,[115] lysozymes,[116,117] trypsin, insulin,[116,118] and catalase.[119] Many studies show that high pressure CO_2 has negligible effect on biological properties of proteins, however, this impact cannot be broadened. For instance, the bioactivity and biochemical integrity of proteins with isoelectric points above 3 such as recombinant human deoxyribonuclease[114] is significantly decreased when exposed to high pressure CO_2. In addition, this approach is not applicable for cell-laden hydrogels and polymer solutions with very high gelation time. The requirement for high pressure CO_2 pump also limits the wide application of this approach for processing of biomaterials in large scale.

3. Microengineering Hydrogels

In conventional tissue engineering approaches, cells are seeded on hydrogels that mimic the biochemical properties of natural ECM. Despite major promising results in reconstruction of many tissues such as cartilage, bladder, and liver, there are still major hurdles such as the lack of control on metabolic activity of encapsulated cells and absence of functional vasculature network to deliver nutrients and oxygen.[21,120–124] Human tissues are complicated ensembles of multiple cell types embedded in complex and well-defined structures of ECM. The organization of ECM is hierarchical from nano- to macro-size with many proteins forming large structures.[124–127] Microfabrication techniques have been employed to develop more efficient approaches for controlling the microenvironment of cells. Different approaches such as emulsion-based techniques, replica molding, photolithography, capillary force molding, and microfluidic systems are used for micro-engineering of hydrogels. These techniques are schematically shown in Fig. 7. In addition, process of each of these methods and their limitations are summarized in Table 2. This section provides an insight about these methods, their application in biomedicine and tissue engineering.

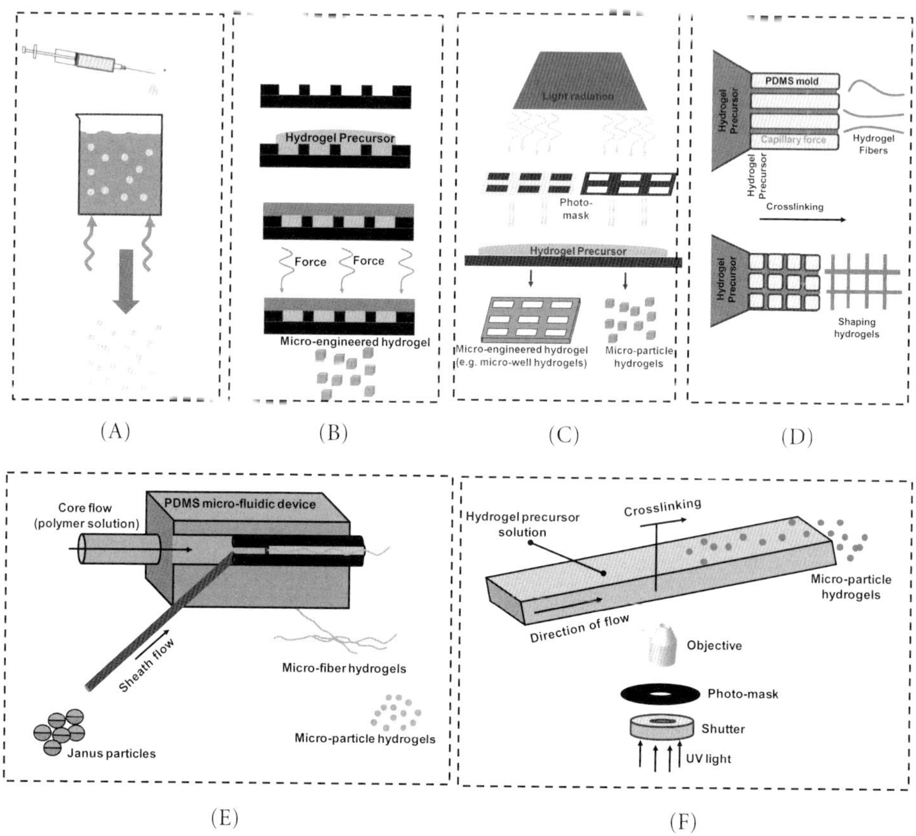

Fig. 7. Different techniques developed for micro-engineering of hydrogels, (A) conventional emulsion-based technique, (B) replica molding, (C) photolithography for fabrication of microwells and microparticle hydrogels, (D) capillary force molding microfluidic device for fabrication of microfibers, (E) microparticles, or Janus particles, and (F) stop photo-lithography for fabrication of microparticle hydrogels.

Table 2. Different micro and nano topography techniques for various hydrogels.

Method	Device/stamp specification	Polymer classification	Advantages	Limiting factors	Ref.
Emulsion-based technique	NA	Natural and synthetic polymers with low viscosity	• Simple and easy to scale up for mass production of microparticle hydrogels	• Pre-fabricated microfluidic channel device is required	[128–130]
Replica Molding/ nano-imprinting	Hydrophobic mold	Thermoresponsive polymers/natural proteins/ elastomers	• Requires low expertise for fabrication • Resolution of less than 10 nm • Applicable for large area of hydrogel (few centimeters)	• Long process time for crosslinking • Pattern formation in two-dimensional (2D) structure	[131–133]
Photo lithography/ light assisted molding	Photo-mask	Photo-crosslinkable polymers	• Very high resolution (<10 nm) • Particles with variety of dimensions • Fabrication of microwells	• Further process is required to assembly of hydrogels for formation of 3D constructs	[9, 134–137]
Capillary force lithography/ micromolding in capillaries	Hydrophilic mold	Elastomers	• Formation of 3D structures with very high resolution,	• Just suitable for elastomers with very low viscosity	[138–143]
Microcontact printing (μCP)	Patterned mold	Polypeptides	• Easy for surface modification of biomaterials with bioactive compounds	• Only 2D modification process • Swelling of poly (dimethylsiloxane) (PDMS) mold decreases the resolution of process	[141, 144, 145]

(Continued)

Table 2. (*Continued*)

Method	Device/stamp specification	Polymer classification	Advantages	Limiting factors	Ref.
Block copolymer lithography	NA	Block copolymer-based hydrogels	• Creation of nano sized pores	• Not applicable for naturally derived proteins and many synthetic polymers	[146, 147]
	Conventional spinning technique	Polymers with low viscosity (elastomers)	• Economically feasible • Very promising results for formation of tubular shape tissues	• Not applicable for fabrication of Janus fibers	[148]
Microfluidic Fabrication of microfiber hydrogels	Orifice with Spinning solvent	Elastomers	• Fabrication of very fine fibers with high surface area	• Organic solvent required as anti-solvent	[149, 150]
	Orifice with coaxial flow	Natural and synthetic polymers	• Continuous techniques • Suitable for cell encapsulation • Fabrication of Janus microfiber	• Required microfluidic device	[148, 150]
Microfluidic fabrication of micro particle hydrogels	Microfluidic-channel /stop photolithography	Natural and synthetic polymers/ photo-crosslinkable	• Possible to finely control the definite number of encapsulated cells in the microparticle hydrogel • Feasible to tune morphology, shape and porosity of hydrogels	• Might not be highly efficient in cell encapsulation of microparticle hydrogels • Pre-fabricated microfluidic channel device is required	[151–153]
Microfluidic fabrication of Janus particles or microfibers	Microfluidic device	Natural and synthetic polymers	• Possible to separate organic and inorganic substances to achieve better biological properties	• Complicated production process • Pre-fabricated microfluidic channel device is required	[154–158]

3.1. Extrusion-dripping emulsion techniques

In emulsion-based techniques such as extrusion-dripping emulsion as shown in Fig. 7(A), a droplet of hydrogel precursor is formed and subsequently delivered either to an anti-solvent reservoir or to a solution containing a crosslinking reagents. In the former approach, the polymer is crosslinked physically or chemically by the addition of a crosslinking agent and these microparticles are collected in a reservoir.[128,129] In the latter approach however, *in situ* gelation of surface layer of polymer precursor leads to formation of hydrogel microparticles.[159,160] The size of microparticles in emulsion-based techniques is directly correlated with the diameter of droplets of precursor before the crosslinking process. The microparticle hydrogels with diameter in the range of 0.5 μm to 0.5 cm can be generated by using this method.

Alginate has been used for cell encapsulation using micro-emulsion technique in which crosslinking by calcium ion is carried out internally or externally.[159,160] In an external gelation, a droplet of alginate solution containing cells is formed in air and then collected in a solution of calcium ions. Calcium ions induce crosslinking and gelation of alginate polymer chain on the surface of this droplet, which prevents diffusion of calcium ions into the core regions and thus protects cells or biological compounds against free ions.[159,160] In internal gelation approach, solutions of alginate and calcium salts are added drop-wise to oil. Drops of alginate solution are formed due to hydrophilic–hydrophobic interaction between water and oil phases. Subsequently, oil is acidified which triggers the release of calcium ions from the calcium salts. The calcium ions then induce gelation of alginate polymer chain, forming alginate microparticle hydrogels. As shown in Fig. 8 the calcium alginate hydrogels, formed by internal gelation are more homogenous compared to the hydrogels formed by external gelation approach. The overall

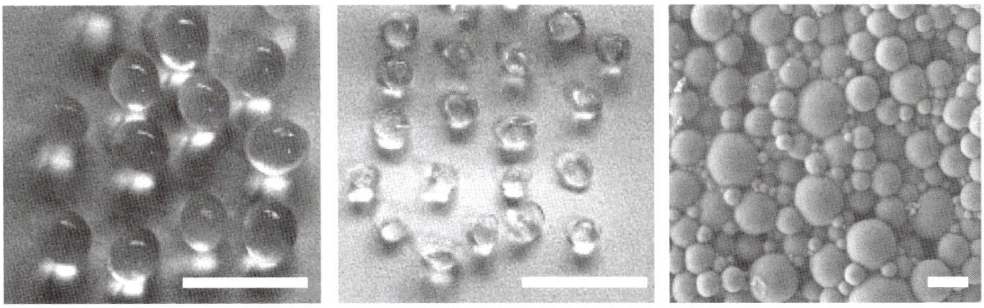

(A) (B) (C)

Fig. 8. Samples of hydrogel particles produced by emulsion-based techniques. (A, scale bar is 1 cm) Microparticles of alginate by internal and (B, scale bar is 1 cm) external crosslinking[159,160] ;(C, scale bar is 10 μm) from heparin/HA.[129]

degree of crosslinking, however, in the internal gelation technique is low that is favorable when high swelling properties are required.[159,160] Heparin/HA microparticles with average diameter of 1 μm are shown in Fig. 8(C).[129] These microparticles can be used for drug delivery and also cell encapsulation applications. For instance, the microparticles of Heparin/hyaluronic hydrogels, produced by this method possessed nanoporous structure, which are potentially favorable for growth factor encapsulation.[129]

Gelatin microparticle hydrogels are fabricated by emulsion technique.[161] In this method a gelatin solution is added drop-wise to an oil bath that is kept at low temperature to form physically crosslinked micron sized hydrogels. These microhydrogels are then collected by filtration and chemically crosslinked with glutaraldehyde.[161] These gelatin hydrogels have also been used for delivery of growth factors such as IGF-1 or TGF-β1. These compounds are loaded into gelatin by keeping the microparticle hydrogels in IGF-1 or TGF-β1 solution for a period of 15 h at 4°C.[161,162] The drug loading has been conducted after crosslinking of gelatin hydrogels to preserve the bioactivity of these growth factors.

In summary, with emulsion-based techniques hydrogel particles with different diameters in the range of 0.5 μm to 1 cm are fabricated. However, in this method there is no control on size distribution of particles. One of the major issues associated with this technique is the random agglomeration of particles, which results in achieving a broad range of particle size.

3.2. Replica molding

As schematically shown in Fig. 7(B) in replica molding technique micron-size patterns or microparticle hydrogels are generated by conformal contact of a hydrophobic mold with the surfaces of polymer solution.[131,132] Various types of naturally derived and synthetic polymers such as thermoresponsive and UV crosslinkable polymers can be processed by this method. Stainless steel and poly(dimethylsiloxane) (PDMS) templates are common molds in this method due to their high mechanical strength.[163] In addition, siloxane-based polymers, photocurable perfluoropolyethers, biodegradable polymers, and photosensitive polymers have also been widely used as a stamp/template[21,164–167] in replica molding. For soft lithography of hydrogels in particular, hydrophobic surface of PDMS is beneficial in separation of stamp from hydrogel surface.[168,169]

Micropattern is generated on the surface of poly(N-isopropylacrylamide) (PNIPAM) hydrogels,[170] as shown in Fig. 9(A). High aspect ratio (fiber-like structure) pillars play an important role in wide range of biomedical applications such as DNA separation,[171] force sensors,[172,173] dry adhesives,[174] and cell response studies.[172,173] Replica molding along with photo-polymerization techniques have been

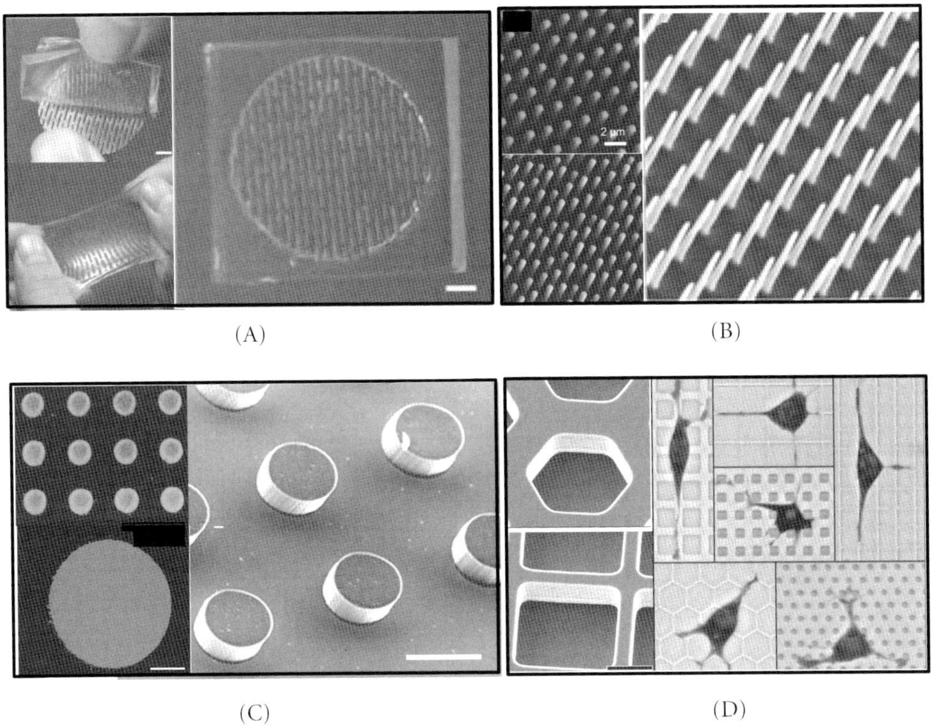

Fig. 9. Replica molding for micro-engineering of hydrogels. (A, scale bar is 3 mm) PNIPAM hydrogels with PDMS mold,[170] (B, scale bar is 2 μm) fabrication of high aspect ratio of PHEMA hydrogels with geometries,[175] (C, scale bar is 100 μm) fabrication of microparticle PEG-based hydrogels and immobilization of BSA as a model protein on its surface,[176] and (D, scale bar is 100 μm) topography and micropatterning on polyacrylamide hydrogels.

used for fabrication of hydrogel pillars from PHEMA, poly(HEMA-N-isopropylacrylamide) (PHEMA–NIPAAM), and poly(ethylene glycol dimethacrylate) (PEGMA) with high aspect ratios as depicted in Fig. 9(B).[175] PEGMA pillar hydrogels exhibited favorable structural stability after swelling in aqueous solution due to high degree of crosslinking in the hydrogel pillars.[175]

Replica molding technique is used for the fabrication of microparticle hydrogels for various biomedical applications such as enzyme and protein immobilizations.[176] For instance, microparticles of PEG-based hydrogels fabricated with replica molding are used for the immobilization of glucose oxidase and peroxidase as model proteins to confirm immobilization efficiency of these hydrogels.[176] A uniform microarchitecture with average diameter of approximately 75 μm is prepared by this method that depicted in Fig. 9(C).[176] Same approach has been used for the formation of microhydrogels of chitosan or alginate.[177] Additionally, replica molding is used for the preparation of microtopography on the surface of hydrogels to guide proliferation of MSCs. As shown in Fig. 9(D), cells are aligned in respect to the topography of hydrogels.

Replica molding is used to fabricate multilayered microfluidic networks for the preparation of microparticles and fibers, develop hydrogel constructs with gradient concentration of drugs, chemicals or reagents throughout their structure.[21,123,178] For example multilayered PEGDA hydrogel is prepared using a PDMS template. The diffusivity of solute (i.e., culture media) is controlled by the degree of crosslinking in PEGDA hydrogel.[179] Feasibility of multilayer molding in this approach makes it favorable for the fabrication of complex cell-laden constructs for different tissue engineering applications.[177] Furthermore, this method is commercially feasible for micropatterning of hydrogels due to its simplicity. However, a long processing time and also 2D patterning are the main drawbacks of this method in biomedicine and tissue engineering.[21,180]

3.3. Photolithography

An optically predefined mask, which selectively blocks the light in some regions, is used in photolithography. Due to selective exposure of light to some region, uncrosslinked regions are subsequently washed and removed by water.[134–137] The photolithography technique is used for the fabrication of microwells and microparticle hydrogels. As depicted in Figs. 7(B) and 7(C) by controlling the illumination of light in this technique micropatterns or microhydrogels are crated with a nanoscale resolution.[9]

Microlanes and microwells are created on the surface of hydrogels. These architectures can support cells against shear stress and therefore, facilitates the alignment of cells on the surface of hydrogels. Photolithography has been used for the formation of micron sized hydrogels with defined shapes for broad range of applications. In this technique, physically predefined molds are used to crosslink hydrogel precursor with a desirable shape and pattern. Photo-crosslinkable polymers are dispersed onto molds and subsequently crosslinked by UV or visible light for a short period of time to form negative replica of mold.[181] In addition to all favorable properties of PDMS molds for soft lithography such as high mechanical strength,[163] cytocompatibility,[182] commercial availability,[21] and easy to detach from hydrogel surface,[168,169] it is also optically transparent to approximately 300 μm that is ideal for photolithography of 3D hydrogels and fabrication of microparticle hydrogels.[169] The dimensions of patterns that are generated by this technique can be finely controlled with the resolution in the range of nano to millimeter scales.[136,137,183]

In summary, it is feasible to fabricate microparticle hydrogel with the diameter in the range of 0.1–10 μm to control microenvironment of individual cell for different biological analysis, 10–400 μm to control the structure of cluster of cells, or in construct with diameter larger than 400 μm to control the interaction between multiple cell clusters.[9] Therefore, this technique has broad biomedical applications. This technique is, however, only applicable for photo-crosslinkable biomaterials.[144] In addition, since photolithography is inherently 2D process for fabrication of micro-particle hydrogels, further processing is required for assembly of the resulted hydrogels to form a 3D structure for different tissue engineering applications.[9,137]

3.4. Capillary force micromolding

In capillary force lithography, elastomers drive into cavity of physical molds as the result of Laplace pressure, which is generated at the interface of liquid and solid surface.[142,184] Laplace pressure also absorbs liquid inside the microchannels for micromolding in capillaries.[138,139] This technique can be used for the fabrication of microfiber hydrogels with different shapes as shown in Fig. 7(D). In these techniques, micromolds must be hydrophobic to generate Laplace pressure to drive liquid and also to allow air and solvents dissipate during the process. To meet such requirement PDMS-based materials have been widely used for the fabrication of molds in this method.

This technique has been used for micropatterning of different hydrogels that have been used for biomedical applications. Capillary molding has been used to produce micro/nano size structures of poly-acrylamide hydrogel.[185] In this approach, poly-acrylamide is crosslinked by redox polymerization techniques, using N,N,N′N′-tetramethyl ethylene diamine and sodium peroxide disulphate. Shibata *et al.* demonstrated the viability of creating microscale patterns such as line and space, posts and grids with this technique. The line and space structure promotes the alignment of cells along the line that resulted in formation of a long and narrow shape cluster of cells.[185]

In summary, the capillary force micro molding technique can be used for constructing 3D micropatterning of hydrogels in large scale. However, its application is limited for topography and fabrication of hydrogels from only elastomers with low viscosity.[186] This is due to the high surface tension in polymer solutions with high viscosity, which prevents the diffusion of hydrogel solutions into the mold cavity. In addition, there is a lack of control on the resolution of generated patterns, which might limits the application of this method for precise biomedical applications.[144]

3.5. Microcontact printing

In microcontact printing (μCP) predefined patterns can be transferred by conformal contact between a stamp and the substrate surface. Different biomaterials, such as naturally derived proteins, and self-assembled monolayer, can be transferred through μCP to another surface.[145] This technique can be used for the fabrication of microwells and microstructures outside[137,187,188] or within microfluidic channels.[189,190]

The stamp used for this purpose must meet several requirements such as low surface energy for efficient transfer, flexibility for conformal contact and inert surface properties to avoid degradation of transferred materials.[6,191] PDMS stamps, prepared by replica molding therefore are deemed to be a favorable candidate for μCP.[144] This method has wide applications for transfer of different bioactive materials to the surface of hydrogels for variety of biomedical applications. The swelling of stamps (mostly PDMS stamps) as the result of conformal contact with bioactive compounds however decreases the accuracy of this technique for very fine micro or nano imprinting.[141] Swelling of stamp during the inking process elevates the size of patterns. The resolution of this technique is therefore, approximately 500 nm for PDMS and 50 nm for hard PDMS with lower water intake properties.[141] The application this technique is also limited due to generation of two dimensional patterns on the surface of hydrogels.

3.6. Microfluidic-based techniques

In various biomedical applications, cells or bioactive reagents are immobilized and encapsulated in hydrogels. Size distribution of hydrogels plays an important role in biomedical applications. In most of the micro-engineering techniques such as emulsion, replica molding and capillary force micromolding there is no fine control over the size, size distribution, and morphology of microhydrogels.

Immune response and fibrosis formation can be minimized by tuning the morphology and particle size of hydrogels.[192] In addition, narrow size distribution of microparticles of hydrogels with diameter in the range of 10 μm to 20 μm enhances mass transfer properties, hence the therapeutic effect of cell-based therapies and cell viability.[191] Microfluidic techniques are superior for the fabrication of microhydrogels and have been utilized to produce particles and fibers with well-defined physic–chemical properties.

The hydrogels in the form of microparticle and microfibers support cells to maintain their cellular function by diffusion of nutrients and oxygen within their structure and also preserve the bioactivity of reagents against surrounding environment.[192,193] These hydrogels are commonly fabricated from natural and biocompatible polymers, therefore, they exhibit low immune responsive behavior.[194] Several strategies that used for the fabrication of microparticle and microfiber hydrogels are discussed in this section.

3.6.1. *Fabrication of microparticle hydrogels*

Microfluidic techniques that are schematically shown in Fig. 7(E) have been used for the production of microparticles for the encapsulation of cells or bioactive compounds. In this approach emulsification within the microfluidic channels results in the formation of microparticles. The characteristics of these microparticles can be finely tuned by controlling the wetting properties of surface of microfluidic channel, viscosity, surface tension, and flow rate ratio between the disperse and continuous liquid phase in the microfluidic device.[152,153,195] Core-shell, hollow, porous microparticles, and Janus particles have been produced by this technique.[196–198]

The various patterns of droplet in droplet hydrogels that is shown in Fig. 10 have been fabricated by designing coaxial microfluidic channels that allow preparation of emulsion of a fluid in another within the microfluidic channel. The schematic diagram of this microfluidic device is shown in Fig. 10. The microarchitecture, size, morphology, and number of microparticles in each individual droplet are controlled by tuning the flow of solution, geometry, and the hydrophilic properties of microfluidic channel. This technique has been used for the creation of droplet-in-droplet, double emulsion microparticle, and droplet-in-droplet-in-droplet, triple emulsion microparticle hydrogels.[196] These multi-core microparticles can be used for multi-stage drug delivery application by loading different bioactive or therapeutic reagents in the cores or the shell of these microparticles. Additionally, this design of microfluidic channels has been used for the encapsulation of gas bubble in a droplet microfluidic[199] and for the cell encapsulation to prepare hydrogels with definite number of cells in each microparticle.[130]

Microparticle hydrogels containing definite number of cells are of benefits for various biomedical applications such as therapeutic cell delivery techniques. For instance, embryonic stem cells (ESCs) are encapsulated in agarose microparticles with diameter of 110 μm. It is viable to tune the size of microparticles by varying the concentration of agarose or alginate solution.[200–202] Furthermore, the cell encapsulation efficiency of nearly 100% is achievable by this technique.[203]

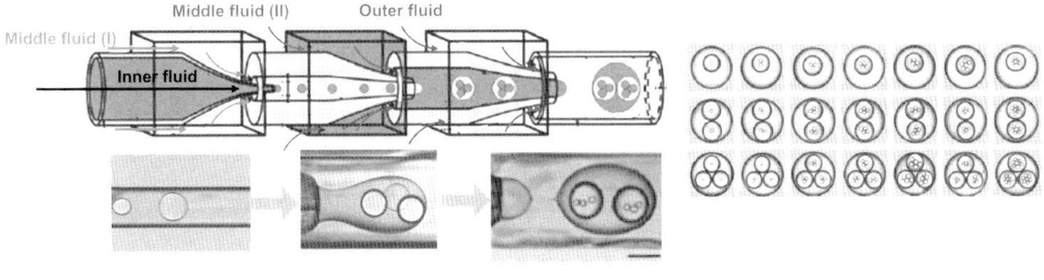

(A) (B)

Fig. 10. (A) Schematic diagram of apparatus for microfluidic emulsification technique used for the fabrication of microparticle hydrogels microfluidic and (B) effect of flow rate on the shape, morphology and the numbers of microparticles in each individual microhydrogel.[196]

Designing a system for the single cell encapsulation is still challenging due to the random operation of this process. It has been attempted to use low cell density in solution to achieve single cell encapsulation. However, the major issue is the minimal cell encapsulation efficiency at this condition.[153] Abeate *et al.* attempted to establish a new approach in designing microfluidic channel to overcome this obstacle. It was found that single cell encapsulation and one particle per droplet can be achieved by aligning the cells in microfluidic channels and also by adjusting the flow rate of polymeric solution to generate a periodic flow of particles.[152] In another approach, high aspect ratio PDMS microfluidic-channel is designed to restrict cells to certain streamlines inside the channel to generate two trains of cells with precisely longitudinal spacing. This self-ordering phenomenon can be used for the encapsulation of single cell inside a microparticle hydrogel.[151]

In summary, microparticle hydrogels with different microarchitecture and morphology can be produced by using microfluidic techniques. However, the success of this method is governed by precise design of microfluidic device.

3.6.2. *Fabrication of Janus microparticles*

Janus hydrogels are anisotropic microparticles constitute of two hemispheres with completely distinct compositions.[206–210] Janus particles with opposite charges have been used for the fabrication of electrical papers.[206] For example, nanoparticles of fluorescent anisotropy are used as nano probes to study molecular interactions.[208]

Different methods have been developed for the fabrication of Janus particles such as selective surface modification,[208,209] electro-hydrodynamic jetting,[211] and self-assembly.[217] Application of these techniques, however, is limited due to high polydispersity of products with random distribution of asymmetric properties in the particles. In more advance approaches for fabrication of Janus particles, microfluidic devices have been used for the generation of mono dispersed microparticles with diameters varied in the range 10–500 μm.[196,198,219] These Janus particles have been used for controlled drug delivery,[213] biological sample labeling and sorting,[155,156] and biomedical imaging.

Chen *et al.* has used the concept of phase separation in microfluidic devices for the fabrication of Janus microparticles.[157] Fig. 11(A) shows the schematic diagram of the double emulsion microfluidic device that has been designed for the preparation of these Janus particles. As an example a monomer solution comprising acrylic acid and benzophenone are passed through a microfluidic channel to encapsulate nanomagnetic particles. Focused UV spot light is then used to create Janus microparticles.[157] The microarchitecture of these Jaunus particles are shown in Fig. 11(B). Due to the presence of magnetic core, hydrogels rotate clockwise by subjecting these hydrogel particles to a magnetic field as shown in Fig. 11(C).

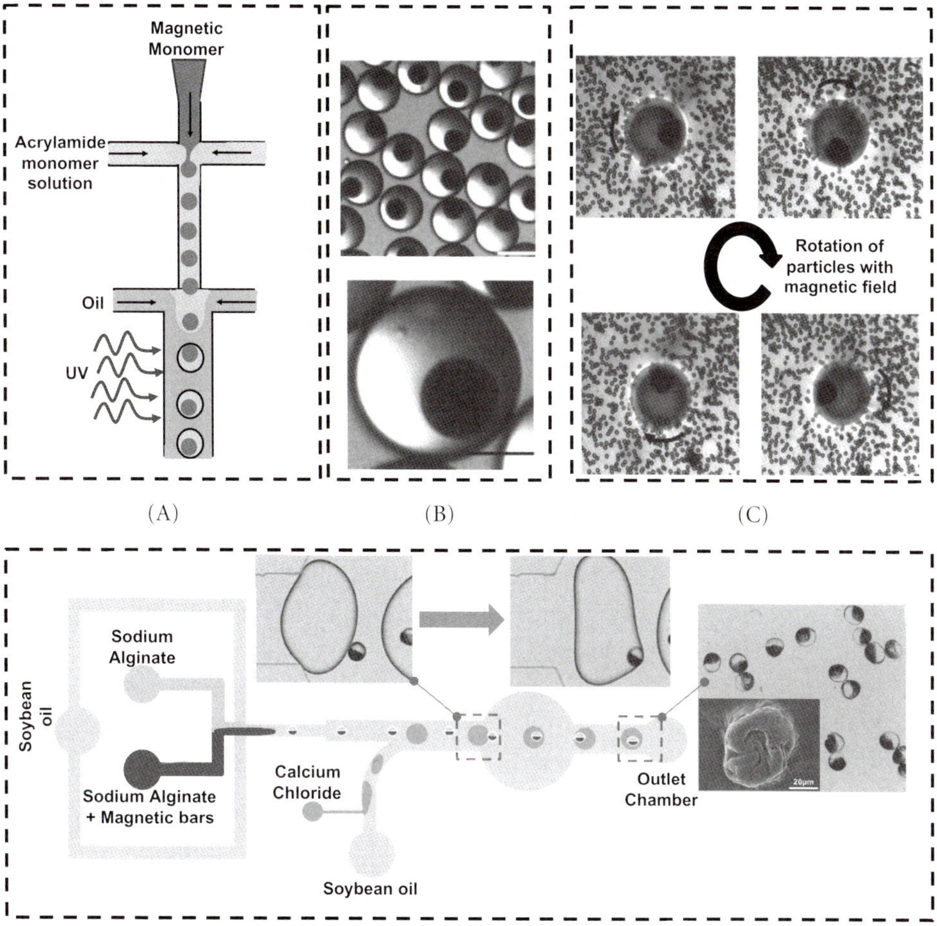

(A) (B) (C)

(D)

Fig. 11. Janus particle formation, (A) schematic diagram of microfluidic device, (B, scale bar is 50 μm) Janus particles with magnetic anisotropic structure, (C) rotation of Janus particles by applying magnetic field to the particle,[157] and (D) fabrication of alginate Janus microparticle hydrogels in a microfludic device, Janus particles exhibits two distinct hemispheres.[154]

In these Janus hydrogels hydrophobic magnetic particles are inserted in the core-shell structure and they are covered with UV crosslinkable polymer hydrogel.[157] This technique may not be suitable for cell encapsulation due to the risk of cytoxicity reaction between the cells and inorganic particles.[158]

Janus particles with two distinct separate hemispheres; containing magnetic substance and biological species are fabricated to inhibit the interaction between biological species and external inorganic particles. Zhao *et al.* has developed a microfluidic device for the fabrication of these Janus hydrogel particles. The schematic of this microfluidic device is shown in Fig. 11(D). Magnetic particles are encapsulated in an alginate microparticle. The diameter of Janus particles fabricated in this study are in the range of 50–65 μm.[154] These microparticle hydrogels can be used as carrier of cells or biochemical substance for cell culture array or cell-based therapies with targeted delivery using magnetic field to drive the particles.[154]

In summary, Janus hydrogel are generated by using microfluidic techniques to fabricate two distinctive regions in a particle. These hydrogels have broad range of applications from optics and biotechnology. The main advantage of the microfluidic for the fabrication of Janus hydrogels is the mono dispersity of particles and the feasibility to tune their characteristics.

3.6.3. *Fabrication of microfibers*

Fibrous constructs can guide the proliferation, alignment, and migration of cells in a certain direction.[214–216] Microfiber hydrogels are of benefit in different tissue engineering applications due to high permeability and diffusivity of nutrient and oxygen within their structure.[217–219] Microfibers can be used for the alignment of cells to generate tubular structures for vascular tissue engineering.[220] Electrospinning and hydrodynamic spinning have been used broadly for the generation of hydrogel fibers.[148,221] However, in recent years microfluidic techniques are used to fabricate microfibers with tunable characteristics.[153] This process for the fabrication of microchannels and fibers is schematically shown in Fig. 12(A). In this technique microfibers are generated by crosslinking of coaxial flow of hydrogel precursor in a microfluidic channel. Core fluid (hydrogel precursor) and sheath fluid are injected into a microchannel and as long as the interfacial energy between the two fluids is low, both fluids flow in the channel and upon the crosslinking of the core flow in the channel the fibers are formed.[153] In coaxial flow-based micro devices, diameter and shape of microfibers are tuned by changing the chemistry, flow rate or the concentration of hydrogel precursors through the capillary glass pipettes or microfluid channel mixers.[148]

By using capillary glass pipettes in a coaxial flow device, calcium alginate microfibers are fabricated for cell encapsulation and protein delivery. In this method the solutions of sodium alginate (2 wt.%) and calcium chloride (100 mM) have been the main flow and the sheath flow, respectively.[222] Shin *et al.*[222] showed the effect of flow rate of hydrogel precursor on the diameter, shape and geometry of microfiber hydrogels. By increasing the flow rate of sodium alginate from 1 μL/min to 5 μL/min, coil shape microfiber are formed as shown in Fig. 12(B). By increasing the core and sheath flow rates, the alginate microfiber diameters are increased from approximately 20–50 μm. These microfiber possessed average

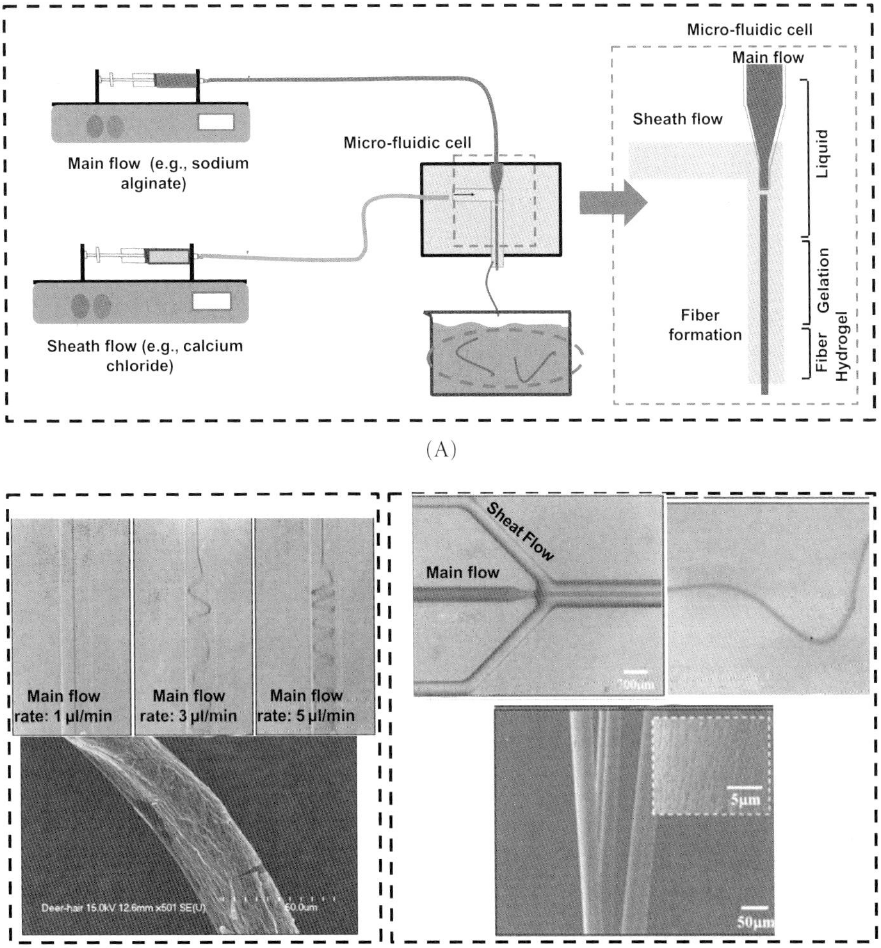

Fig. 12. Microfiber hydrogel fabrication using microfluidic device. (A) The schematic overview of microfluidic-based technique for fabrication of microfiber hydrogels, (B) fabrication of alginate microfiber hydrogels using microfluidic techniques glass capillary tune microdevice [222] and (C) cylindrical microfluidic channel.[223]

diameter of nearly 30 μm with relatively rough surface as shown in Fig. 12(B). This design of microfluidic device has been used for cell encapsulation within the microfibers.[222] In addition to capillary glass pipettes, coaxial flows were modulated in microfluidic channel mixers formed by convex hemi-cylindrical microchannels. Calcium alginate microfibers with various compositions have been produced by this new design of microfluidic device and used for the formation of microfiber of alginate hydrogels with the diameters between 50 μm and 150 μm. The main advantage of this approach compared to glass capillary pipette microdevices is the degree of freedom to fabricate microfluidic channels with different hydrophilic properties, shape, and geometry to tune the microstructure of fabricated hydrogels. This approach can be scaled up for the fabrication of microfibers.[223] Chitosan microfibers have been produced by using coaxial flow microfluidic channel devices. Human hepatocarcinoma cells, cultured within the structure of chitosan microfiber hydrogel possesses high liver-specific function due to high diffusivity of nutrients within the hydrogel systems.[224] Chitosan fibers with length of nearly 1 mm and diameters in the range of 70–150 μm have been fabricated.[224] In addition to naturally derived biomaterials such as chitosan and alginate, this technique has been used for fabrication of hydrogel fibers from synthetic polymers such as PEGDA, with more tunable properties. Additionally it is feasible to use photo-crosslinkable polymers in combination with microfluidic devices for formation of hydrogel fibers.

Microfibers of photo-crosslinkable polymers have been produced using microfluidic technique.[225–227] For instance, PVA and 4-hydroxy butyl acrylate have been photo-crosslinked *in situ* with UV.[228] Photo-crosslinking technique has also been used for the fabrication of Janus polyurethane microfibers in microfluidic devices. These fibers contained two distinct compartments with porous and non-porous microstructure. The porous section of the Janus microfiber promoted the cell adhesion while the non-porous part increased the mechanical strength of the microfiber.[229]

In summary, several microfluidic techniques have been developed for the fabrication of microfeatures in hydrogels. These techniques have capability to finely tune the diameters and porosity of microparticles and microfibers by variation of process parameters. These methods have been used for the fabrication of cell-encapsulated microfibers and microparticles for biomedical applications such as delivery of therapeutic cells and as building blocks for fabrication of 3D scaffolds for tissue engineering applications.

3.7. Bottom–up assembly of micro hydrogels for tissue engineering

In nature many tissues are made up of assemblies of small tissue molecules as repeating functional groups. As an illustration, liver is composed of lobules, kidney is made up of nephrons, and muscle is made from bundles of microfibers.[180] Therefore, bottom–up assembly of micro-engineered hydrogels has been developed to create complex tissue micro architecture to promote the regeneration of functional tissues in tissue engineering applications.[230] Even though the bottom-up assembly is infancy a few strategies have been established that include "lock and key assembly", secondary crosslinking and micro masonry assembly process.[126,231–233] These three techniques for assembly of microhydrogels are schematically shown in Fig. 13.

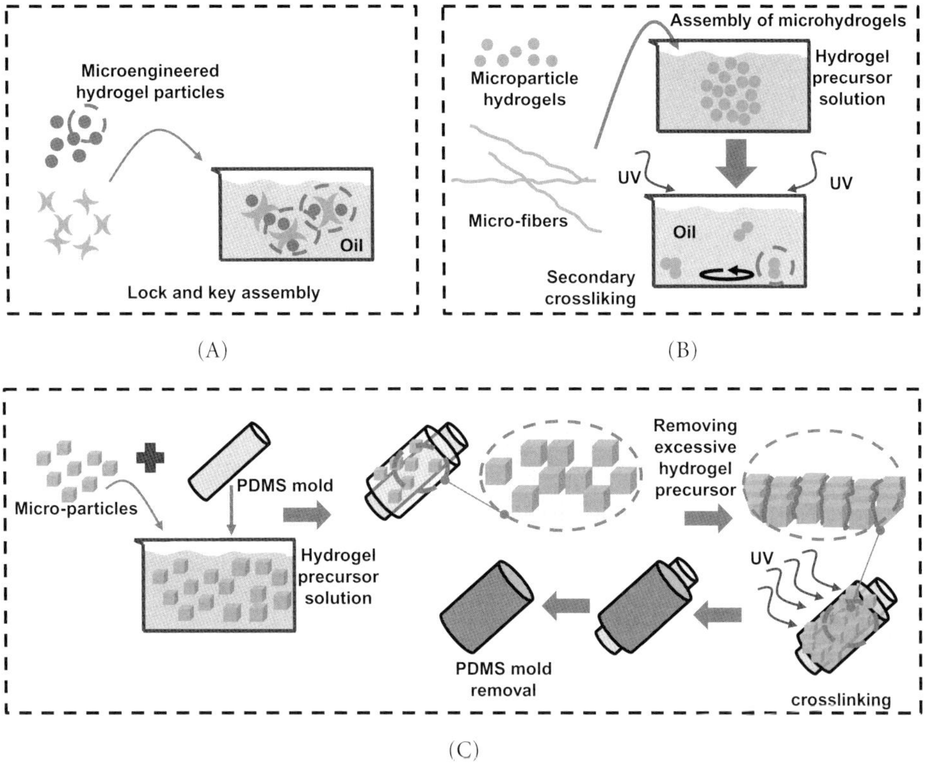

Fig. 13. Bottom–up assembly of hydrogels, (A) "lock and key" assembly of hydrogels, (B) secondary crosslinking of hydrogels, drives by capillary force, and (C) micro masonry assembly process.

In the lock and key assembly technique, the critical factor is the type of force that is used to assemble the building blocks. Hydrophilic and hydrophobic surfaces demonstrate inherent tendency to minimize interaction with each other. The differences in chemical properties at a hydrophobic–hydrophilic liquid interface and at an air–liquid interface have been used to assemble micron sized hydrogels. These effects lead to assembly of microhydrogels as only few patterns can be followed by microhydrogels to assemble to minimize the energy of system.[126,231] For instance, in microhydrogel assembly in oil (hydrophilic–hydrophobic interaction in liquid) the hydrogels are driven together to decrease the total surface area in contact with hydrophobic liquid and decrease the surface interaction. By controlling the shape of the micron sized hydrogels it is feasible to fabricate lock and key assembly where the shape of different microhydrogels is matched to create meso-scale hydrogel with tunable microarchitecture.[126,231] Cell-laden PEGDA hydrogels containing various shapes is assembled in oil by using lock and key approach. In this study, PEGDA solution containing cells is placed in a glass substrate and exposed to UV light through a shadow photomask containing various micropatterns to prepare individual microparticles of PEG hydrogel. These microparticles are assembled in oil phase due to the surface tension exist in oil and water interface.[126,231] It was observed that agitation accelerated the assembly of microparticle hydrogels. The major issues in lock and key approach for assembly of microhydrogels are low mechanical strength and poor physical integrity; also the limitation in maximum size of building block assembly that cannot exceed a few millimeters.

In secondary crosslinking approach for assembly of micro-engineered hydrogels, microparticles are initially fabricated and then soaked in a polymeric solution. The microparticles suspended in polymer solution are then added to oil, after which microparticles are physically assembled due to the hydrophilic–hydrophobic surface tension. This followed by the chemical crosslinking of assemblies to form 3D structure of hydrogels. This process is schematically shown in Fig. 13(B). The assembly of microparticle in this technique is tuned by retention time in oil and also the stirring speed.[234] Lack of control on the shape of assembled hydrogels and also the need for secondary crosslinking are the main drawbacks associated with this technique.[234]

In micro masonry assembly process individual building blocks of microhydrogels are placed on a hydrophobic mold such as a PDMS template. The excess polymer solution is then removed to induce the assembly of microparticle hydrogels. The molded microparticles are then crosslinked to form 3D construct of hydrogels. The schematic overview of this method is shown in Fig. 13(C). For instance this method is used to generate hepatocyte-laden hydrogel assembly structures with hollow tube like shapes.[235] The main drawback associated with the bottom-up approach is the need for secondary crosslinking process of microparticle hydrogels when large constructs (with dimensions above 1 cm) are required. The secondary crosslinking approach is required to assure adequate physical integrity and bonding between the microhydrogel particles. Other novel approaches such as DNA-glue or polypeptide sequestering has been proposed for bottom-up approach to promote assembly of building block that might provide more efficient means for assembly of microhydrogels in future.

4. Conclusions

Hydrogels are hydrophilic networks of polymers that are chemically or physically crosslinked. They are the material of choice as scaffolds for tissue engineering due to their resemblance to natural ECM. The microarchitecture of hydrogels substantially affects the permeability of nutrients, therapeutic reagents and oxygen. Therefore, several different techniques have been developed to tune the microarchitecture of hydrogels for broad range of biomedical applications such as drug delivery and tissue engineering. This review provides a brief overview of current techniques available to create a desirable pore size in a hydrogel. The limitations and advantages of each method have been discussed. Additionally, different micro-engineering techniques for fabrication of microparticle, microfiber and Janus particle hydrogels are described. These micro-engineered hydrogels can mimic the microenvironment of native ECM. The ultimate aim in this approach is to assemble microhydrogels as the building-blocks in bottom-up approaches to fabricate a 3D structure of an innate tissue. There are, however, major challenges in fabrication of 3D constructs from microhydrogels that still need to be resolved. It is anticipated that in near future scientists address the current issues in these emerging and forefront technologies in bottom-up approaches for assembly of microhydrogels. Artificial organs or tissues that are fabricated by these methods therefore can be ultimately used to manage the current shortage of donors for organ transplantation.

References

1. R. S. Langer and J. P. Vacanti, Tissue engineering. *Sci.*, **260**, 920 (1993).
2. R. M. Nerem and A. Sambanis, Tissue engineering: From biology to biological substitutes. *Tissue Eng.*, **1**, 3 (1995).
3. L. E. Freed, J. C. Marquis, A. Nohria, J. Emmanual, A. G. Mikos, and R. Langer, Neocartilage formation *in vitro* and *in vivo* using cells cultured on synthetic biodegradable polymers. *J. Biomed. Mater. Res.*, **27**, 11 (1993).
4. B. V. Slaughter, S. S. Khurshid, O. Z. Fisher, A. Khademhosseini, and N. A. Peppas, Hydrogels in regenerative medicine. *Adv. Mater.*, **21**, 3307 (2009).
5. N. A. Peppas, *Hydrogels in Medicine and Pharmacy*. Florida: CRC Press (1987).
6. N. A. Peppas, J. Z. Hilt, A. Khademhosseini, and R. Langer, Hydrogels in biology and medicine: From molecular principles to bionanotechnology. *Adv. Mater.*, **18**, 1345 (2006).
7. N. Annabi, J. W. Nichol, X. Zhong, C. Ji, S. Koshy, A. Khademhosseini *et al.*, Controlling the porosity and microarchitecture of hydrogels for tissue engineering. *Tissue Eng. Part B Rev.* **16**, 371(2010).
8. E. Jabbari and S. Nozari, Swelling behavior of acrylic acid hydrogels prepared by G-radiation crosslinking of polyacrylic acid in aqueous solution. *Eur. Polym. J.*, **36**, 2685 (2000).
9. A. Khademhosseini and R. Langer, Microengineered hydrogels for tissue engineering. *Biomaterials*, **28**, 5087, (2007).
10. B. B. Mandal and S. C. Kundu, Cell proliferation and migration in silk fibroin 3D scaffolds. *Biomaterials*, **30**, 2956 (2009).
11. S. M. Lien, L.-Y. Ko, and T.-J. Huang, Effect of pore size on ecm secretion and cell growth in gelatin scaffold for articular cartilage tissue engineering. *Acta Biomater.*, **5**, 670 (2009).

12. J. H. Park, B. G. Chung, W. G. Lee, J. Kim, M. D. Brigham, J. Shim *et al.*, Microporous cell-laden hydrogels for engineered tissue constructs. *Biotechnol. Bioeng.*, **106**,138 (2009).
13. I. V. Yannas, E. Lee, D. P. Orgill, E. M. Skrabut, and M. GF, Synthesis and characterization of a model extracellular matrix that induces partial regeneration of adult mammalian skin. *Proc. Natl. Acad. Sci. USA*, **86**, 933 (1989).
14. C. M. Hwang, S. Sant, M. Masaeli, N. N. Kachouie, B. Zamanian, S.-H. Lee *et al.*, Fabrication of three-dimensional porous cell-laden hydrogel for tissue engineering. *Biofabrication*, **2**, 035003/1 (2010).
15. K. Whang, K. E. Healy, D. R. Elenz, E. K. Nam, D. C. Tsai, C. H. Thomas *et al.*, Engineering bone regeneration with bioabsorbable scaffolds with novel microarchitecture. *Tissue Eng.*, **5**, 35 (1999).
16. M. C. Wake, C. W. Jr. Patrick, and A. G. Mikos, Pore morphology effects on the fibrovascular tissue growth in porous polymer substrates. *Cell Transplant*, **3**, 339 (1994).
17. T. D. Roy, J. L. Simon, J. L. Ricci, E. D. Rekow, V. P. Thompson, and J. R. Parsons, Performance of degradable composite bone repair products made via three-dimensional fabrication techniques. *J Biomed Mater Res.*, **66**, 283 (2003).
18. D. J. Griffon, M. R. Sedighi, D. V. Schaeffer, J. A. Eurell, and A. L. Jonson, Chitosan scaffolds: Interconnective pore size and cartilage engineering. *Acta Biomater.*, **2**, 313 (2006).
19. H. J. Kim, U. J. Kim, G. Vunjak-Novakovic, B. H. Min, and D. L. Kaplan, Influence of macroporous protein scaffolds on bone tissue engineering from bone marrow stem cells. *Biomaterials*, **26**, 4442 (2005).
20. H.-W. Kim, H.-E. Kim, and V. Salih, Stimulation of osteoblast responses to biomimetic nanocomposites of gelatin–hydroxyapatite for tissue engineering scaffolds. *Biomaterials*, **26**, 5221 (2005).
21. A. Khademhosseini, R. Langer, J. Borenstein, and J. P. Vacanti, Microscale technologies for tissue engineering and biology. *Proc. Natl. Acad. Sci. USA*, **103**, 2480 (2006).
22. R. A. Quirk, R. M. France, K. M. Shakesheff, and S. M. Howdle, Supercritical fluid technologies and tissue engineering scaffolds. *Curr. Opin. Solid State Mater. Sci.*, **8**, 313 (2005).
23. M. H. Sheridan, L. D. Shea, M. C. Peters,and D. J. Mooney, Bioabsorbable polymer scaffolds for tissue engineering capable of sustained growth factor delivery. *J. Control Release*, **64**, 91 (2000).
24. N. Annabi, A. Fathi, S. M. Mithieux, P. Martens, A. S. Weiss, and F. Dehghani, The effect of elastin on chondrocyte adhesion and proliferation on poly([var epsilon]-caprolactone)/elastin composites. *Biomaterials*, **32**, 1517 (2011).
25. N. Annabi, A. Fathi, S. M. Mithieux, A. S. Weiss, and F. Dehghani, Fabrication of porous pcl/elastin composite scaffolds for tissue engineering applications. *J. Supercrit. Fluid.*, **59**, 157 (2011).
26. D. Horak, H. Hlidkova, J. Hradil, M. Lapcikova, and M. Slouf, Superporous poly (2-hydroxyethyl methacrylate)-based scaffolds: Preparation and characterization. *Polymer*, **49**, 2046 (2008).

27. Y. Gong, Q. Zhou, C. Gao, and J. Shen, *In vitro* and *in vivo* degradability and cytocompatibility of poly(L-lactic acid) scaffold fabricated by a gelatin particle leaching method. *Acta Biomater.*, **3**, 531 (2007).
28. S. W. Suh, J. Y. Shin, J. Kim, J. Kim, C. H. Beak, D. -I. Kim *et al.*, Effect of different particles on cell proliferation in polymer scaffolds using a solvent-casting and particulate leaching technique. *ASAIO J.*, **48**, 460 (2002).
29. J. Zhang, L. Wu, D. Jing, and J. A. Ding, Comparative study of porous scaffolds with cubic and spherical macropores. *Polymer*, **46**, 4979 (2005).
30. M. Dadsetan, T. E. Hefferan, J. P. Szatkowski, P. K. Mishra, S. I. Macura, L. Lu *et al.*, Effect of hydrogel porosity on marrow stromal cell phenotypic expression. *Biomaterials*, **29**, 2193 (2008).
31. S. Kubinova, D. Horak, and E. Sykova, Cholesterol-modified superporous poly (2-hydroxyethyl methacrylate) scaffolds for tissue engineering. *Biomaterials*, **30**, 4601 (2009).
32. D. Horak, A. Sitnikov, E. Guseinov, L. Kokov, M. Titova, A. Adamyan *et al.*, Poly (hema) —based embolic material in endovascular surgery of liver. *Polim. Med.*, **32**, 48 (2002).
33. V. Guarino, M. A. Alvarez-Perez, A. Borriello, T. Napolitano, and L. Ambrosio, Conductive pani/pegda macroporous hydrogels for nerve regeneration. *Adv. Healthcare Mater.*, **2**, 218 (2013).
34. J. Kim, M. J. Yaszemski, and L. Lu, Three-dimensional porous biodegradable polymeric scaffolds fabricated with biodegradable hydrogel porogens. *Tissue Eng. Part C*, **15**, 583 (2009).
35. R. C. Thomson, M. C. Wake, M. J. Yaszemski, and A. G. Mikos biodegradable polymer scaffolds to regenerate organs. *Adv. Polym Sci.*, **122**, 245 (1995).
36. W.-Q. Xiao, J.-K. He, J. W. Nichol, L.-Y. Wang, C. B. Hutson, B. Wang *et al.*, Synthesis and characterization of photocrosslinkable gelatin and silk fibroin interpenetrating polymer network hydrogels. *Acta Biomater.*, **7**, 2384 (2011).
37. L. Xiao, Y. Wang, and Q. Xu, A study on the biocompatibility of neural stem cells with a newly created biomaterial of hyaluronic acid-based scaffold. *Shenjing Jiepouxue Zazhi*, **26**, 481 (2010).
38. X. Wu, L. Black, G. Santacana-Laffitte, and C. W. Jr. Patrick, Preparation and assessment of glutaraldehyde-crosslinked collagen–chitosan hydrogels for adipose tissue engineering. *J. Biomed. Mater.* **81A**, 59 (2007).
39. K. P. T. Sudheesh, S. Srinivasan, V. -K. Lakshmanan, H. Tamura, S. V. Nair, and R. Jayakumar, *B*-Chitin hydrogel/nano hydroxyapatite composite scaffolds for tissue engineering applications. *Carbohydr. Polym.*, **85**, 584 (2011).
40. S. Stokols and M. H.Tuszynski, The fabrication and characterization of linearly oriented nerve guidance scaffolds for spinal cord injury. *Biomaterials*, **25**, 5839 (2004).
41. S. Stokols and M. H.Tuszynski, Freeze dried agarose scaffolds with uniaxial channels stimulate and guide linear axonal growth following spinal cord injury. *Biomaterials*, **27**, 443 (2006).

42. H. Tan, C. M. Ramirez, N. Miljkovic, H. Li, J. P. Rubin, and K. G. Marra, Thermosensitive injectable hyaluronic acid hydrogel for adipose tissue engineering. *Biomaterials*, **30**, 6844 (2009).
43. Y.-G. Lee, H.-S. Kang, M.-S. Kim, and T.-I. Son, Thermally crosslinked anionic hydrogels composed of poly(vinyl alcohol) and poly(gamma-glutamic acid): Preparation, characterization, and drug permeation behavior. *J. Appl. Polym. Sci. Symp.* **109**, 3768 (2008).
44. W. C. Lin, D. G. Yu, and M. C. Yang, Blood compatibility of novel poly([gamma]-glutamic acid)/polyvinyl alcohol hydrogels. *Colloid Surface B*, **47**, 43 (2006).
45. M.-H. Ho, P.-Y. Kuo, H.-J. Hsieh, T.-Y. Hsien, L.-T. Hou, J.-Y. Lai *et al.*, Preparation of porous scaffolds by using freeze-extraction and freeze-gelation methods. *Biomaterials*, **25**,129 (2004).
46. S. A. Sell, P. S. Wolfe, K. Garg, J. M. McCool, I. A. Rodriguez, G. L. Bowlin. The use of natural polymers in tissue engineering: A focus on electrospun extracellular matrix analogues. *Polymers* (Basel, Switz)., **2**, 522 (2010).
47. D. H. Reneker and I. Chun. Nanometer diameter fibers of polymer, produced by electrospinning. Nanotechnology, **7**, 216 (1996).
48. W. -J. Li, C. T. Laurencin, E. J. Caterson, R. S. Tuan, and F. K. Ko. Electrospun nanofibrous structure: A novel scaffold for tissue engineering. *J. Biomed. Mater. Res.*, **60**, 613 (2002).
49. Q. P. Pham, U. Sharma, and A. G. Mikos, Electrospun Poly(E-Caprolactone) Microfiber and Multilayer Nanofiber/Microfiber Scaffolds: Characterization of Scaffolds and Measurement of Cellular Infiltration. *Biomacromolecules*, **7**, 2796 (2006).
50. Q. P. Pham, U. Sharma, and A. G. Mikos, Electrospinning of polymeric nanofibers for tissue engineering applications: A review. *Tissue Eng.*, **12**, 1197 (2006).
51. S. Heydarkhan-Hagvall, K. Schenke-Layland, A. P. Dhanasopon, F. Rofail, H. Smith, B. M. Wu *et al.*, Three-dimensional electrospun ecm-based hybrid scaffolds for cardiovascular tissue engineering. *Biomaterials.*, **29**, 2907 (2008).
52. C.P. Barnes, S. A. Sell, E. D. Boland, D. G. Simpson, and G. L. Bowlin, Nanofiber technology: Designing the next generation of tissue engineering scaffolds. *Adv. Drug Deliv. Rev.*, **59**, 1413 (2007).
53. S. A. Sell, M. J. McClure, K. Garg, P. S. Wolfe, and G. L. Bowlin, Electrospinning of collagen/biopolymers for regenerative medicine and cardiovascular tissue engineering. *Adv. Drug Deliv. Rev.*, **61**, 1007 (2009).
54. K. Jayaraman, M. Kotaki, Y. Zhang, X. Mo, and S. Ramakrishna, Recent advances in polymer nanofibers. *J. Nanosci. Nanotechnol.*, **4**, 52 (2004).
55. J. F. Mano, G. A. Silva, H. S. Azevedo, P. B. Malafaya, R. A. Sousa, S. S. Silva *et al.*, Natural origin biodegradable systems in tissue engineering and regenerative medicine: Present status and some moving trends. *J. R Soc.*, **4**, 999 (2007).
56. A. Koski, K. Yim, and S. Shivkumar, Effect of molecular weight on fibrous pva produced by electrospinning. *Mater. Lett.*, **58**, 493 (2004).

57. T. Lin, H. Wang, H. Wang, and X. Wang, The charge effect of cationic surfactants on the elimination of fibre beads in the electrospinning of polystyrene. *Nanotechnology*, **15**, 1375 (2004).
58. R. Nayak, I. L. Kyratzis, Y. B. Truong, R. Padhye, and L. Arnold, Melt-electrospinning of polypropylene with conductive additives. *J. Mater. Sci.*, **47**, 6387 (2012).
59. K. D. McKeon-Fischer, D. H. Flagg, and J. W. Freeman, Coaxial electrospun poly(ε-caprolactone), multiwalled carbon nanotubes, and polyacrylic acid/polyvinyl alcohol scaffold for skeletal muscle tissue engineering. *J. Biomed. Mater Res. Part A*, **99A**, 493 (2011).
60. L. Li and Y. -L. Hsieh, Ultra-fine polyelectrolyte hydrogel fibers from poly (acrylic acid)/poly (vinyl alcohol). *Nanotechnology*, **16**, 2852 (2005).
61. B. Zhang, R. Lalani, F. Cheng, Q. Liu, and L. Liu, Dual-functional electrospun poly(2-hydroxyethyl methacrylate). *J Biomed Mater Res. Part A*, **99A**, 455 (2011).
62. S. Y. Chew, Y. Wen, Y. Dzenis, and K. W. Leong, The role of electrospinning in the emerging field of nanomedicine. *Curr Pharm Des.*, **12**, 4751 (2006).
63. J. A. Matthews, G. E. Wnek, D. G. Simpson, and G. L. Bowlin, Electrospinning of collagen nanofibers. *Biomacromolecules*, **3**, 232 (2002).
64. J. Liu, *Investigation of the Appropriate Collagen-Based Electrospun Materials for Vascular Tissue Engineering* 2008.
65. E. N. Lamme, L. R. T. J. Van, A. Jonker, M. J. Van, and E. Middelkoop, Living skin substitutes: Survival and function of fibroblasts seeded in a dermal substitute in experimental wounds. *J Invest Dermatol.*, **111**, 989 (1998).
66. J. -W. Xu, T. S. Johnson, P. M. Motarjem, G. M. Peretti, M. A. Randolph, and M. J. Yaremchuk, Tissue-engineered flexible ear-shaped cartilage. *Plast. Reconstr. Surg.*, **115**, 1633 (2005).
67. S. Neuenschwander and S. P. Hoerstrup, Heart valve tissue engineering. *Transplant Immunol.*, **12**, 359 (2004).
68. M. Li, M. J. Mondrinos, M. R. Gandhi, F. K. Ko, A. S. Weiss, and P. I. Lelkes, Electrospun protein fibers as matrices for tissue engineering. *Biomaterials*, **26**, 5999 (2005).
69. L. Nivison-Smith, J. Rnjak, and A. S. Weiss, Synthetic human elastin microfibers: Stable cross-linked tropoelastin and cell interactive constructs for tissue engineering applications. *Acta Biomater.*, **6**, 354 (2010).
70. G. Kim Taek, J. Chung Hyun, and G. Park Tae, Macroporous and nanofibrous hyaluronic acid/collagen hybrid scaffold fabricated by concurrent electrospinning and deposition/leaching of salt particles. *Acta Biomater.*, **4**, 1611 (2008).
71. S. N. Jayasinghe, Cell electrospinning: A novel tool for functionalising fibres, scaffolds and membranes with living cells and other advanced materials for regenerative biology and medicine. *Analyst*, **138**, 2215 (2013).
72. A. Barbetta, G. Rizzitelli, R. Bedini, R. Pecci, and M. Dentini, Porous gelatin hydrogels by gas-in-liquid foam templating. *Soft Matter.*, **6**, 1785 (2010).
73. A. Barbetta, R. J. Carnachan, K. H. Smith, Zhao, N. R. Cameron, R. Kataky *et al.*, Porous polymers by emulsion templating. *Macromol. Symp.*, **226**, 203 (2005).

74. A. Barbetta, M. Dentini, M. S. de Vecchis, P. Filippini, G. Formisano, and S. Caiazza, Scaffolds based on biopolymeric foams. *Adv. Funct. Mater.*, **15**, 118 (2005).
75. A. Barbetta, E. Barigelli, and M. Dentini, Porous alginate hydrogels: Synthetic methods for tailoring the porous texture. *Biomacromolecules*, **10**, 2328 (2009).
76. A. Barbetta, A. Gumiero, R. Pecci, R. Bedini, and M. Dentini, Gas-in-liquid foam templating as a method for the production of highly porous scaffolds. *Biomacromolecules*, **10**, 3188 (2009).
77. V. Keskar, N. W. Marion, J. J. Mao, and R. A. Gemeinhart, *In vitro* evaluation of macroporous hydrogels to facilitate stem cell infiltration, growth, and mineralization. *Tissue Eng. A*, **15**, 1695 (2009).
78. H. Tai, V. K. Popov, K. M. Shakesheff, and S. M. Howdle, Putting the fizz into chemistry: Applications of supercritical carbon dioxide in tissue engineering, drug delivery and synthesis of novel block copolymers. *Biochem. Soc. Trans.*, **35**, 516 (2007).
79. J. J. A. Barry, S. N. Nazhat, F. R. A. J. Rose, A. H. Hainsworth, C. A. Scotchford, and S. M. Howdle, Supercritical carbon dioxide foaming of elastomer/heterocyclic methacrylate blends as scaffolds for tissue engineering. *J. Mater. Chem.*, **15**, 4881(2005).
80. C. Ji, N. Annabi, A. Khademhosseini, and F. Dehghani, Fabrication of porous chitosan scaffolds for soft tissue engineering using dense gas Co_2. *Acta Biomater.*, **7**, 1653 (2011).
81. C. Ji, A. Khademhosseini, and F. Dehghani, Enhancing cell penetration and proliferation in chitosan hydrogels for tissue engineering applications. *Biomaterials*, **32**, 9719 (2011).
82. C. Ji, N. Annabi, M. Hosseinkhani, S. Sivaloganathan, and F. Dehghani, Fabrication of poly-dl-lactide/polyethylene glycol scaffolds using the gas foaming technique. *Acta Biomater.*, **8**, 570 (2012).
83. F. Dehghani and N. Annabi, Engineering porous scaffolds using gas-based techniques. *Curr. Opin. Biotechnol.*, **22**, 661 (2011).
84. A. Barbetta, A. Carrino, M. Costantini, and M. Dentini, Polysaccharide based scaffolds obtained by freezing the external phase of gas-in-liquid foams. *Soft Matter.*, **6**, 5213 (2010).
85. K. M. Huh, N. Baek, and K. Park, Enhanced swelling rate of poly(ethylene glycol)-grafted superporous hydrogels. *J. Bioact. Compat. Polym.*, **20**, 231 (2005).
86. J. Chen, H. Park, and K. Park, Synthesis of superporous hydrogels. Hydrogels with fast swelling and superabsorbent properties. *J. Biomed. Mater. Res.*, **44**, 53 (1999).
87. H. V. Chavda and C. N. Patel, Effect of crosslinker concentration on characteristics of superporous hydrogel. *Int. J. Pharm. Invest.*, **1**, 17 (2011).
88. E. Behravesh, S. Jo, K. Zygourakis, and A. G. Mikos, Synthesis of *in situ* cross-linkable macroporous biodegradable poly(propylene fumarate-co-ethylene glycol) hydrogels. *Biomacromolecules*, **3**, 374 (2002).
89. I. G. Beskardes, T. T. Demirtas, M. D. Durukan, and M. Gumusderelioglu, Microwave-assisted fabrication of chitosan-hydroxyapatite superporous hydrogel composites as bone scaffolds. *J. Tissue Eng. Regen. Med.*, (2012).

90. H. A. Abd El-Rehim, E. -S. A. Hegazy, and D. A. Diaa, Characterization of superabsorbent material based on carboxymethylcellulose sodium salt prepared by electron beam irradiation. *J. Macromol. Sci. Part A*, **43**, 101 (2006).
91. Y. V. Matrunchik, E. V. Vorob'eva, N. P. Krut'ko, and I. I. Basalyga, Influence of different-nature surfactants on the properties of polyacrylic acid-based polymer hydrogel. *Dokl. Nats. Akad. Nauk. Belarusi.*, **53**, 68 (2009).
92. K. Varaprasad, N. N. Reddy, N. M. Kumar, K. Vimala, S. Ravindra, and K. M. Raju, Poly(acrylamide-chitosan) hydrogels: Interaction with surfactants. *Int. J. Polym. Mater.*, **59**, 981 (2010).
93. N. Hassan, P. V. Messina, V. I. Dodero, and J. M.Ruso, Rheological properties of ovalbumin hydrogels as affected by surfactants addition. *Int. J. Biol. Macromol.*, **48**, 495 (2011).
94. J. Berger, M. Reist, J. M. Mayer, O. Felt, N. A. Peppas, and R. Gurny, Structure and interactions in covalently and ionically crosslinked chitosan hydrogels for biomedical applications. *Eur. J. Pharm. Biopharm.*, **57**, 19 (2004).
95. D Capitani, A. A. A. De, V. Crescenzi, G. Masci, A. L. Segre, Nmr study of a novel chitosan-based hydrogel. *Carbohydr. Polym.*, **45**, 245 (2001).
96. J. J. A. Barry, M. M. C. G. Silva, V. K. Popov, K. M. Shakesheff, and S. M. Howdle, Supercritical carbon dioxide: Putting the fizz into biomaterials. *Phil. Trans. R. Soc. A*, **364**, 249 (2006).
97. C. B. Park, D. F. Baldwin, and N. P. Suh, Effect of the pressure drop rate on cell nucleation in continuous processing of microcellular polymers. *Polym. Eng. Sci.*, **35**, 432 (1995).
98. X. Zhu, L. Lee, J. Jackson, Y. Tong, and C. Wang, Characterization of porous poly(d,l-lactic-co-glycolic acid) sponges fabricated by supercritical CO_2 gas-foaming method as a scaffold for three-dimensional growth of Hep3b cells. *Biotechnol. Bioeng.*, **100**, 998 (2008).
99. C. Palocci, A. Barbetta, A. La Grotta, and M. Dentini, Porous biomaterials obtained using supercritical CO_2–water emulsions. *Langmuir.*, **23**, 8243 (2007).
100. B. Tan, J.-Y. Lee, and A. I. Cooper, Emulsion-templated porous materials using concentrated carbon dioxide-in-water emulsions and inexpensive hydrocarbon surfactants. *Abstracts of Papers*, 234*th ACS National Meeting*, Boston, MA, United States, August 19–23 (2007) IEC.
101. B. Tan, J. -Y. Lee, and A. I. Cooper, Synthesis of emulsion-templated poly(acrylamide) using CO_2-in-water emulsions and poly(vinyl acetate)-based block copolymer surfactants. *Macromolecules*, **40**, 1945 (2007).
102. B. Tan, J.-Y. Lee, S. W. Choi, and J. H. Kim, Preparation of porous $CaCO_3$/Pam composites by CO_2 in water emulsion templating method. *Eur. Polym. J*, **43**, 4814 (2007).
103. J.-Y. Lee, B. Tan, and A. I. Cooper, CO_2-in-water emulsion-templated poly(vinyl alcohol) hydrogels using poly(vinyl acetate)-based surfactants. *Macromolecules*, **40**, 1955 (2007).

104. S. Partap, I. Rehman, J. R. Jones, and J. A. Darr, Supercritical carbon dioxide in water emulsion-templated synthesis of porous calcium alginate hydrogels. *Adv. Mater.*, **18**, 501 (2006).
105. S. Partap, A. K. Hebb, I. Rehman, and J. A. Darr, Formation of porous natural-synthetic polymer composites using emulsion templating and supercritical fluid assisted impregnation. *Polym. Bull*, **58**, 849 (2007).
106. M. Temtem, L. M. C. Silva, P. Z. Andrade, S. F. Dos, dS. C. Lobato, J. M. S. Cabral *et al.*, Supercritical CO_2 generating chitosan devices with controlled morphology. Potential application for drug delivery and mesenchymal stem cell culture. *J. Supercrit. Fluid.*, **48**, 269 (2009).
107. C. Tsioptsias and C. Panayiotou, Foaming of chitin hydrogels processed by supercritical carbon dioxide. *J. Supercrit. Fluid.*, **47**, 302 (2008).
108. C. Ji, A. Barrett, L. A. Poole-Warren, N. R. Foster, and F. Dehghani, The development of a dense gas solvent exchange process for the impregnation of pharmaceuticals into porous chitosan. *Int. J. Pharm.*, **391**,187 (2010).
109. W. S. Dodds, L. F. Stutzman, and B. J. Sollami, Carbon dioxide solubility in water. *Ind. Eng. Chem.*, **1** (1956).
110. N. Annabi, S. M. Mithieux, S. W. Anthony, and F. Dehghani, Development and characterisation of a novel elastin hydrogel. *Mater. Res. Soc. Symp. Proc.*, (2009).
111. N. Annabi, S. M. Mithieux, E. A. Boughton, A. J. Ruys, A. S. Weiss, and F. Dehghani, Synthesis of highly porous crosslinked elastin hydrogels and their interaction with fibroblasts *in vitro*. *Biomaterials*, **30**, 4550 (2009).
112. N. Annabi, S. M. Mithieux, A. S. Weiss, and F. Dehghani, The fabrication of elastin-based hydrogels using high pressure Co_2. *Biomaterials*, **30**, 1 (2009).
113. M. L. Floren, S. Spilimbergo, A. Motta, and C. Migliaresi, Carbon dioxide induced silk protein gelation for biomedical applications. *Biomacromolecules*, **13**, 2060 (2012).
114. R. T. Bustami, H. -K. Chan, T. Sweeney, F. Dehghani, and N. R. Foster Generation of fine powders of recombinant human deoxyribonuclease using the aerosol solvent extraction system. *Pharm. Res.*, **20**, 2028 (2003).
115. F. Dehghani, N. Annabi, P. Valtchev, S. M. Mithieux, A. S. Weiss, S. G. Kazarian *et al.*, Effect of dense gas Co_2 on the coacervation of elastin. *Biomacromolecules*, **9**, 1100 (2008).
116. M. A. Winters, B. L. Knutson, P. G. Debenedetti, H. G. Sparks, T. M. Przybycien, C. L. Stevenson *et al.*, Precipitation of proteins in supercritical carbon dioxide. *J. Pharm. Sci.*, **85**, 586 (1996).
117. A. Striolo, A. Favaro, N. Elvassore, A. Bertucco, and V. Di Noto, Evidence of conformational changes for protein films exposed to high-pressure Co_2 by FT–IR spectroscopy. *J. Supercrit. Fluid.*, **27**, 283(2003).
118. S. D. Yeo, P. G. Debenedetti, S. Y. Patro, and T. M. Przybycien. Secondary structure characterization of microparticulate insulin powders. *J. Pharm. Sci.*, **83**, 1651 (1994).
119. S. D. Yeo, G. Lim, P. G. Debenedetti, and H. Bernstein, Formation of microparticulate protein powders using a supercritical fluid antisolvent. *Biotechnol. Bioeng.*, **41**, 341 (1993).

120. S. Nehrer, R. Dorotka, S. Domayer, D. Stelzeneder, and R. Kotz, Treatment of full-thickness chondral defects with Hyalograft C in the knee: A prospective clinical case series with 2 to 7 years' follow-up. *Am. J. Sports Med.*, **37**(1), 81S.
121. K. M. Kulig and J. P. Vacanti, Hepatic tissue engineering. *Transpl. Immunol.*, **12**, 303 (2004).
122. M. Shin, K. Matsuda, O. Ishii, H. Terai, M. Kaazempur-Mofrad, J. Borenstein *et al.*, Endothelialized networks with a vascular geometry in microfabricated poly(dimethyl siloxane). *Biomed. Microdevices*, **6**, 269 (2004).
123. J. T. Borenstein, E. J. Weinberg, B. K. Orrick, C. Sundback, M. R. Kaazempur-Mofrad, and J. P.Vacanti, Microfabrication of three-dimensional engineered scaffolds. *Tissue Eng.*, **13**, 1837 (2007).
124. S. Khetan and J. A. Burdick, Patterning hydrogels in three dimensions towards controlling cellular interactions. *Soft Matter.*, **7**, 830 (2011).
125. J. C. Gore, J. Xu, D. C. Colvin, T. E. Yankeelov, E. C. Parsons, and M. D. Does, Characterization of tissue structure at varying length scales using temporal diffusion spectroscopy. *NMR Biomed.*, **23**, 745 (2010).
126. Y. Du, M. Ghodousi, E. Lo, M. K. Vidula, O. Emiroglu, and A. Khademhosseini, Surface-directed assembly of cell-laden microgels. *Biotechnol. Bioeng.*, **105**, 655 (2009).
127. J. W. Nichol and A. Khademhosseini, Modular tissue engineering: Engineering biological tissues from the bottom-up. *Soft Matter.*, **5**, 1312 (2009).
128. X. Xu, J. Zhao, and X. Jia, Hyaluronic acid-based, heparin decorated hydrogel particles for cartilage repair. *Polym. Prepr. (Am. Chem. Soc., Div. Polym. Chem.)*, **51**, 410 (2010).
129. X. Xu, A. K. Jha, R. L. Duncan, and X. Jia, Heparin-decorated, hyaluronic acid-based hydrogel particles for the controlled release of bone morphogenetic protein 2. *Acta Biomater.*, **7**, 3050(2011).
130. K. L. Spiller, Y. Liu, J. L. Holloway, S. A. Maher, Y. Cao, W. Liu *et al.*, A novel method for the direct fabrication of growth factor-loaded microspheres within porous nondegradable hydrogels: Controlled release for cartilage tissue engineering. *J. Controlled Release*, **157**, 39 (2012).
131. Y. Xia, E. Kim, X.-M. Zhao, J. A. Rogers, M. Prentiss, and G. M. Whitesides, Complex optical surfaces formed by replica molding against elastomeric masters. *Sci.*, **273**, 347 (1996).
132. L. J. Guo, Nanoimprint lithography: Methods and material requirements. *Adv. Mater.*, **19**, 495 (2007).
133. X. M. Zhao, Y. Xia, and G. M. Whitesides, Fabrication of three-dimensional microstructures. Microtransfer molding. *Adv. Mater.*, **8**, 837 (1996).
134. T. V. Liu and S. N. Bhatia, Three-dimensional tissue fabrication. *Adv Drug Delivery Rev.*, **56**, 1635 (2004).
135. J. Voldman, M. L. Gray, and M. A. Schmidt, Microfabrication in biology and medicine. *Annu Rev Biomed Eng.*, **1**, 401 (1999).
136. K. Subramani and M. A. Birch, Micropatterning of poly (ethylene glycol)-diacrylate (PEGDA) hydrogel by soft-photolithography for analysis of cell-biomaterial interactions. *J. Biomimetics Biomater. Tissue Eng.*, **2**, 3 (2009).

137. A. Revzin, R. J. Russell, V. K. Yadavalli, W. G. Koh, C. Deister, D. D. Hile *et al.*, Fabrication of poly(ethylene glycol) hydrogel microstructures using photolithography. *Langmuir.*, **17**, 5440 (2001).
138. E. Kim, Y. Xia, and G. M. Whitesides, Polymer microstructures formed by molding in capillaries. *Nature*, **376**, 581 (1995).
139. P. C. Duineveld, M. Lilja, T. Johansson, and O. Inganaes, Diffusion of solvent in Pdms elastomer for micromolding in capillaries. *Langmuir.*, **18**, 9554 (2002).
140. K. Y. Suh and H. H. Lee, Capillary force lithography: Large-area patterning, self-organization, and anisotropic dewetting. *Adv. Funct. Mater.*, **12**, 405 (2002).
141. A. P. Quist, E. Pavlovic, and S. Oscarsson, Recent advances in microcontact printing. *Anal. Bioanal. Chem.*, **381**, 591(2005).
142. K. Y. Suh, Y. S. Kim, and H. H. Lee, Capillary force lithography. *Adv. Mater*, **13**, 1386 (2001).
143. A. Khademhosseini, J. Yeh, S. Jon, G. Eng, K. Y. Suh, J. A. Burdick *et al.*, Molded polyethylene glycol microstructures for capturing cells within microfluidic channels. *Lab Chip.*, **4**, 425 (2004).
144. H. N. Kim, A. Jiao, N. S. Hwang, M. S. Kim, D. H. Kang, D. -H. Kim *et al.*, Nanotopography-guided tissue engineering and regenerative medicine. *Adv. Drug Deliv. Rev.*, Ahead of Print.
145. R. J. Jackman, J. L. Wilbur, and G. M. Whitesides, Fabrication of submicrometer features on curved substrates by microcontact printing. *Sci.*, **269**, 664 (1995).
146. M. Park, C. Harrison, P. M. Chaikin, R. A. Register, and D. H. Adamson, Block copolymer lithography: Periodic arrays of ~1011 holes in 1 square centimeter. *Sci.*, **276**, 1401 (1997).
147. I. Y. Tsai, M. Kimura, R. Stockton, J. A. Green, R. Puig, B. Jacobson *et al.*, Fibroblast adhesion to micro- and nano-heterogeneous topography using diblock copolymers and homopolymers. *J. Biomed. Mater. Res., Part A*, **71A**, 462 (2004).
148. B. G. Chung, K. -H. Lee, A. Khademhosseini, S.-H. Lee, Microfluidic fabrication of microengineered hydrogels and their application in tissue engineering. *Lab Chip.*, **12**, 45 (2012).
149. A. K. Agrawal, M. Jassal, A. Vishnoi, N. S. Save, Temperature responsive fibers with anisotropic transitional behavior. *J. Appl. Polym. Sci.*, **95**, 681 (2005).
150. M. Hu, R. Deng, K. M. Schumacher, M. Kurisawa, H. Ye, K. Purnamawati *et al.*, Hydrodynamic spinning of hydrogel fibers. *Biomaterials*, **31**, 863 (2010).
151. J. F. Edd, C. D. Di, K. J. Humphry, S. Koster, D. Irimia, D. A. Weitz, *et al.*, Controlled encapsulation of single-cells into monodisperse picolitre drops. *Lab Chip.*, **8**, 1262 (2008).
152. A. R. Abate, C.-H. Chen, J. J. Agresti, D. A. Weitz, Beating poisson encapsulation statistics using close-packed ordering. *Lab Chip.*, **9**, 2628 (2009).
153. J. Wan, Microfluidic-based synthesis of hydrogel particles for cell microencapsulation and cell-based drug delivery. *Polymers*, **4**, 1084 (2012).

154. L. B. Zhao, L. Pan, K. Zhang, S. S. Guo, W. Liu, Y. Wang, *et al.*, Generation of janus alginate hydrogel particles with magnetic anisotropy for cell encapsulation. *Lab Chip.*, **9**, 2981 (2009).
155. U. Lehmann, C. Vandevyver, V. K. Parashar, and M. A. M. Gijs, Droplet-based DNA purification in a magnetic lab-on-a-chip. *Angew. Chem. Int. Edit.*, **45**, 3062 (2006).
156. H.-S. Kim, O.-T. Son, K.-H. Kim, S.-H. Kim, S. Maeng, and H.-I. Jung, Separation of apoptotic cells using a microfluidic device. *Biotechnol. Lett.*, **29**, 1659 (2007).
157. C.-H. Chen, A. R. Abate, D. Lee, E. M. Terentjev, and D. A. Weitz. Microfluidic assembly of magnetic hydrogel particles with uniformly anisotropic structure. *Adv. Mater.*, **21**, 3201 (2009).
158. N. Lewinski, V. Colvin, and R. Drezek, Cytotoxicity of nanoparticles. *Small*, **4**, 26 (2008).
159. L. W. Chan, H. Y. Lee, and P. W. S. Heng, Mechanisms of external and internal gelation and their impact on the functions of alginate as a coat and delivery system. *Carbohydr. Polym.*, **63**, 176 (2006).
160. L. W. Chan, H. Y. Lee, and P. W. S. Heng, Production of alginate microspheres by internal gelation using an emulsification method. *Int. J. Pharm.*, **242**, 259 (2002).
161. H. Park, J. S. Temenoff, Y. Tabata, A. I. Caplan, R. M. Raphael, J. A. Jansen, *et al.*, Effect of dual growth factor delivery on chondrogenic differentiation of rabbit marrow mesenchymal stem cells encapsulated in injectable hydrogel composites. *J. Biomed. Mater. Res. Part A*, **88A**, 889 (2009).
162. T. A. Holland, Y. Tabata, and A. G. Mikos, Dual growth factor delivery from degradable oligo(poly(ethylene glycol) fumarate) hydrogel scaffolds for cartilage tissue engineering. *J. Controlled Release*, **101**, 111 (2005).
163. C.-L. Wu, H.-C. Lin, C.-H. Huang, M.-C. Yip, and W. Fang Mechanical Properties of Pdms/Cnts Nanocomposites. *Mater. Res. Soc. Symp. Proc.* 2008;1056E:No pp. given.
164. J. W. Nichol, H. Bae, N. N. Kachouie, B. Zamanian, M. Masaeli, A. Khademhosseini, *Microscale Technologies for Tissue Engineering and Stem Cell Differentiation.* Singapore: World Scientific (2011).
165. K. R. King, C. C. J. Wang, M. R. Kaazempur-Mofrad, J. P. Vacanti, and J. T. Borenstein Biodegradable Microfluidics. *Adv. Mater.*, **16**, 2007 (2004).
166. G. Vozzi, C. Flaim, A. Ahluwalia, and S. Bhatia, Fabrication of Plga scaffolds using soft lithography and microsyringe deposition. *Biomaterials*, **24**, 2533 (2003).
167. J. Atencia and D. J. Beebe, Controlled microfluidic interfaces. *Nature*, 437, 648 (2005).
168. S. K. Sia and G. M. Whitesides, Microfluidic devices fabricated in poly(dimethylsiloxane) for biological studies. *Electrophoresis*, **24**, 3563 (2003).
169. G. M. Whitesides, E. Ostuni, S. Takayama, X. Jiang, D. E. Ingber, Soft lithography in biology and biochemistry. *Annu. Rev. Biomed. Eng.*, **3**, 335 (2001).
170. L. Song, M. Zhu, Y. Chen, and K. Haraguchi. Surface-patterning of nano composite hydrogel film by direct replica molding and subsequent change in pattern size. *Polym. J.*, **40**, 800 (2008).

171. N. Kaji, Y. Tezuka, Y. Takamura, M. Ueda, T. Nishimoto, H. Nakanishi *et al.*, Separation of long DNA molecules by quartz nanopillar chips under a direct current electric field. *Anal. Chem.*, **76**, 15 (2004).
172. O. Du Roure, A. Saez, A. Buguin, R. H. Austin, P. Chavrier, P. Siberzan *et al.*, Force mapping in epithelial cell migration. *Proc. Natl. Acad. Sci. USA.*, **102**, 2390 (2005).
173. J. L. Tan, J. Tien, D. M. Pirone, D. S. Gray, K. Bhadriraju, and C. S. Chen, Cells lying on a bed of microneedles: An approach to isolate mechanical force. *Proc. Natl. Acad. Sci. USA.*, **100**, 1484 (2003).
174. A. K. Geim, S. V. Dubonos, I. V. Grigorieva, K. S. Novoselov, A. A. Zhukov, S. Y. Shapoval Microfabricated adhesive mimicking gecko foot-hair. *Nat. Mater.*, **2**, 461 (2003).
175. D. Chandra, J. A. Taylor, and S. Yang Replica molding of high-aspect-ratio (sub-) micron hydrogel pillar arrays and their stability in air and solvents. *Soft Matter.*, **4**, 979 (2008).
176. D.-N. Kim, W. Lee, and W.-G. Koh, Micropatterning of proteins on the surface of three-dimensional poly(ethylene glycol) hydrogel microstructures. *Anal. Chim. Acta.*, 609, **59** (2008).
177. G. T. Franzesi, B. Ni, Y. Ling, and A. Khademhosseini, A controlled-release strategy for the generation of cross-linked hydrogel microstructures. *J. Am. Chem. Soc.*, **128**, 15064 (2006).
178. C. J. Bettinger, E. J. Weinberg, K. M. Kulig, J. P. Vacanti, Y. Wang, J. T. Borenstein *et al.*, Three-dimensional microfluidic tissue-engineering scaffolds using a flexible biodegradable polymer. *Adv. Mater.*, **18**, 165 (2006).
179. M. P. Cuchiara, A. C. B. Allen, T. M. Chen, J. S. Miller, and J. L. West, Multilayer microfluidic PEGDA hydrogels. *Biomaterials*, **31**, 5491 (2010).
180. I. Wheeldon, A. F. Ahari, and A. Khademhosseini, Microengineering hydrogels for stem cell bioengineering and tissue regeneration. *JALA*, **15**, 440 (2010).
181. H. Geckil, F. Xu, X. Zhang, S. Moon, and U. Demirci, Engineering hydrogels as extracellular matrix mimics. *Nanomedicine*, **5**, 469 (2010).
182. C.-H. Lin, W.-C. Jao, Y.-H. Yeh, W.-C. Lin, and M.-C. Yang, Hemocompatibility and cytocompatibility of styrenesulfonate-grafted pdms-polyurethane-hema hydrogel. *Colloids Surf. B*, **70**, 132 (2009).
183. P. Panda, S. Ali, E. Lo, B. G. Chung, T. A. Hatton, A. Khademhosseini *et al.*, Stop-flow lithography to generate cell-laden microgel particles. *Lab Chip.*, **8**, 1056 (2008).
184. K.-Y. Suh, M. C. Park, and P. Kim, Capillary force lithography: A versatile tool for structured biomaterials interface towards cell and tissue engineering. *Adv. Funct. Mater.*, **19**, 2699 (2009).
185. H. Shibata, Y. J. Heo, and S. Takeuchi, *Simple Molding Fabrication for Polyacrylamide Hydrogel.* IEEE (2011).
186. B. Kim, M. Park, Y. S. Kim, and U. Jeong, Thermal expansion and contraction of an elastomer stamp causes position-dependent polymer patterns in capillary force lithography. *ACS Appl. Mater. Interfaces*, **3**, 4695 (2011).

187. V. Liu and S. Bhatia, Three-dimensional photopatterning of hydrogels containing living cells. *Biomed. Microdevices*, **4**, 257 (2002).
188. W.-G. Koh, A. Revzin, and M. V. Pishko, Poly(ethylene glycol) hydrogel microstructures encapsulating living cells. *Langmuir.*, **18**, 2459 (2002).
189. W.-G. Koh , L. J. Itle, and M. V. Pishko, Molding of hydrogel microstructures to create multiphenotype cell microarrays. *Anal. Chem.*, **75**, 5783 (2003).
190. W. Zhan, G. H. Seong, and R. M. Crooks, Hydrogel-based microreactors as a functional component of microfluidic systems. *Anal. Chem.*, **74**, 4647 (2002).
191. D. Kuckling, Responsive hydrogel layers-from synthesis to applications. *Colloid. Polym. Sci.*, **287**, 881 (2009).
192. S. Sakai, C. Mu, K. Kawabata, I. Hashimoto, and K. Kawakami, Biocompatibility of subsieve-size capsules versus conventional-size microcapsules. *J. Biomed. Mater. Res. Part A*, **78A**, 394 (2006).
193. S. Sugiura, T. Oda, Y. Izumida, Y. Aoyagi, M. Satake, A. Ochiai *et al.*, Size control of calcium alginate beads containing living cells using micro-nozzle array. *Biomaterials*, **26**, 3327 (2005).
194. G. Orive, R. M. Hernandez, G. A. Rodriguez, R. Calafiore, T. M. Chang, P. de Vos *et al.*, History, challenges and perspectives of cell microencapsulation. *Trends Biotechnol.*, **22**, 87 (2004).
195. G. Orive, R. M. Hernandez, A. Murua, and J. L. Pedraz, Recent advances in the use of encapsulated cells for effective delivery of therapeutics. *Ther. Delivery*, **1**, 387 (2010).
196. D. F. Williams, On the nature of biomaterials. *Biomaterials*, **30**, 5897 (2009).
197. S. L. Anna, N. Bontoux, and H. A. Stone, Formation of dispersions using "flow focusing" in microchannels. *Appl. Phys. Lett.*, **82**, 364 (2003).
198. L.-Y. Chu, A. S. Utada, R. K. Shah, J.-W. Kim, D. A. Weitz, Controllable monodisperse multiple emulsions. *Angew. Chem. Int. Ed.*, **46**, 8970 (2007).
199. S. Xu, Z. Nie, M. Seo, P. Lewis, E. Kumacheva, H. A. Stone *et al.*, Generation of monodisperse particles by using microfluidics: Control over size, shape, and composition. *Angew. Chem. Int. Ed.*, **44**, 3799 (2005).
200. R. F. Shepherd, J. C. Conrad, S. K. Rhodes, D. R. Link, M. Marquez, D. A. Weitz *et al.*, Microfluidic assembly of homogeneous and janus colloid-filled hydrogel granules. *Langmuir.*, **22**, 8618 (2006).
201. J. Wan, A. Bick, M. Sullivan, and H. A. Stone, Controllable microfluidic production of microbubbles in water-in-oil emulsions and the formation of porous microparticles. *Adv. Mater.*, **20**, 3314 (2008).
202. G. Orive, M. de Castro, H.-J. Kong, R. M. Hernandez, S. Ponce, D. J .Mooney *et al.*, Bioactive cell-hydrogel microcapsules for cell-based drug delivery. *J. Controlled Release*, **135**, 203 (2009).
203. C. A. Hoesli, K. Raghuram, R. L. J. Kiang, D. Mocinecova, X. Hu, J. D. Johnson *et al.*, Pancreatic cell immobilization in alginate beads produced by emulsion and internal gelation. *Biotechnol. Bioeng.*, **108**, 424 (2010).

204. L. Li, A. E. Davidovich, J. M. Schloss, U. Chippada, R. R. Schloss, N. A. Langrana *et al.*, Neural lineage differentiation of embryonic stem cells within alginate microbeads. *Biomaterials*, **32**, 4489 (2011).
205. A. Kumachev, J. Greener, E. Tumarkin, E. Eiser, P. W. Zandstra, and E. Kumacheva, High-throughput generation of hydrogel microbeads with varying elasticity for cell encapsulation. *Biomaterials*, **32**, 1477 (2011).
206. T. Nisisako, T. Torii, T. Takahashi, and Y. Takizawa, Synthesis of monodisperse bicolored janus particles with electrical anisotropy using a microfluidic co-flow system. *Adv. Mater.*, **18**, 1152 (2006).
207. D. Dendukuri, T. A. Hatton, and P. S. Doyle, Synthesis and self-assembly of amphiphilic polymeric microparticles. *Langmuir.*, **23**, 4669 (2007).
208. J. Choi, Y. Zhao, D. Zhang, S. Chien, Y. H. Lo, Patterned fluorescent particles as nanoprobes for the investigation of molecular interactions. *Nano Lett.*, **3**, 995 (2003).
209. J. C. Love, B. D. Gates, D. B. Wolfe, K. E. Paul, G. M. Whitesides, Fabrication and wetting properties of metallic half shells with submicron diameters. *Nano Lett.* **2**, 891 (2002).
210. M. Fialkowski, A. Bitner, and B. A. Grzybowski, Self-assembly of polymeric microspheres of complex internal structures. *Nat Mater.*, **4**, 93 (2005).
211. K.-H. Roh, D. C. Martin, and J. Lahann, Biphasic janus particles with nanoscale anisotropy. *Nat Mater.*, **4**, 759 (2005).
212. M.-Y. Zhao, L.-H. Li, C.-R. Zhou, and L. Lu, Preparation and characterization of the calcium alginate hydrogels as injectable cartilage scaffolds. *Gongneng Cailiao*, **41**, 1353 (2010).
213. C. Alexiou, R. Jurgons, R. J. Schmid, C. Bergemann, J. Henke, W. Erhardt *et al.*, Magnetic drug targeting — biodistribution of the magnetic carrier and the chemotherapeutic agent mitoxantrone after locoregional cancer treatment. *J. Drug. Targeting.*, **11**, 139 (2003).
214. E. A. A. Neel, A. M. Young, S. N. Nazhat, and J. C. Knowles, A facile synthesis route to prepare microtubes from phosphate glass fibres. *Adv. Mater.*, **19**, 2856 (2007).
215. C. M Hwang, A. Khademhosseini, Y. Park, K. Sun, S. -H. Lee, Microfluidic chip-based fabrication of plga microfiber scaffolds for tissue engineering. *Langmuir.*, **24**, 6845 (2008).
216. B. R. Lee, K. H. Lee, E. Kang, D. -S. Kim, and S. -H. Lee, Microfluidic wet spinning of chitosan-alginate microfibers and encapsulation of Hepg2 cells in fibers. *Biomicrofluidics*, **5**, 022208/1 (2011).
217. J. M. Rosiak, P. Ulanski, L. A. Pajewski, F. Yoshii, and K. Makuuchi, Radiation formation of hydrogels for biomedical purposes. some remarks and comments. *Radiat. Phys. Chem.*, **46**, 161 (1995).
218. R. A. Stile, W. R. Burghardt, K. E. Healy, Synthesis and characterization of injectable poly(n-isopropylacrylamide)-based hydrogels that support tissue formation *in vitro*. *Macromolecules*, **32**, 7370 (1999).
219. N. Zhang and D. H. Kohn, Using polymeric materials to control stem cell behavior for tissue regeneration. *Birth Defects Res. C*, **96**, 63 (2012).

220. K. H. Lee, S. J. Shin, Y. Park, and S. -H. Lee, Synthesis of cell-laden alginate hollow fibers using microfluidic chips and microvascularized tissue-engineering applications. *Small*, **5**, 1264 (2009).
221. T. Takei, N. Kishihara, S. Sakai, and K. Kawakami, Novel technique to control inner and outer diameter of calcium-alginate hydrogel hollow microfibers, and immobilization of mammalian cells. *Biochem. Eng. J.*, **49**, 143 (2010).
222. S.-J. Shin, J.-Y. Park, J.-Y. Lee, H. Park, Y.-D. Park, K.-B. Lee *et al.*, "On the Fly" continuous generation of alginate fibers using a microfluidic device. *Am. Chem. Soc.* **23**, 9104 (2007).
223. E. Kang, S. J. Shin, K. H. Lee, and S. -H. Lee, Novel Pdms cylindrical channels that generate coaxial flow, and application to fabrication of microfibers and particles. *Lab Chip.*, **10**, 1856 (2010).
224 K. H. Lee, S. J. Shin, C. -B. Kim, J. -K. Kim, Y. -W. Cho, B. -G. Chung *et al.*, Microfluidic synthesis of pure chitosan microfibers for bio-artificial liver chip. *Lab Chip.*, **10**, 1328 (2010).
225. M. D. Brigham, A. Bick, E. Lo, A. Bendali, J. A. Burdick, and A. Khademhosseini, Mechanically robust and bioadhesive collagen and photocrosslinkable hyaluronic acid semi-interpenetrating networks. *Tissue Eng. Part A*, **15**, 1645 (2009).
226. C. Chung, J. Mesa, G. J. Miller, M. A. Randolph, T. J. Gill, and J. A. Burdick, Effects of auricular chondrocyte expansion on neocartilage formation in photocrosslinked hyaluronic acid networks. *Tissue Eng.*, **12**, 2665 (2006).
227. Q. Li, C. G. Williams, D. D. N. Sun, J. Wang, K. Leong, and J. H. Elisseeff, Photocrosslinkable polysaccharides based on chondroitin sulfate. *J. Biomed. Mater. Res. Part A*, 68A, **28** (2003).
228. W. Jeong, J. Kim, S. Kim, S. Lee, G. Mensing, and D. J. Beebe, Hydrodynamic microfabrication via "on the fly" photopolymerization of microscale fibers and tubes. *Lab on a Chip — Miniaturisation for Chemistry and Biology.*, **4**, 576 (2004).
229. J.-H. Jung, C.-H. Choi, S. Chung, Y.-M. Chung, and C.-S. Lee, Microfluidic synthesis of a cell adhesive janus polyurethane microfiber. *Lab Chip.*, **9**, 2596 (2009).
230. C. B. Little and M. M. Smith, Animal models of osteoarthritis. *Curr. Rheumatol. Rev.*, **4**, 175 (2008).
231. Y. Du, E. Lo, S. Ali, A. Khademhosseini, Directed assembly of cell-laden microgels for fabrication of 3D tissue constructs. *Proc. Natl. Acad. Sci. USA*, **105**, 9522 (2008).
232. G. M. Whitesides and M. Boncheva, Beyond molecules: Self-assembly of mesoscopic and macroscopic components. *Proc. Natl. Acad. Sci. USA*, **99**, 4769 (2002).
233. W. Shen, G. Wang, and F. Ding. Self-assembly of the clusters with anisotropy. *Nanjing Daxue Xuebao, Ziran Kexue.*, 38, **216** (2002).
234. B. Zamanian, M. Masaeli, J. W. Nichol, M. Khabiry, M. J. Hancock, H. Bae *et al.*, Interface-directed self-assembly of cell-laden microgels. *Small*, **6**, 937 (2010).
235. J. G. Fernandez and A. Khademhosseini, Micro-masonry: Construction of 3D structures by microscale self-assembly. *Adv. Mater.*, **22**, 2538 (2010).

Chapter 6

Controlling Hydrogel Biodegradability

**Wesley N. Sivak*, Danielle M. Minteer†, Bernd Lannau*
and Kacey G. Marra‡,§**

*Department of Plastic Surgery, University of Pittsburgh, Pittsburgh, PA, USA

†Department of Bioengineering, University of Pittsburgh, Pittsburgh, PA, USA

‡Departments of Plastic Surgery and Bioengineering, McGowan Institute for Regenerative Medicine, University of Pittsburgh, Pittsburgh, PA, USA

§marrak@upmc.edu

Hydrogels are hydrophilic, three-dimensional (3D) network polymers, consisting of crosslinked natural, synthetic, or natural/synthetic hybrid materials. Hydrogels are capable of swelling and retaining large amounts of fluid, often with structures closely resembling natural tissues. Biomimetic hydrogels have been shown to support cellular growth and infiltration and can further act as reservoirs for the controlled delivery of bioactive molecules. Polymeric hydrogels can be designed to be degradable, largely due to the number and nature of chemical or physical crosslinks between the macromolecular chains. Hydrolytic degradation can be controlled to varying degrees via manipulation of material properties (e.g., hydrophilicity, stereochemistry, molecular weight, ionic strength, or oxidation state), material processing techniques, enzymatic susceptibility, or response to various environmental stimuli (e.g., temperature, pH, electric and magnetic fields, antibodies, or inflammation). This review examines the current literature regarding various hydrogels and factors used to control their degradation rates.

1. Introduction

A hydrogel is a hydrophilic, three-dimensional (3D) network, consisting of crosslinked natural, synthetic, or natural/synthetic hybrid polymers.[1] Due to the presence of chemical or physical crosslinks between the polymer chains, hydrogels do not dissolve but instead swell as they absorb water. Swelling reaches equilibrium as the elastic retractile force, exerted by the crosslinks, is balanced out by the thermodynamic force of the swelling.[2,3] These crosslinks consist of covalent bonds, hydrogen bonding, van der Waals interactions or physical entanglements.[4] Due to its elastic properties, a hydrogel can quickly and fully recover to its original dimensions following small deformations (<20%).[5] The swelling ability of the hydrogel greatly influences its resultant physical properties. Examples include the permeability to hydrophilic or hydrophobic drugs, biocompatibility, mechanical characteristics and the rate of degradation.[6] Depending on the indication, the rate of degradation can be the key parameter in determining the overall success of the hydrogel. As a consequence, there has been a significant amount of research devoted to regulating the degradation rate of biocompatible hydrogel materials, exemplified by the numerous applications of hydrogels within the discipline of tissue engineering.

Hydrogels have the unique ability to encapsulate living cells and can further serve as a reservoir for spatial and temporal dependent delivery of bioactive molecules.[1,5] Hydrogels are able to encapsulate living cells largely due to their high water content and the resulting ease of nutrient diffusion. It has been demonstrated that encapsulated cells will eventually contribute to production of extracellular matrix (ECM) components.[7] Low molecular weight precursors to ECM components that are initially secreted by encapsulated cells can diffuse freely into the matrix of the hydrogel. However, it is not sufficient until degradation occurs, that larger ECM molecules, such as collagen, are able to infiltrate the hydrogel structure and develop an interface with the surrounding tissue environment. Thus, it is important that hydrogels are designed with control over the gel structure, closely matching its degradation rate to the ECM secretion of incorporated cells or adjoining tissues.[7] If hydrogel degradation occurs too quickly, the production of ECM proteins (i.e., proteoglycans and collagen) will be insufficient for proper tissue remodeling and regrowth. Lack of sufficient ECM contributes to the final macroscopic geometry, mechanical properties, and bioactivity of the tissue regenerate. Conversely, degradation that occurs too slowly can result in altered cellular signaling and function. Cell surface receptors may be stimulated or inhibited by the ECM constituents, leading to unfavorable alterations of certain intracellular cascades. Ultimately, it is the degradation rate of the hydrogel that influences the final type and architecture of tissue produced.[7,8]

Synchronizing the degradation rate of a hydrogel to a target tissue can prove a formidable task.

Researchers have achieved measures of control by altering the chemical structure of the polymers used to fabricate a hydrogel, as well as varying the crosslinking density.[9] A hydrogel consists of polymer chains and crosslinks between these chains; degradation can be attained through the scission of either the polymer backbone or the crosslinks. As scission occurs, the mean distance between consecutive crosslinks (i.e., the mesh size) increases, leading to an overall decrease in the compactness of the network. As the number of intact crosslinks decreases, the equilibrium between the thermodynamic force of the swelling and the elastic retractile force shifts, leading to an increased influx of the water.[6] A hydrogel will retain its structural integrity as crosslinks are cleaved, but only up to a certain point.[10] Past this point, polymer chains from the bulk are solvated and released into solution. This event coincides with a sharp decrease of the mass of the hydrogel — a process referred to as "reverse gelation".[7]

With few exceptions, the vast majority of hydrogels are engineered to degrade hydrolytically, hydrolyzing through a chemical linkage present in the crosslinks or in the main chain polymer of the hydrogel. Alpha-hydroxy esters (e.g., lactic acid and epsilon-caprolactone), amides, urethane-ureas, and phosphoesters are examples of hydrolytically labile linkages traditionally used in hydrogels for tissue engineering applications. Hydrogels composed from such materials begin to degrade the moment that they come into contact with an aqueous environment.[7] Peptide sequences are also vulnerable to hydrolytic degradation via an enzymatic process, and hydrogels can also be specifically engineered to contain these sequences in order to obtain desired rates of degradation. Often matrix metalloproteinases, and more specific, collagenases, hyaluronidases and chondroitinases are used for enzymatic degradation, as these enzymes are ubiquitous within normal and regenerating tissues and regulate *in vivo* ECM remodeling.[11] Unlike in hydrolytic degradation, enzymes may also be exogenously delivered and provide the researcher temporal control over hydrogel degradation.[7]

The hydrogel's physical environment can also have profound implications upon its degradation rate. For example, solutes present in the *in vivo* environment or new tissue deposition can lead to dissolution of the polymer chains or the disruption of hydrogen bonding interactions associated with the crosslinks.[12–15] Furthermore, the *in vivo* environment is known to further alter the cleavage of ester bonds in biopolymers.[7] External stimuli in the form of pH changes,[7,16–22] temperature shifts,[21–43] alterations in ionic strength,[43–45] electric fields,[45–47] magnetic fields,[48–50] ultrasonic pulses,[51–53] antibody exposure,[54,55] and even activation of inflammatory cascades[56,57] can be utilized to alter the physical environment of the hydrogel and impact its degradation rate in a favorable manner.

Due to the fact that the degradation is affected by many different variables, engineers can fine-tune each variable in ways that lead to hydrogels with the desired trigger signal and rate of degradation. However, one must always remain cognizant of the fact that it is challenging to control hydrogel properties in an independent manner due to the interdependency between hydrogel properties.

This review will summarize the current methods and strategies employed to control hydrogel biodegradability.

2. Material Properties

Ensuring adequate performance of a hydrogel depends on specifying, characterizing, and controlling many of the resultant material properties including elasticity, compressibility, viscoelastic behavior, tensile strength, failure strain, and degradation rate. Although the hydrogel environment is often in excess of 90% water, slight variations in hydrogel chemistry have been shown to greatly shift macroscopic properties in a favorable manner.[58] In hydrogels, these properties can be attributed to the intrinsic properties of the main chain polymer, which are then further altered by the degree of crosslinking characteristics (i.e., amount, type, and size of crosslinking molecules) and environmental conditions. Proper selection of constituent materials comprising the main chain polymer has been used by many authors to exert measures of control over the degradative characteristics of hydrogels; a summary of key studies can be found in Table 1.

2.1. Hydrophilicity and hydrophobicity

The susceptibility of constituent polymers to hydrolytic degradation is a vitally important parameter allowing hydrogel systems to be designed with varying degrees of sensitivity. Degradation kinetics can be controlled through the underlying chemistry; for example, ester linkages associated with lactic acid degrade much more rapidly than ester linkages of caprolactone.[59] A variety of biodegradable synthetic polymers, including poly(L-lactic acid) (PLLA), poly(glycolic acid) (PGA), poly(ethylene glycol) (PEG), polycaprolactones, polyorthoesters, polyanhydrides, and polycarbonates have been extensively characterized and widely used to fabricate hydrogel scaffolds.[60] Their ease of chemical synthesis on large scales, combined with the Federal Drug Administration (FDA) approval of several of these polymers has ushered the application of synthetic polymers toward many hydrogel applications. The ability to co-polymerize, combine and control the hydrophilic–hydrophobic interactions of many of these polymers has given tissue engineers the flexibility to tailor the mechanical and degradation properties of a material for specific applications, particularly those at tissue interfaces, which often require gradients of several material properties.[61]

Polymers such as PLA, PGA and poly(lactic-co-glycolic acid) (PLGA) have degradation rates that can be related to polymer composition, crystallinity, and topological structure.[62] The hydrolytic degradation is largely governed by hydrophilic–hydrophobic interactions and can be controlled by varying ratios of polymers. A study by Sawhney *et al.* has shown that incorporation of alpha-hydroxy acid oligomers augmented the degradability of the PEG-based hydrogel matrices under physiological conditions.[59] They were able to demonstrate that the degradation time of the hydrogels could be tailored from 1 day to 4 months by varying the type of alpha-hydroxy acid incorporated (e.g., glycolic or lactic acid). The authors attributed these observations to the alterations in hydrophobic domains of the main chain polymer governing hydrolysis.

Akala *et al.* synthesized novel pH-sensitive hydrogels based on biocompatible copolymers of N,N-dimethylacrylamide with tert-butylacrylamide (to improve mechanical properties), acrylic acid (to introduce pH-sensitivity) and crosslinking agents containing aromatic azo bonds (degradable by the azoreductase activity in the colon).[17] The influence of the length (and consequently hydrophobicity) of the alkanoyl (propionyl, hexanoyl, and lauroyl) residues and their concentration in the hydrogel on the kinetics of swelling were investigated, and the rate of side-chain hydrolysis was found to be dependent on the length of the alkyl and the content of the hydrolyzable co-monomer in the hydrogel. In a related endeavor, Kim *et al.* developed novel biodegradable poly(ethylene glycol)-based hydrogels incorporating sebacate diacrylate (PEGSDA).[63] The results of an *in vitro* degradation study demonstrated that these hydrogels were biodegradable with weight losses about 66% and 32% for 25% and 50% PEGSDA respectively after 8 weeks of incubation in phosphate-buffered saline at 37°C.

A hydrophilic polymer's degradation rate and pattern can also be tailored by grafting hydrophobic moieties to pendant hydroxyl groups.[64] A simple type of hydrolytic degradation can be incorporated into PEG gels by adding short PLA blocks on either side of the PEG core.[59,65] The degradation rates of these hydrolytically degrading gels can be controlled by adjusting the length of PLA blocks, the initial macromonomer concentration, or by co-polymerizing two or more macromonomer molecules to create gels with multimodal mass loss profiles.[66,67] Markland *et al.* synthesized a novel polypeptide hydrogel by crosslinking poly(L-glutamic acid) (PLG) with PEG.[16] The PLG–PEG hydrogel was shown to be highly hydrophilic, and the extent of swelling varied with pH, increasing at higher ionization of the PLG. Modification of the polypeptide by changing its hydrophobicity and degree of ionization was an effective method for altering the overall extent of pH-responsive swelling and degradation. Ichi *et al.* investigated a series of PEG hydrogels crosslinked by a hydrolyzable polyrotaxane comprised of many α-cyclodextrins (α-CD) and characterized the hydrolytic erosion behavior (see Fig. 1).[68] From the result of the erosion studies, the time to reach complete gel erosion was prolonged by decreasing the polyrotaxane content and increasing the PEG/α-CD ratio. The PEG/α-CD ratio, indicating the number of PEG chains linked with one α-CD molecule, is considered to make the environment of the

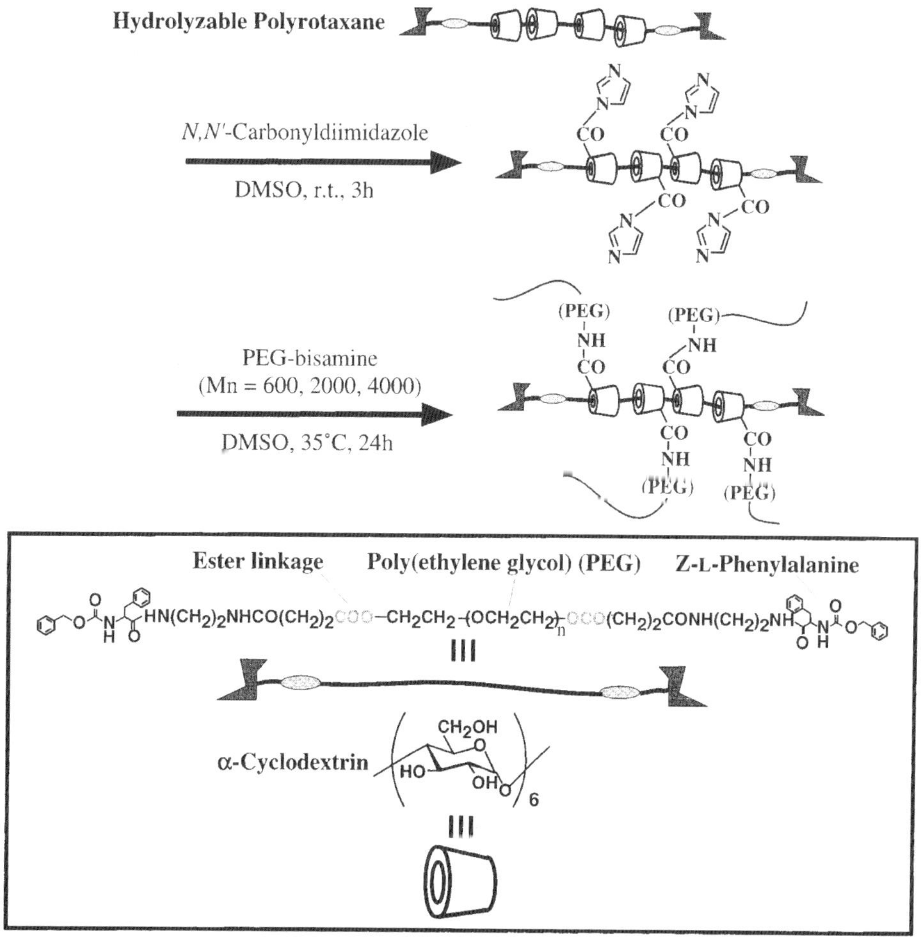

Fig. 1. Preparation of PEG hydrogels crosslinked by the Polyrotaxane.[68]

polyrotaxane more aqueous and lead to the hydrolysis of ester linkages in the polyrotaxane. However, the higher PEG/α-CD ratio prolonged the time of the hydrogel erosion. Their results indicate the enhanced stability of ester hydrolysis in the hydrogels with highly swollen states. Such an anomalous phenomenon was attributed to the structural characteristic of the polyrotaxane where ester linkages were included within the cavity of α-CDs, resulting in their enhanced stability.

The swelling properties of hydrogels are crucial for substance exchange when they are used as injectable scaffolds for biomedical applications. Degradation rates have been shown to correspond to the extent of swelling under certain experimental conditions. Tan *et al.* reported a new class of biocompatible and biodegradable composite hydrogels derived from water-soluble chitosan and oxidized hyaluronic acid (HA) which gel upon mixing, without the addition of a chemical cross-linking agent.[69] The gelation is attributed to the Schiff base reaction between

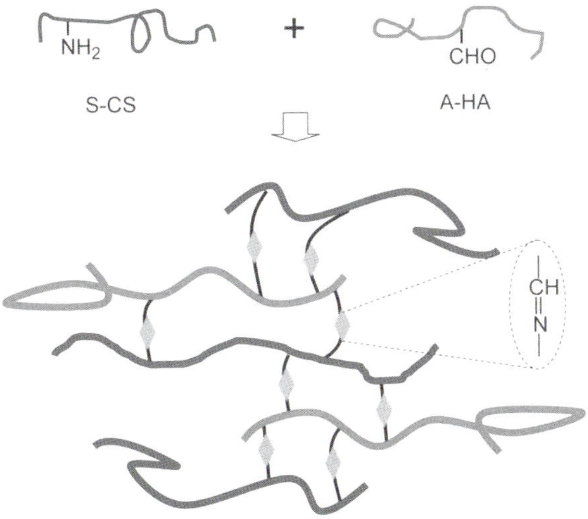

Fig. 2. The scheme of S-CS and A-HA composite hydrogel via Schiff's base crosslinking reaction.[69]

amino and aldehyde groups of polysaccharide derivatives (see Fig. 2). The amount of N-succinyl-chitosan (S-CS) and aldehyde hyaluronic acid (A-HA) used in the hydrogel synthesis significantly affected the hydrogels' swelling properties. Both S-CS and A-HA have an abundant number of hydrophilic groups, such as hydroxyl, amino and carboxyl groups, which can easily produce hydration with water. The S-CS/A-HA hydrogels with 1/9 and 9/1 ratios revealed less cross-linking, consequently increasing the exposure of polymer chains to water molecules, and significantly leading to increased water absorption and faster degradative weight loss.

Interestingly, Bryant *et al.* demonstrated that the presence of cells slowed degradation of biodegradable PEG gels containing PLA as the degradable linkage.[58] This finding was attributed, in part, to differences in water contents between the cell-free and cell-laden gels. The *in vivo* environment is known to accelerate cleavage of ester bonds, and can significantly accelerate the degradation of hydrolytically biodegradable PEG–PLA-based gels.[18,19] Changez *et al.* developed interpenetrating network hydrogels (IPNs) based on poly(acrylic acid) and gelatin and evaluated their *in vitro* and *in vivo* biodegradation in addition to *in vivo* release of gentamicin sulphate.[70] *In vitro* and *in vivo* degradation studies demonstrated that, with the increase of acrylic acid content in the polymer, the rate of degradation decreases; a reverse phenomenon was observed with increasing gelatin content in the hydrogel. The rate of *in vivo* degradation was much lower than *in vitro* degradation. Incorporation of gentamicin sulphate in hydrogels led to further reductions in degradation. In tuning the degradation of the hydrogel, there are many factors that must be considered, including the type and length of the degradable linker as well as the application environment. These factors will directly influence the structural evolution of the hydrogel, which subsequently impact the spatial deposition of newly synthesized tissues.

2.2. Stereochemistry

Stereochemistry has long provided a foundation for understanding structure and reactivity. The relative spatial arrangement of atoms that form the structure of molecules and influences their manipulation, can affect the physical or biological properties of the resulting material and the manner in which the material reacts toward its chemical environment. For example, the ability to control PLA D,L imparts control over on the resulting material modulus.[71] This occurs through the crystallinity of the PLA blocks since pure L or D polymers are semi-crystalline but mixtures of D and L produce amorphous materials. Nature is inherently chiral because the building blocks of life (amino acids, nucleotides, and sugars) are chiral and appear in nature in enantiomerically pure forms. Hence, any substances, created to interact with or modify biological systems, interact with a chiral environment. For decades, the FDA has required that drugs be produced in enantiomerically pure forms, or that rigorous tests be performed to ensure that both enantiomers are safe following the thalidomide tragedy of the 1950s.[72]

Differences in the stereochemistry of precursors can favorably alter the material properties of a resulting hydrogel, including the degradation rate. Chung *et al.* developed a novel temperature-sensitive and *in situ* forming hydrogel system based on Pluronic F127.[21] A series of multi-block Pluronic copolymers linked by D-lactide and L-lactide oligomers with different spacer lengths were synthesized, and pairs of multiblock copolymers having the corresponding enantiomeric D- or L-lactide oligomer spacer, were blended to form stereo-complexed hydrogels (see Fig. 3). The resultant physically crosslinked Pluronic hydrogels exhibited significantly altered sol–gel phase transition behaviors with much lower critical gelation concentrations and temperatures, compared to the uncomplexed multi-block or Pluronic homopolymer hydrogels. Mass erosion results revealed that multi-block and stereo-complexed hydrogels exhibited differing delayed erosion behaviors through diffusion/erosion-coupled mechanisms. Furthermore, the stereo-complexed hydrogels had increased mechanical strength with high resistance to rapid dissolution in aqueous medium.

Stereocomplexation refers to synergistic interactions that occur between polymer chains or small molecules of the same chemical composition but different stereochemistry. De Jong *et al.* obtained hydrogels, physically crosslinked through stereo-complex formation, by mixing aqueous solutions of dextran with either L-lactic acid or D-lactic acid.[73] The authors were able to show that under

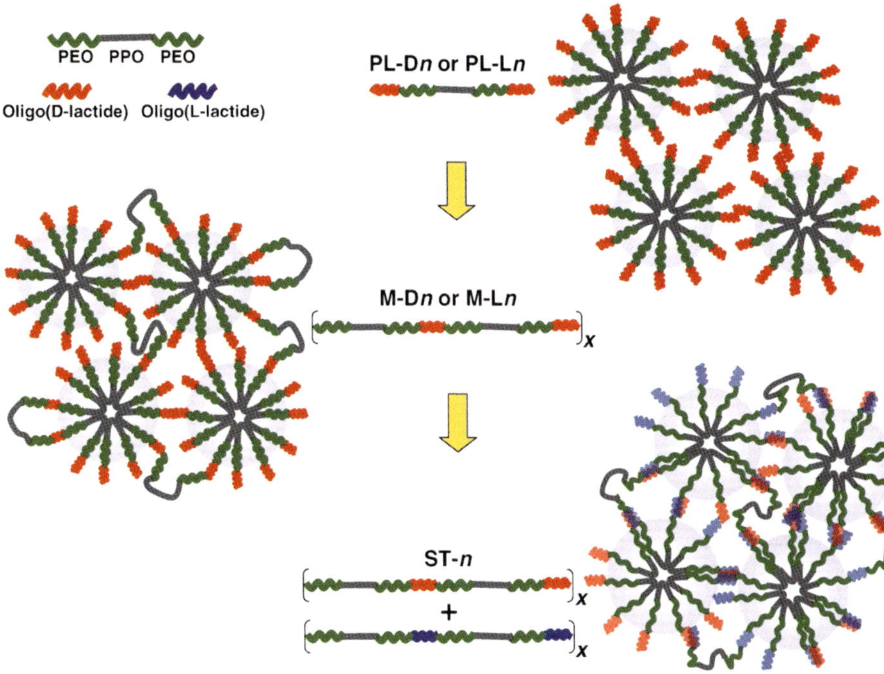

Fig. 3. Schematic illustration for molecular structure of hydrogels formed by PL copolymer end-capped with oligolactide (PL-Dn or PL-Ln), multi-blocks (M-Dn or M-Ln), and stereo-complexed multi-blocks (ST-n).[24]

physiological conditions the gels were fully degradable over periods ranging from 1 to 7 days. The degradation times depended on the composition of the hydrogel (i.e., the number of lactate grafts, the length and polydispersity of the grafts and the initial water content). The authors concluded that the degradation of the stereo-complex hydrogel started with hydrolysis of the carbonate ester, which links the lactate graft to dextran (see Fig. 4). Lim *et al.* reported on the synthesis and characterization of stereo-complexed hydrogels, composed of enantiomeric oligo-lactates coupled to Poly(2-hydroxyethyl methacrylate) (pHEMA).[74] The pendant oligo-L-lactate and oligo-D-lactate chains were able to interact and physical crosslinks were formed. It was shown that the hydrogels containing stereo-complex crystallinities, degraded slower than materials with optically pure crystalline domains. The degradation rate could be further tuned by modifying the degree of polymerization of the oligolactates.

Van Nostrum *et al.* reported on a stereo-complexed hydrogel in which the dextran backbone was replaced by 2-hydroxypropyl methacrylamide (HPMA).[75] In these hydrogels, the oligolactate side chains were acetylated, preventing rapid chain end scission — making slow random chain scission the main action of

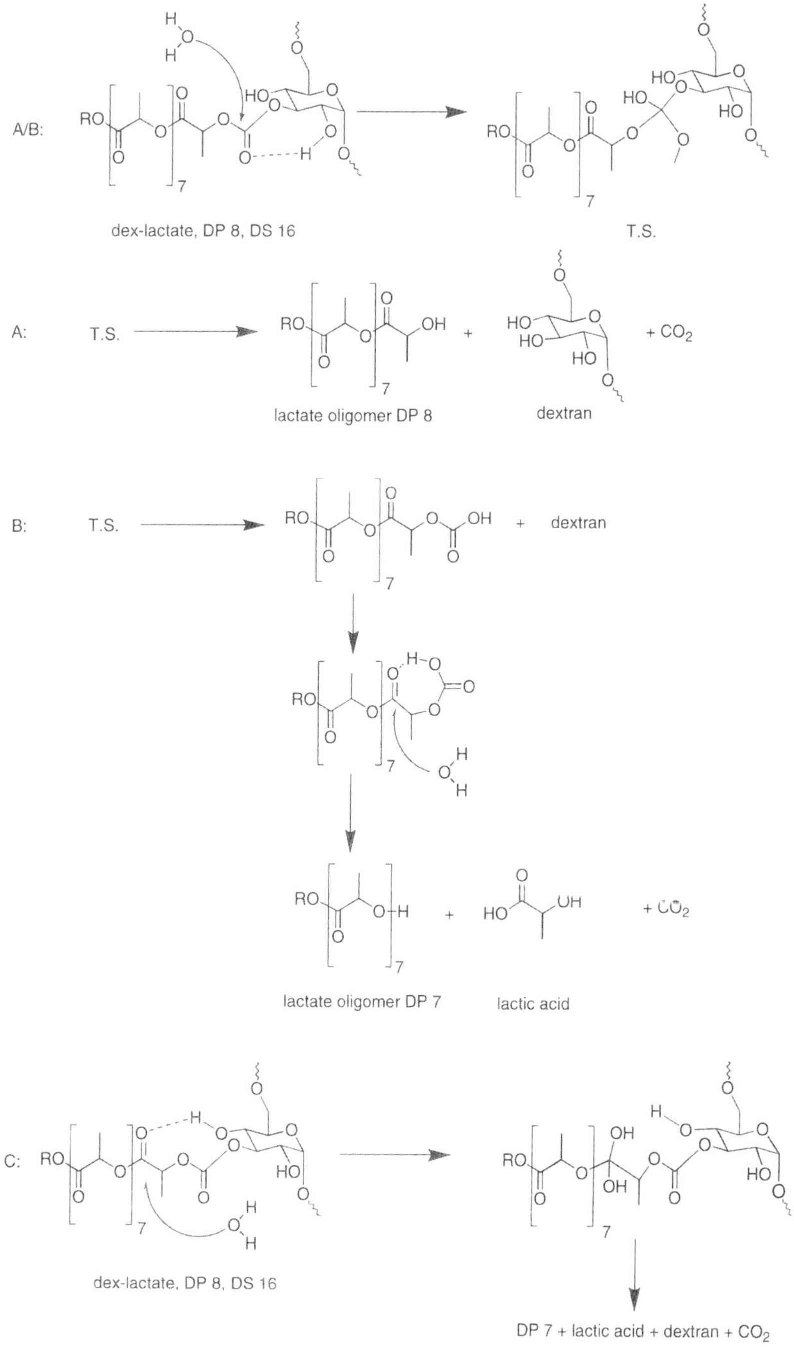

Fig. 4. Suggested mechanisms of hydrolysis of dex-lactate (T.S., transition state).[73]

degradation — leading to longer degradation times up to 60 days. Hiemstra *et al.* chemically modified PEG-(PLLA) 8/PEG- poly(d, l-lactic acid) (PDLA)8 hydrogels in order to combine physical entanglements with photopolymerization.[76] For this purpose, PEG–PLLA and PEG–PDLA star block copolymers were functionalized with methacrylate groups, either at the PLA chain ends or at the PEG chain ends (see Fig. 5). It was found that the methacrylates hardly interfered with the stereocomplexation. On the other hand, after UV-polymerization, the hydrogels showed significantly higher storage moduli and prolonged degradation times when compared to only photopolymerized gels. Additionally, low photoinitiator concentrations were needed when stereocomplexation had already occurred. Interestingly, hydrogels in which the methacrylates were coupled to the PEG ends degraded much slower than those gels in which the PLA ends where methacrylated. The authors further demonstrated that degradation times can be tailored by varying the degree and place of methacrylation in the hydrogel precursors. However, be mindful of the significant limitations of stereocomplexation and the relatively

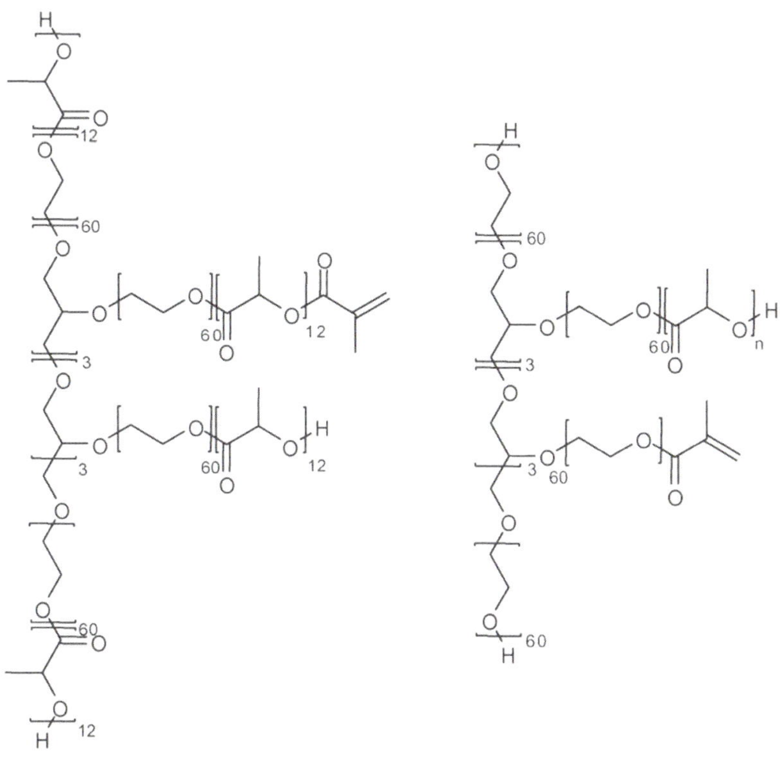

(A) (B)

Fig. 5. (A) Eight-arm PEG–PLA12–MA star block copolymers, (B) PEG–MA/PLAn (n = 12 or 16) star block copolymers.[40]

restricted range of polymer compositions which can be used; even small changes in the stoichiometry or otherwise changing the composition of matter within the gelators can significantly weaken or altogether eliminate the stereochemical interactions.[20]

2.3. Molecular weight

The degradation behavior of materials can often be controlled by altering the molecular weight of its components.[77] For example, Park examined the degradation behaviors of PDLA microspheres prepared from starting materials with two different molecular weights (17,000 and 41,000).[78] During a 53-day *in vitro* degradation assay, the lower molecular weight microspheres exhibited significant earlier degradation with reduced glass transition temperature, while the higher molecular weight polymeric microsphere did not show any detectable changes for over 50 days. Moreover, it has also been reported that the mass loss properties of materials formed via radical chain polymerization reactions are greatly influenced by the kinetic chain length.[66,79] In a material where longer kinetic chains are present, more segments must be broken before erosion from the bulk occurs; this in turn increases overall degradation time and delays dissolution.

Hydrogels follow these trends, and the components utilized to construct the main chain polymer can be selected based upon molecular weight to tailor material properties for a specific application. The degradation of hydrogels, when controlled in this manner, generally relies upon blending of constituent materials with differing molecular weights. Boontheekul *et al.* characterized hydrogels formed using a combination of partial oxidation of polymer chains and a bimodal molecular weight distribution of polymer.[12] Specifically, alginates were partially oxidized to a theoretical extent of 1% with sodium periodate, which created acetal groups susceptible to hydrolysis. The ratio of low molecular weight to high molecular weight alginates used to form gels was also varied, while maintaining the gel forming ability of the polymer. The rate of degradation was controlled by the ratio of high to low molecular weight alginates, as indicated by the reduction of mechanical properties and corresponding number of crosslinks, dry weight loss, and molecular weight decrease. This approach offers control over the degradation rate through a bimodal molecular weight distribution, but can also alter the fluid and solid properties of resulting hydrogels.

Hydrogels were formed by van de Wetering *et al.* using conjugate addition of PEG multiacrylates and dithiothreitol (DTT) for encapsulation and sustained release of human growth hormone (hGH).[10] By varying the molecular weight of the multi-arm PEG acrylates, control over gel swelling, degradation, and hGH release, from a few hours to a few months, was obtained. Protein release from the degrading PEG-based gel networks was also modeled as a diffusion process with a time-dependent diffusion coefficient, calculated from swelling measurements, molecular weight changes, and theoretical mesh sizes. Others have noted that other reported PEG-based hydrogel materials degrade faster than their materials formed from PEG acrylates crosslinked via photopolymerization.[80] The rate at which that degradation occurs was controlled by a number of factors, but depended heavily upon the initial water content of the swollen network. The initial water content of the gel, in turn, was a function of the molecular weight of the PEG acrylate.

Almany *et al.* also reported a novel hydrogel system based upon denatured fibrinogen fragments that were PEGylated with PEG-diacrylates, mixed with photoinitiator and exposed to UV light in the presence of a cell suspension.[81] The fibrinogen backbone of the hydrogel material provides proteolytic sensitivity via naturally occurring substrates for fibrinolysis, but interestingly, the molecular weight of the PEG constituent also independently affected the degradation results (see Fig. 6). The elastic modulus of the PEG-fibrinogen hydrogel was also dependent on the molecular weight of the PEG constituent and proportional to the percent polymeric composition. Kong *et al.* formulated calcium-crosslinked alginate hydrogels consisting of alginates having different molecular weights, where the molecular weight of the G blocks, in the polymer chains was varied in order to alter the size of the polymer segments responsible for ionic cross linking.[82] Their results demonstrate controlled degradation of hydrogels via manipulations of the molecular weight of key components, without utilizing conventional chemical or

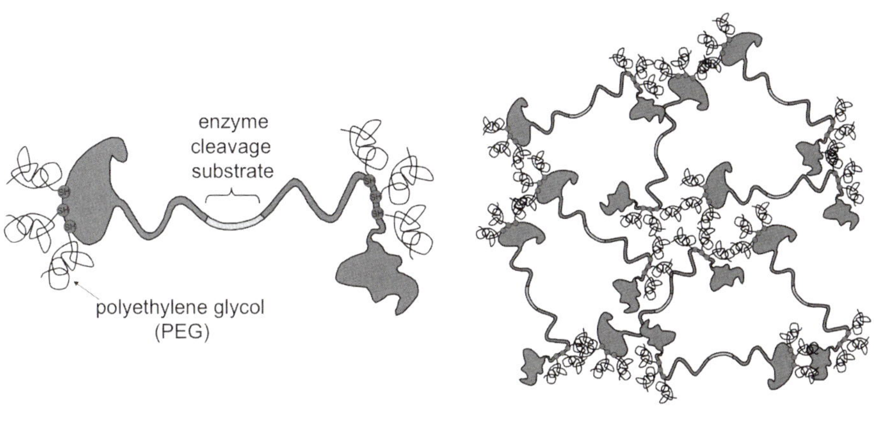

(A) PEGylated Denatured Fibrinogen (B) PEG-Fibrinogen Hydrogel Assembly

Fig. 6. Schematic illustration of the PEG-fibrinogen hydrogel assembly. PEGylated fibrinogen fragments (A) contain a natural protease cleavage site (yellow) and multiple unpaired thiols (red) for covalent conjugation of functionalized PEG by Michael-type addition reaction. PEG-fibrinogen hydrogel assembly (B) is accomplished by photoinitiation of unreacted PEG-DA, resulting in a hydrogel network of PEGylated fibrinogen.[81]

enzymatic degradation pathways. Modification of the gel degradation rate with this approach also proved effective in improving the quality *in vivo* of engineered cartilage tissues.

In a follow-up study, Kong *et al.* further hypothesized that adjusting the molecular weight distribution of polymers that are hydrolytically labile but capable of forming gels would allow one to alter the degradation rate of the gels over a broad range, while limiting the range of their elastic moduli.[15] This hypothesis was tested with binary alginate hydrogels formed from both ionic and covalently crosslinked partially oxidized (1% uronic acid residues), low molecular weight (MW ~ 60,000 g/mol) and high molecular weight alginates (MW ~ 120,000 g/mol). Increasing the fraction of low molecular weight alginates to 0.50 maintained a similar elastic modulus to that for the high molecular weight alginate gels, but led to faster degradation irrespective of the crosslinking mode. This result was attributed to a faster separation between crosslinked domains upon chain breakages for the low molecular weight alginates, coupled with their faster chain scission than the high molecular weight alginates. Furthermore, the more rapidly degrading oxidized binary hydrogels facilitated the formation of new bone tissues from transplanted bone marrow stromal cells, as compared with the non-oxidized high MW hydrogels. Finally, Bryant *et al.* fabricated biodegradable poly(ethylene glycol)-co-poly(lactic acid) (PEG–PLA) hydrogels via photopolymerization.[58] The dominating gel property with respect to degradation appeared to be the crosslinking density in the absence of cells and the PLA length (i.e., molecular weight) in the presence of cells.

2.4. Ionic strength

Electrostatic interactions have been widely investigated for augmenting hydrogel materials, again achieved through alteration of the ionic charge of incorporated materials.[20] Hydration of hydrogels begins with the initial saturation of hydrophilic species, beginning with ionic and polar residues contained within the matrix. Slowly, hydrophobic areas will reach an equilibrium state with the aqueous environment. Additional swelling water that is imbibed after the ionic, polar and hydrophobic groups become saturated with bound water is called "free water" or "bulk water", and is assumed to fill the space between the network chains, and/or the center of larger pores, macropore or voids.[83] The free water is responsible for mass transport phenomena throughout a hydrogel and largely determines many of the fundamental properties of hydrogels. Careful selection of highly hydrophilic species, such as ionic pendant groups, can significantly impact the bound and free water environments present in a hydrogel. Furthermore, incorporated charged species can interact with one another or competitively interact with other ionic species within the surrounding environment, giving rise to altered rates of degradation.

Kong *et al.* examined controlled degradation rates of hydrogels and release of encapsulated plasmid DNA (pDNA) utilizing ionic crosslinked polysaccharide hydrogels.[84] The hydrogel degradation rates were varied over a broad range, and pDNA release correlated with the gel degradation rate. Degradable hydrogels were then used for the local and sustained delivery of a pDNA encoding for vascular endothelial growth factor (VEGF) in the ischemic hindlimbs of mice, and local pDNA release significantly improved the recovery of blood perfusion as compared with a bolus injection of VEGF encoding pDNA. In another study, Kong *et al.* utilized ionic and covalently crosslinked partially oxidized (1% uronic acid residues) alginate hydrogels to assess if the degradation rate of the gels could be altered over a broad range.[15] The concentration of ionic crosslinks present in the gel were found to be responsible for faster degradation responses, irrespective of any chemical crosslinking mode.

Van Tomme *et al.* assessed the effect of positively and negatively charged microspheres upon the degradation behavior of dextran-based hydrogels.[85] By varying the crosslink density of the microspheres and the water content of the hydrogels (75–85%) the degradation times of the gels could be tailored from 65 to 140 days. Furthermore, it was demonstrated that the degradation times increased from 30 to 75, 85, 105, and 125 days for 100/0, 75/25, 50/50, 25/75 and 0/100 positively/negatively charged microspheres, respectively. Incorporation of rhodamine-B-dextran in both the anionic and cationic microspheres resulted in a degradation controlled release with a tailorable release profile depending on the positive/negative charge microsphere ratio. The authors demonstrated that the possibility to tailor the network properties and degradation behavior of dextran-based hydrogel systems was attributable to not only the presence of charge upon the incorporated microspheres, but also whether that charge was positive or negative. Similarly, a US patent filing by Feijen also suggests that by altering ionic strength and the composition of the hydrogel matrix, one can control degradation kinetics, the degree of uptake of a particular pharmacologically active agent, and the overall timed release profile of incorporated drugs.[43]

Hwang *et al.* evaluated silk-elastin-like protein polymers (SELPs) of varying ratios and lengths of silk and elastin blocks capable of hydrogel formation as matrices for controlled delivery of pDNA.[86] Influence of polymer structure, ionic strength of the media and gelation time on degradation and DNA release from two structurally related hydrogels, SELP-47K and SELP-415K, was evaluated. SELP-415K, which has twice the number of elastin units as that of SELP-47K, demonstrated higher degradation and release than that of SELP-47K. DNA release from these hydrogels was found to be an inverse function of polymer concentration and cure time. Interestingly, the authors concluded that ionic strength of the media principally governed the rate of degradation and subsequent pDNA release. Markland *et al.* also reported novel polypeptide hydrogel has been synthesized by crosslinking PLG with PEG, where the PLG–PEG hydrogel was shown to be highly hydrophilic, and the extent of swelling and degradation increasing at higher ionization levels of the PLG.[16] Aside from electrostatic effects, such as ion–ion repulsion and internal ion osmotic pressure, circular dichroism studies showed that swelling response, and likely subsequent degradation, was also affected by secondary structural attributes associated with the polypeptide backbone.

Alginates have been used in a variety of medical applications including cell encapsulation and drug stabilization and delivery, because it gels under gentle conditions, has low toxicity, and is readily available.[3] It is a linear polysaccharide copolymer of (1–4)-linked β-d-mannuronic acid (M) and α-l-guluronic acid (G) monomers and is derived primarily from brown seaweed and bacteria.[87,88] Gels are formed when divalent cations such as Ca^{2+}, Ba^{2+}, or Sr^{2+} cooperatively interact with blocks of G monomers to form ionic bridges between different polymer chains.[87] The crosslinking density and thus mechanical properties and pore size of the ionic crosslinked gels can be readily manipulated by varying the M to G ratio in addition to the molecular weight of the polymer chain. Ionic crosslinked alginate hydrogels do not specifically degrade but undergo slow, uncontrolled dissolutions. Mass is lost through ion exchange of calcium followed by dissociation of individual chains, which results in loss of mechanical stiffness over time.[46] Jeon *et al.* engineered alginate hydrogels with hydrolytically degradable ester linkages incorporated during the photopolymerization process.[89] They concluded there was still limited control over the mechanical properties, swelling ratios, and degradation profiles of purely ionically crosslinked alginate hydrogels, likely due to the uncontrollable loss of divalent cations into the surrounding environment.[90,91]

2.5. Oxidation state

Few materials can undergo significant oxidation without destroying the properties necessary for hydrogel formation. However as already alluded to, hydrolytically degradable forms of alginate can be synthesized by partial oxidation of alginate and an alginate derivative, polyguluronate, to form oxidized alginate and poly(aldehyde guluronate) (PAG), respectively.[13,92] These materials do indeed retain the ability to form hydrogels after such a transformation. Boontheekul *et al.* characterized hydrogels formed using a combination of partial oxidation of polymer chains and a bimodal molecular weight distribution of polymer.[12] Specifically, alginates were partially oxidized to a theoretical extent of 1% with sodium periodate, which created acetal groups susceptible to hydrolysis (see Fig. 7). The ratio of low molecular weight to high molecular weight alginates used to form gels was also varied, while maintaining the gel forming ability of the polymer. The rate of degradation was found to be controlled by both the oxidation and the ratio of high to low molecular weight

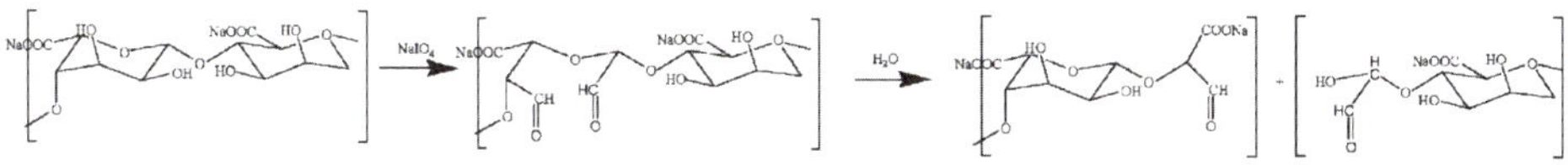

Fig. 7. Periodate oxidation of alginate creates an open chain adduct that is susceptible to hydrolytic scission.[12]

alginates, as monitored by the reduction of mechanical properties and corresponding number of crosslinks, dry weight loss, and molecular weight decrease. This approach offers control over the degradation rate by varying the degree of oxidation, as increasing the degree of oxidation accelerated the rate of degradation. The authors also concluded that the modifications to the alginates, shifted the mechanism of degradation from calcium-mediated cation exchange to hydrolytic chain scission.

Cha *et al.* hypothesized that a biodegradable polymeric crosslinker would allow for decoupling of the dependency between the properties of various hydrogel materials.[93] To investigate, they synthesized oxidized methacrylic alginate (OMA) by partially oxidizing alginate to generate hydrolytically labile units and conjugating methacrylic groups. The OMA was then used to crosslink poly(ethylene glycol) methacrylate and poly(N-hydroxymethyl acrylamide) to form 3D hydrogel systems. OMA significantly improved rigidity and toughness of both hydrogels as compared with a small molecule crosslinker, and also controlled the degradation rate of hydrogels depending on the oxidation degree, without altering their initial mechanical properties. The use of OMA as a crosslinker allowed for tuning the hydrogel degradation rate with the degree of oxidation while minimally changing initial hydrogel stiffness. This refined control of hydrogel degradation rate was related to the independency of the initial number of elastically effective crosslinks and the dependency of gel degradation rate on the number of oxidized uronic acid residues of OMA.

3. Material Processing

Hydrogels have been used as scaffolds for tissue engineering applications because of their similarities with ECM and excellent biological capability. The degree of porosity has a substantial effect on the mechanical properties, with the stiffness of the scaffold decreasing as porosity increases, and the mechanical characteristics varying greatly with fluid flux caused by deformation.[94,95] The features of individual and/or clusters of pores combine to create the hydrogel microarchitecture, controlling many aspects of material performance.[96] Thus, control of scaffold porosity and microarchitecture plays a key role in regulating hydrogel properties. Material processing techniques to control the overall porosity of hydrogels include solvent casting/particle leaching, freeze-drying, gas foaming, and electrospinning; combinations of these methods have been used to fabricate porous hydrogels for many tissue engineering applications. In addition, more advanced control of specific pore features and microarchitecture has been achieved through various micropatterning and micromolding techniques.[97–101]

3.1. Solvent casting/particle leaching

Solvent casting/particle leaching begins with the dispersion of a porogen with controlled particle size into a polymer solution. The polymer is then cast and solidified, producing a polymer–porogen network. The solute particles are subsequently leached, or dissolved away by immersing the material in a selective solvent, resulting in the formation of a porous network. A wide variety of porogens have been employed for this technique depending on the hydrogel and application. Historically, salt particles are most commonly used because they are inexpensive, widely available, easy to handle, and stable under an assortment of processing conditions.[102] Alternative porogen materials, including sugars, paraffin, and gelatin, have also been employed with hydrogels.[103–105] The nature of the porogen has been demonstrated to play an important role in the interconnectivity of pores and the degradation rates achieved.[106] Porogen geometry has also been shown to influence the structure of the porous network formed using particle leaching. It has been demonstrated that spherical particles result in more interconnected pores than cubic particles at the same final porosity.[107]

Park *et al.* used salt leaching to produce PEG–poly(e-caprolactone) (PCL) -based hydrogels using NaCl as a porogen (pore size distribution: 180–400 mm) and dimethyl sulfoxide as a solvent *in vitro* and *in vivo* test of PEG–PCL-based hydrogel scaffold for cell delivery application.[108] After leaching with distilled water, a highly porous and interconnected matrix with enhanced swelling properties was formed and demonstrated degradation rates dependent upon pore size. Similar processing techniques using NaCl have recently been applied to (PEG)-fumarate, alginate-g-poly(N-isopropylacrylamide) (PNIPAAm), pHEMA, and other hydrogel systems.[109–111]

A major advantage of the solvent casting method is that pore size and overall porosity can be tuned by changing the particle size and concentration within the pre-polymer, respectively. Additionally, this technique can be performed feasibly on a small scale, making it widely available and well suited for use during the development stages of a new hydrogel system. However, using the solvent casting method there is little control over the orientation and the degree of interconnectivity of pores. Owing to limitations associated with removing solid particles from the hydrogel, this technique is usually restricted to the fabrication of commonly thin hydrogel sheets (typically less than 500 mm that must later be assembled into a larger construct. It should be noted that many particle leaching methods rely on the use of cytotoxic organic solvents that require lengthy drying times to assure complete removal and are not compatible with cell viability.[102]

3.2. Freeze-drying

Freeze-drying, also known as lyophilization, has been used extensively for the fabrication of porous hydrogels for tissue engineering. This method uses rapid cooling to produce thermodynamic instability within a system and causes phase separation, locking the structure in place. The solvent is then removed by sublimation under vacuum leaving behind voids in the regions it previously occupied. This technique has been applied by Wu *et al.* to produce porous collagen–chitosan hydrogels.[112] After preparation of a 9:1 collagen:chitosan blend, glutaraldehyde solution was added to crosslink the mixture before freeze-drying. The freezing temperature before lyophilization was shown to have an impact on the degradation characteristics of the resulting hydrogel. In particular, samples that were frozen at −20°C and −80°C resulted in open pore structures and faster degradation after lyophilization, whereas parallel sheet structure and slower degradation was obtained at −196°C. Moreover, the swelling ratio diminished from 4,400% to 2,000% as the temperature decreased from −20°C to −196°C due to the reduction of contact surface area.

Freeze-drying techniques are suitable for a wide range of hydrogel materials, including natural and synthetic hydrophilic polymers to produce interconnected porous structures. However, these methods encounter difficulty in precisely tuning pore size since the hydrogel architecture formed using this method is extremely sensitive to the kinetics of the thermal quenching process. Other issues associated with this technique are the low structural stability and generally weak mechanical properties of the fabricated materials. The freeze-drying process often results in the formation of a surface skin because the matrix may collapse at the scaffold–air interface due to the interfacial tension caused by solvent evaporation.[113] This surface skin may interfere with degradation mechanisms that the materials may normally undergo.

To address these issues, an alternative freeze gelation process has been utilized to produce porous hydrogels for chitosan and alginate. In a study by Ho *et al.* a frozen chitosan solution (−20°C) was immersed in a precooled NaOH–ethanol solution to adjust its pH to allow for gelation of chitosan below its freezing point.[113] Since the polymer was already gelled in the frozen state, the solvent could be removed with drying at room temperature without the formation of a surface skin. A highly interconnected porous hydrogel with the pores that ranged from 60 to 150 micrometers and porosity of 90% was produced using this technique. The degradation kinetics of the material did not appear to be significantly altered by the process. *In vitro* studies indicated that seeded rat osteoblast-like cells were able to attach, spread, and proliferate both inside and on the surface of the resulting hydrogel. Compared with conventional freeze-drying, this method has improved energy efficiency, and is amenable to scale up.

3.3. Gas foaming

Gas foaming utilizes the nucleation and growth of gas bubbles dispersed throughout a polymer to generate a porous structure. The gas bubbles can either be formed by a foaming-blowing agent via chemical reaction or be released from a pre-saturated gas–polymer mixture at a high pressure. The most commonly used foaming agent for fabricating porous hydrogels is sodium bicarbonate owing to its ability to generate CO_2 in mildly acidic solutions.[102] As an example, Huh *et al.* used sodium bicarbonate to fabricate an acrylic acid–acryl amide porous hydrogel by crosslinking acrylic acid and acryl amide with N,N'-methylenebisacrylamide.[114] The resultant hydrogel showed an interconnected structure with pore size ranging from 100 to 250 mm and 100% equilibrium swelling ratio.

Keskar *et al.* used sodium bicarbonate as a blowing agent to create hydrogels from photo-crosslinkable PEG diacrylate covalently linked to the peptide sequence arginine-glycine-aspartic acid (RGD) to promote cell adhesion on this otherwise cell-repellant hydrogel material.[115] The degradation rates of the materials obtained varied considerably, as this process proved to be difficult to control. However, the scaffold was found to support the adhesion and long term viability of human mesenchymal stem cells (MSCs) and facilitated mineralization when exposed to osteogenic medium. Interestingly, human MSCs were also capable of binding to porous PEG-based gels even in the absence of the RGD adhesion sequence, suggesting that structure of the scaffold was sufficient for cell attachment. Ammonium bicarbonate is another gas blowing agent that has been used to produce interconnected pores inside hydrogels via its decomposition to CO_2 and NH_3. As an example, ammonium bicarbonate was added during the irradiation of carboxymethylcellulose–sodium and poly-acrylamide to induce porosity and was shown to enhance the swelling ratio in comparison with hydrogels prepared in the absence of a blowing agent.[116]

Owing to the wide availability of the most common blowing agents, this method provides an inexpensive platform to introduce porosity into hydrogel materials. The blowing agents used are generally cell friendly, and this technique can be employed without the use of organic solvent, making it well suited for tissue engineering applications. However, it can be difficult to control the resulting pore sizes obtained utilizing these procedures, which can significantly impact the degradation rate of the hydrogel materials.

3.4. Electrospinning

The basic premise of electrospinning is the use of an externally applied electric field to draw fibers from a charged polymer solution held by surface tension at the end of a capillary tube. The polymer is charged by applying a high voltage and is then drawn as a thin jet toward an oppositely charged collector plate by electrostatic force. The resulting material properties such as fiber diameter, porosity, degradation, and morphology can be controlled by various parameters such as applied voltage, viscosity, solution conductivity, and temperature.[117]

Electrospinning has been used by Li *et al.* to fabricate porous hydrogels of Polyvinyl alcohol (PVA) and polyacrylic acid (PAA).[118] Using this method, a PVA and PAA solution mixture at different ratios was placed in a glass capillary with the 0.4 mm inner diameter tip, which was tilted downward at an angle between 0 and 30 degrees depending on the solution viscosity. An ultra-fine, submicron fibrous hydrogel was formed through the electrospinning process. The majority of the interfiber pores were found inter-connected, which is desirable for tissue engineering applications to allow cell–cell interaction and migration. The swelling and degradation behavior of the fibrous hydrogel membrane was found to be dependent on the strength of the applied electric field.

4. Enzymatic Activity

Natural polymers, such as silk, HA, and fibrinogen degrade from the action of proteases. Silk film and fiber degradation has been attributed to several proteases, including *a*-chymotrypsin and collagenases,[119,120] and a trypsin inhibitor isolated from the water extract from silkworm cocoon–cocoon shell associated trypsin inhibitor (CSTI).[121] Exposure to these enzymes has been found to result in expedited silk film degradation over silk fibers based on weight loss.[122] Vepari and Kaplan. has discovered that silk weight loss after exposure to enzymes is accompanied by a change in average molecular weight of silk from 120 kDa for control silk films to 53 kDa for silk films degraded with *a*-chymotrypsin after 17 days.[122] Additionally, an increase in the crystallinity of the silk was observed with degradation and tensile properties of silk fibers decreased without change in molecular weight of the silk fibers.

Silk combined with elastin like protein polymers, at varying ratios and lengths, are known as silk-elastin like protein polymers (SELPs), form hydrogels and have been studied as control vehicles for pDNA delivery.[86] Hwang *et al.* evaluated the influence of polymer structure, ionic strength of the media and gelation time on DNA release from two structurally related hydrogels, SELP-47K and SELP-415K. Results indicated that release is a function of polymer structure, concentration and cure time, as SELP-415K, which has twice the number of elastin units as that of SELP-47K, demonstrated higher release than that of SELP-47K. DNA release was found to be an inverse function of polymer concentration and cure time, with higher release at lower polymer concentration and shorter cure time. Hwang *et al.* also established that ionic strength of the culture media governed rate of release.

HA is enzymatically degraded by hyaluronidase and is known to be resorbable through numerous metabolic pathways.[123] HA is hydrophilic, non-adhesive and quickly degraded *in vivo*; however, crosslinking individual HA polymer chains together decreases their degradation rates.[124] HA is readily modified, and Baier *et al.* measured *in vitro* enzymatic degradation of gylcidyl methacrylate-HA (GMHA) as a function of time by incubating the gels in hyaluronidase and monitoring the mass of the hydrogel. Increasing methacrylation on GMHA resulted in a decreased degradation rate, indicating correlation between methacrylation and the degree of crosslinking. Tan *et al.* observed the weight loss and enzymatic resistance of two AHA–g–PNIPAAm copolymer hydrogels as a function of incubation time in PBS at 37°C over 28 days.[125] They found that the grafting ratio of PNIPAAm has a significant influence on the weight loss behavior of copolymer hydrogels. The addition of hyaluronidase resulted in a more rapid weight loss of AHA–g–PNIPAAm copolymer, with both copolymer hydrogels exceeding 40% weight loss when incubated in 100 U/mL hyaluronidase/PBS at 37°C throughout 28 days.

Fibrinogen is a soluble glycoprotein converted into fibrin by thrombin in the coagulation cascade, and because of the biocompatibility of fibrinogen, it is commonly used in tissue engineering. Furthermore, fibrinogen is a natural substrate for tissue remodeling and contains several relevant cell-signaling domains including a protease degradation substrate and cell-adhesion motifs.[126,127] Almany *et al.* PEGylated denatured fibrinogen fragments with PEG-diacrylates, mixed with photoinitiator and exposed to UV light to form a hydrogel material in a cell suspension.[81] Such a hydrogel material maintains highly malleable mechanical properties in addition to upholding biological functionality through the backbone of the polymeric network. A fibrinogen backbone provides the PEG–fibrinogen hydrogels' inherent degradability by way of cell-activated protease activity and cell-specific adhesion that are not available with PEG alone.[128]

5. Environmental Signals

A review in 2002 noted hydrogels as being "one of the upcoming classes of polymer-based controlled-release drug delivery systems."[129] Over the past 11 years, the focus of the field has advanced from studying hydrogel swelling responses to establishing degradation properties of hydrogels as applications in stimuli–responsive drug release in the area of tissue engineering. This section will explore degradation properties of hydrogels in pH, temperature, UV, photo-crosslinking, radioactive, and electro-responsive applications.

Gupta *et al.* clarifies the discrepancies between the terms "gels" and "hydrogels" by explaining, that the two terms both refer to polymeric networks and may be similar in chemical regards, but are different physically. The review describes gel as: "technically being semi-solid systems comprising small amount of solid, dispersed in relatively larger amounts of liquid, yet possessing more solid-like than liquid-like character,"[129] while denoting a hydrogel as having a defining characteristic of "crosslinked network of hydrophilic polymers" and "the ability to absorb large amounts of water and swell while maintaining their 3D structure."[129] Figure 8 depicts a graphic of the physical varieties between gels and hydrogels.

Several environmental and biological stimuli have been proven to elicit swelling responses within hydrogels, including pH,[7,16–22] temperature,[21–43] ionic strength,[43–45] light radiation,[14,44,58,90,130–138] time,[139–145] ultrasonic radiation,[51–53] magnetic field,[48–50] electric field,[45–47] antibody,[54,55] and inflammation.[56,57]

5.1. pH

One particularly common method to approach hydrogel crosslinking (and/or de-crosslinking) is triggering responses from ionizable functional groups by change in pH. Generating charge along the polymer backbone, causes an electric repulsion and an increase in hydrodynamic volume of the polymer.[21] Through pH change, biodegradation may occur while ionic species in extracellular fluid bind competitively with the gel components, expediting crosslink break down. Additionally, pH changes may ionize or protonate the functional groups that cause gelation and, often times, enable delivery of the gel precursors in a single syringe, encouraging application to tissue engineering and regenerative medicine.[20] Examples of pH-induced polymers include: PAA, polymethacrylic acid (PMAA), poly(ethylene imine), poly(L-lysine), and poly(N,N-dimethyl aminoethyl methacrylamide).

Researchers have taken advantage of pH-sensitive techniques to elicit responses of various hydrogels while studying effects of chain length and, consequently, hydrophobicity and found that the rate of hydrolysis is dependent on length and content of the hydrolyzable monomers within the network structure.[17,22] Matrix degradation directly affects drug release from a hydrogel; furthermore, composition of the copolymers, crosslinking density, and network structure are all functions of how the hydrogel is synthesized.[7,16] For example, *in vivo* studies have proven accelerated ester bond cleavage.[18,19]

A specific example exists within hydrogels which contain acidic co-monomers that ionizes at a high pH and an azo aromatic crosslink which is degradable by enzymes produced by microbial flora of the colon.[7] Applying such a pH-induced

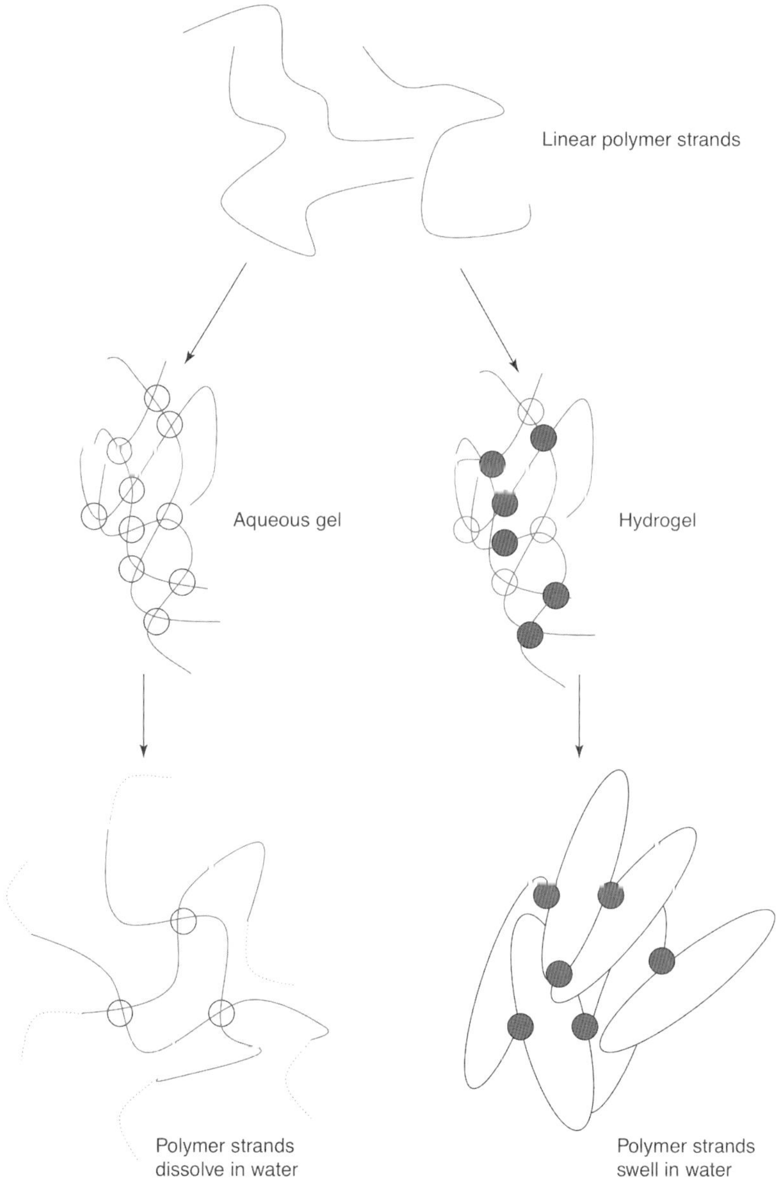

Fig. 8. Polymer strands forming a gel and a hydrogel, showing different behavior in an aqueous environment. Solid circles represent covalent crosslinks and hollow circles represent virtual crosslinks formed by entanglements.[129]

hydrogel for drug delivery to the stomach, a slow equilibrium degree of swelling would occur, preserving the drug against the low-pH environment. As the hydrogel passes through the GI tract and pH increases, hydrogel swelling increases. Upon reaching the colon, the hydrogel has swelled enough to reveal the crosslinks to azoreductase activity produced by colonic bacteria and hydrogel matrix begins to degrade, releasing the drug.[7]

5.2. Temperature

Thermosensitive hydrogels have served as drug and gene delivery vehicles, surface coatings, and as biological separations.[25–33] Drug release from hydrogels is affected by many different parameters, including chain length, concentration of a drug, degradability of hydrogel, hydrophobicity, pore size, and presence of interactions between the hydrogel and the incorporated drug. Typically, the release mechanism from a biodegradable hydrogel is initially diffusion-controlled, then a combination of diffusion and degradation.[23]

A well-studied thermosensitive hydrogel is pNIPAAm and its copolymers.[21,34,35] pNIPAAm is soluble below 32°C and precipitates above 32°C in water [36] and through controlling polymer composition, the transition of pNIPAAm can be controlled. The lower critical solution temperature (LCST) describes such phase transition temperature and above the LCST, hydrogen bonds break and water is expelled from the polymer, causing precipitation. However, pNIPAAm is not biodegradable; to compensate, it is often combined with other materials possessing such capabilities, such as dextran, a complex polysaccharide composed of many glucose molecules.

Huang *et al.* prepared a series of thermosensitive hydrogels with completely biodegradable properties for aqueous encapsulation and controlled release of hydrophilic drug.[37] The hydrogels were prepared through free radical polymerization of N-isopropylacrylamide (NIPAAm) monomer and a dextran macromer containing multiple hydrolytically degradable oligolactate-2-hydroxyethyl methacrylate units (Dex-lactateHEMA). Results of swelling measurement demonstrated four hydrogels with weight ratios of NIPAAm:Dex-lactateHEMA 7:2, 6:3, 5:4, and 4:5 (w/w) were thermoresponsive with a LCST of 32°C. Swelling and degradation rates of the hydrogels strongly depended on temperature and hydrogel composition. Methylene blue and bovine serum albumin (BSA), were loaded into the hydrogels during the synthesis process to model hydrophilic drug release. Molecular size of the drugs, hydrophilicity and degradation of the hydrogels, and temperature were all found to play important roles in controlling drug release. In other studies, pNIPAAm-based polymers were chemically incorporated with enzymatically biodegradable poly (amino acid) or dextran. However, the enzymes needed to decompose these polymers are localized in limited biological systems, therefore, application of such devices may be limited.

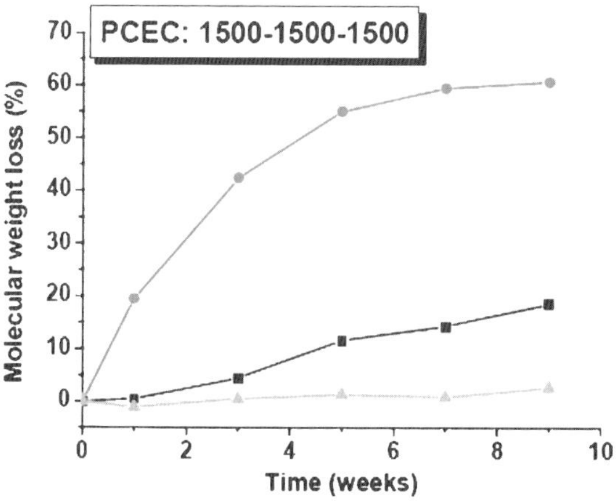

Fig. 9. *In vitro* degradation behavior of PCEC copolymer (S1). J: PCEC copolymer incubated in PBS solution (pH 7.4) at 37°C; D: PCEC copolymer incubated in HCl/H_2O solution (pH 1.2) at 37°C; N: PCEC copolymer incubated in PBS solution (pH 7.4) at 4°C.[146]

Others have explored thermosensitive tri-block copolymers as drug delivery systems.[23,39,146] Specifically, Gong *et al.* established a biodegradable and injectable drug delivery system based on thermosensitive poly(e-caprolactone)–poly(ethylene glycol)–poly(caprolactone) (PCEC) hydrogel. PCEC hydrogel undergoes a temperature-dependent solution–gel–solution transition, which flows at ambient temperature and becomes non-flowing hydrogel at 37°C. *In vitro* release behaviors of a hydrophilic small-molecule drug, a hydrophobic small molecule drug and a macromolecular protein drug, from PCEC hydrogel were shown to be released from the PCEC hydrogel system over a sustained period (see Fig. 9).

Jeong *et al.* studied drug release from poly(ethylene glycol)–poly(lactic-co-glycolic acid)–poly(ethylene glycol) (PEG–PLGA–PEG) triblock copolymers as a biodegradable, thermosensitive injectable drug delivery vehicle.[23] At the appropriate composition, PEG–PLGA–PEG is a free flowing solution at room temperature and becomes a hydrogel at 37°C. Ketoprofen (hydrophilic drug) and spironolatone (hydrophobic drug), were released from the PEG–PLGA–PEG triblock copolymer hydrogel by injecting the solutions into a 37°C aqueous environment. Ketoprofen was found to be released over 2 weeks with a first-order release profile, while spironolactone was released over 2 months with an S-shaped release profile.

Frequently, hydrogels that are both temperature and pH-sensitive have been studied.[40–42] Kim *et al.* reports a novel pH and thermo-sensitive hydrogel as a scaffold for autologous bone tissue engineering.[41] The polymer was synthesized by adding pH-sensitive sulfamethazine oligomers (SMOs) to both ends of a thermo-sensitive poly(e-caprolactone-co-lactide)–poly(ethylene glycol)–poly (e-caprolactone-co-lactide) (PCLA–PEG–PCLA) tri-block copolymer, yielding a pH/thermo-sensitive SMO–PCLA–PEG–PCLA–SMO block copolymer. The synthesized block copolymer solution rapidly formed a stable gel under physiological conditions (pH 7.4, 37°C), whereas it formed a solution at pH 8.0 and 37°C, implying injectability. Conjugation of the SMO groups impeded the *in vivo* degradation rate and reduced resulting inflammation from acidic by-products, due to buffering effects afforded by the sulfonamide moieties. As time following subcutaneous implantation in nude mice increased to 2, 5, or 7 weeks, the sizes of gross gels decreased, indicating that the hydrogels were degraded and had been absorbed *in vivo*. Throughout the experimental period of 7 weeks, the hydrogels maintained gel-like shapes, but the size shrunk due to hydrogel degradation from hydrolysis of the polyester blocks. The same gel was studied by Shim *et al.* who found that the degradation rate of SMO–PCLA–PEG–PCLA–SMO decreased substantially compared with the control block copolymer of PCLA–PEG–PCLA, due to the buffering effect of the sulfonamide group.[147] At physiological conditions, pH of the PCLA–PEG–PCLA block copolymer solution decreased dramatically from 7.4 to 2.2 upon hydrolytic degradation. However, within the SMO–PCLA–PEG–PCLA–SMO block copolymer solution, no pH change was observed during the first week. After the first week, pH of the solution decreased slowly, and, eventually, after 1 month, stabilized at 5.5 due to buffering effects of the SMO sulfonamide moieties on the acidic monomers produced by the PCLA units during degradation. The authors concluded that the enhanced stability of SMO–PCLA–PEG–PCLA–SMO may be utilized for sustained drug delivery systems or long-term cell therapy.

By varying temperature, ionic strength, and the composition of the hydrogel matrix, Feigen *et al.* found that they are able to control degradation kinetics, the degree of uptake of a particular pharmacologically active agent, and the overall timed release profile.[43] In a US patent, Feijen *et al.* explains a discovered biodegradable hydrogel which has significantly enhanced biocompatibility in that blood compatibility is substantially improved, immunogenicity is minimized, and the hydrogel is enzymatically degraded to endogenous, non-toxic compounds.

In a study conducted by Chung *et al.* a novel temperature-sensitive and *in situ* forming hydrogel system based on Pluronic F127 was developed and evaluated.[24] A series of multi-block Pluronic copolymers linked by D-lactide and L-lactide oligomers with different spacer lengths were synthesized and a pair of multi-block copolymers with corresponding enantiomeric D- or L-lactide oligomer spacer was blended to form stereo-complexed hydrogels. The resultant physically crosslinked Pluronic hydrogels exhibited significantly altered solution to hydrogel phase transition behaviors with lower critical gelation concentrations and temperatures compared to the uncomplexed multi block or Pluronic homopolymer hydrogels. The stereocomplexed hydrogels had increased mechanical strength with high resistance to rapid dissolution in aqueous medium. When hGH was incorporated in the strereo-complexed multi-block Pluronic copolymers, hGH was released in sustained and zero-order fashion for 13 days by diffusion/erosion coupling.

5.3. Photo-crosslinked and UV-induced

Photo-crosslinked hydrogels have been gaining increased attention throughout the past few years in biomedical applications because aqueous macromer solutions containing cells and/or bioactive factors are able to be delivered in a minimally invasive manner, then rapidly crosslinked in physiological conditions *in situ* following brief exposure to ultraviolet (UV) light.[90,129,133,137] The photo-crosslinking process is initiated by chemicals called photoinitiators which generate free radicals following exposure to UV or visible light. The free radicals convert aqueous macromer solutions into hydrogels.[137] Short exposure to low-intensity light and the appropriate choice of a photoinitiator allow photopolymerization to occur with limited deleterious effects to cells and bioactive molecules.[132,135] Mechanical properties and swelling behavior of photo-crosslinked hydrogels may be readily controlled by varying the photo-curable moiety.[136,138] The photoinitiated reaction allows rapid polymerization rates in cytocompatible conditions, evidenced by high cell viability of encapsulated cells after culture *in vitro*.[90]

Jeon *et al.* engineered alginate hydrogels with hydrolytically-degradable ester linkages incorporated during photopolymerization.[90] Changing the polymer crosslinking density by varying the degree of alginate methacrylation was quantified through examination of hydrogel swelling behavior, elastic moduli, and degradation profiles. The viability of cells cultured with synthesized macromer and also both in the presence of and inside of photo-crosslinked hydrogels was examined *in vitro*. Alginates have reversible gelling properties in aqueous solutions relevant to the ionic interactions between divalent cations.[44] Ionic crosslinked alginate does not damage cells during the gelling process and is biocompatible; therefore, interest in the use of alginate hydrogels for drug delivery, cell encapsulation, and tissue regeneration has grown.

In their study, Jeon *et al.* developed a photo-crosslinked and biodegradable hydrogel using methacrylated alginate as the first report of photo-crosslinked and biodegradable alginate hydrogels with controllable swelling ratios, elastic moduli, and degradation rates.[14] They found that physical properties of the hydrogel could be tuned by varying the extent of alginate methacrylation, and the alginate hydrogels exhibited low cytotoxicity and excellent cytocompatibility.

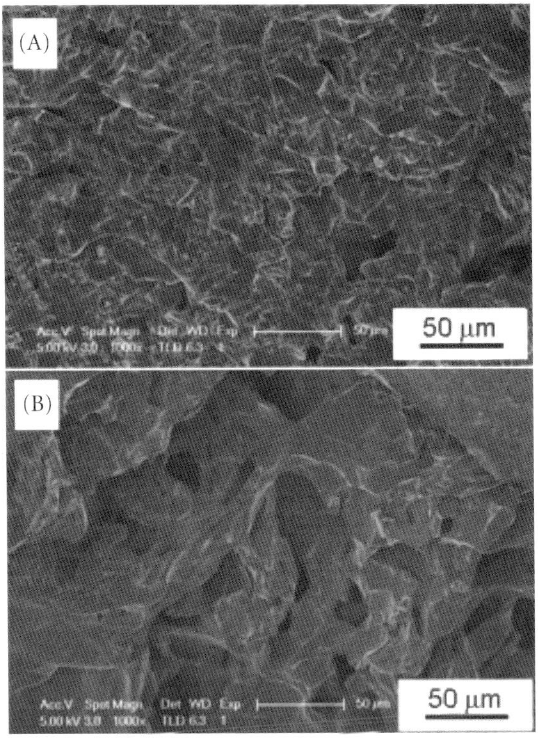

Fig. 10. SEM micrographs of degraded Gel-3 after incubatin in PBS at pH 7.4 and 37°C for 106 days: (A) the surface region; (B) the cross-section.[131]

Du *et al.* report novel biodegradable hydrogels by photo-crosslinking macromers based on polyphosphoesters and PEG which were synthesized by ring-opening polymerization of the cyclic phosphoester monomer 2-(2-oxo-1,3,2-dioxaphospholoyloxy) ethyl methacrylate (OPEMA) with PEG as the initiator and stannous octoate as the catalyst.[131] Content of polyphosphoester in the macromer was controlled by varying the feed ratio of OPEMA:PEG and hydrogels were fabricated by exposing aqueous solutions of macromers with 0.05% (w/w) photoinitiator to UV light irradiation. Du *et al.* demonstrated that crosslinking density and pH values strongly affect degradation rates and the macromers were compatible with osteoblasts culture (see Fig. 10).

While Du *et al.* used photo-crosslinkable hydrogels as a scaffold for cell culture, Lee *et al.* applied the technology of photo-crosslinking for sustained release profile of protein within a thermosensitive, biodegradable hydrogel.[134] The hydrogels were based on Pluronic tri-block copolymers with two terminal hydroxyl groups in Pluronic F-127 acrylated to form a Pluronic macromer. Once photo crosslinked by

UV radiation, Pluronic hydrogels exhibited decreased swelling ratio with increasing temperature and change in the swelling ratio when temperature was cycled between 10°C and 37°C. The hydrogels degraded slowly due to the cleavage of ester linkage in the acrylated Pluronic terminal end. When lysozyme was loaded in the hydrogels, bi-phasic protein release profiles were attained with an intial burst-free and rapid controlled release profile for one week followed by slower, sustained release thereafter. The release rates are controlled by varying the amount of Pluronic macromer for photopolymerization.

Bryant *et al.* demonstrated that slight variations in hydrogel chemistry control hydrogel degradation, evolving macroscopic properties, and ultimately the secretion and distribution of ECM molecule through studying biodegradable poly(ethylene glycol)-co-poly(lactic acid) (PEG–PLA) hydrogels that were fabricated via photopolymerization.[58] Chondrocytes were photo-encapsulated in the gels, and changes in the PEG–PLA repeat unit increased total collagen synthesis after 6 weeks *in vitro*. By tuning scaffold chemistry, and subsequently, gel structure and degradation behavior, Bryant's group established methods on how to better guide tissue evolution and development. The study demonstrated that degradation behavior of PEG–PLA hydrogels depends on the presence of cells and culture environment.

5.4. Electro-responsive

An overlying theme in tissue engineering and regenerative medicine is precise control over drug release from implantable devices, focusing specifically on optimal drug concentration and timing from biodegradable scaffolds.[148] Electrically controlled drug release from polyelectrolyte hydrogels has been demonstrated *in vitro* and *in vivo*.[149–151] Responsive drug release from hydrogels is caused by electro-induced changes in the gels, which de-swell, swell or erode in response to an electric field; therefore, by alternating application and removal of an electric field, pulsatile drug release profiles may been attained.[152–154] Electrically-responsive drug release is influenced by a number of factors such as the nature of the drug and of the gel, experimental set-up, and magnitude of the electric field.[148]

Leavitt *et al.* utilized locally deposited polymer depots as a vehicle for immobilization and local delivery of radionuclides *in vivo*.[155] According to their US Patent, radionuclides are incorporated into the developed hydrogel in their elemental forms, as inorganic compounds, or are attached to a larger molecule or incorporated into the polymer, by physical or chemical methods. The authors employed ancillary structure to control the rate of release. Common standard radionuclides may be used, including radionuclides of iodine, iridium, radium, cesium, yttrium, or other elements. The method patented by Leavitt *et al.* provides three approaches to controlling total drug dosage delivered to a site, simultaneously controlling exposure to other areas of the body. First, the total amount of isotope can be varied; second, the half-life of the isotope can be selected, providing an upper limit of the applied dose; third, the lifetime of the radioisotope in the local delivery depot can be controlled.

In a drug delivery review, Kikuchi describes electrically-stimulated swelling and de-swelling characteristics of polyelectrolyte hydrogels as presented by Kishi *et al.* [47] Kishi *et al.* developed an electric stimuli-induced drug release system using a chemo-mechanical system which allowed the hydrogel to exhibit reversible swelling and shrinking behavior in response to on–off switching of electric stimulus. Through their system, drug molecules within the polyelectrolyte gels may be forced from the electric stimuli-induced gel contraction along with solvent flow. D'Emanuele and Staniforth[45] investigated feedback-controlled drug delivery based on the electrophoresis of an ionic drug. In this system, drug release was regulated in either a positive or a negative manner by appropriate control of the electric field between a pair of platinum electrodes placed on either side of rate controlling polymer hydrogel membrane.

6. Biologic Responses

Inflammatory and immune responses of the body are imperative as well as interactions with the injected or implanted device. Yui *et al.* observed inflammatory-induced hydroxyl radicals and designed drug delivery systems which responded to the hydroxyl radicals and degraded in a limited manner.[56,57] The authors used hyaluronic acid (HA), which, in a healthy patient, degrades via hyaluronidase at a low amount. However, when HA is injected at inflammatory sites, HA degradation via hydroxyl radicals is dominant and rapid.[156] Yui *et al.* prepared crosslinked HA with ethyleneglycol diglycidylether or polyglycerol polyglycidylether. The altered HA gels degraded only when the hydroxyl radicals were generated through the Fenton reaction between Fe^{+2} ions and hydrogen peroxide (H_2O_2) *in vitro.*

Wang *et al.* studied regeneration of 3D silk fibroin scaffolds via an organic solvent, hexafluoroisopropanol (HFIP),[157] compared to an all-aqueous preparation process. The group found that aqueous-derived scaffolds were less resistant to macrophage degradation than the HFIP-derived scaffolds and that the immune system played a significant role in the degradation rate of the aqueous-derived scaffolds but did not show similar impact on HFIP-derived scaffolds. HFIP-derived scaffolds as prepared from higher concentration silk fibroin solutions permitted

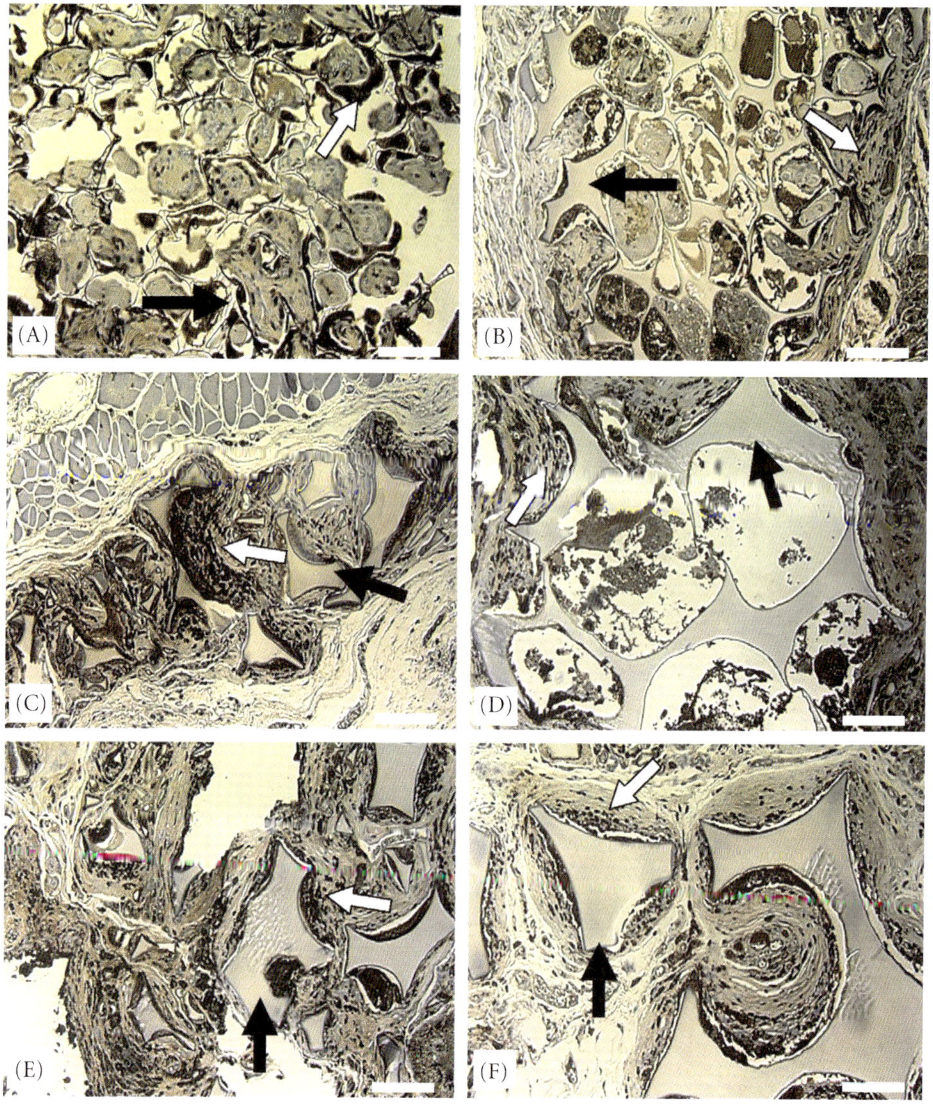

Fig. 11. Macrophage response to subcutaneously implanted HFIP-derived silk fibroin scaffolds in Lewis rats at the end of 12 months. Images (A), (C), and (E) are for scaffolds prepared from 6% silk fibroin solution. Images (B), (D), and (F) are for scaffolds prepared from 17% silk fibroin solution. Pore size in images (A) and (B) is 100–200 mm, in (C) and (D) is 500–600 mm, and in (E) and (F) is 850–1000 mm. Bars 1⁄4 100 mm. Solid arrows 1⁄4 remaining scaffolds. Blank arrows 1⁄4 ED1 positive cells.[157]

less access to macrophage invasion, exhibiting more resistance to macrophage-mediated degradation (see Fig. 11). Novel gels were developed by Miyata *et al.* which responded to change in concentration of bioactive compounds to alter swelling and de-swelling characteristics.[54,55,158] Introduction of stimuli-responsive crosslinked structures into hydrogels were studied with focus on antigen–antibody complex formation as the crosslinking units in the gel with the rationale that specific antigen recognition of an antibody may provide the basis for a new device fabrication.

7. Conclusion

A vast body of literature addresses factors influencing the control of hydrogel degradation. In a broad sense, hydrolysis controls hydrogel degradation. Ultimately, hydrogel degradation is a function of the physiological environment in which the material will be placed and the properties of the hydrogel, relying upon enzymatic destruction of the polymer of interest and, therefore, the, chemistry crosslinking the polymer together. Properties of the studied polymer, crosslinking agents, as well as synthesis procedures determine the behavior of a hydrogel in any specific environment. Distinction of hydrogel degradation results from variation in monomer size and sequence, polymer chain length, hydrophobicity/hydrophilicity, oxidation states, moieties, stereochemistry, crosslinking agents, and several others as highlighted throughout this review chapter. Environmental characteristics, such as temperature, pH, ionic strength, light radiation, ultrasonic radiation, magnetic field, electric field, antibody, urea, inflammation, and drug, have profound effects on the structure, crosslinking, and, therefore, degradation control of hydrogels. Researchers exploit sensitivity towards such environmental factors and have so been able to construct "intelligent" hydrogels that display tailored characteristics depending on the surrounding environment. One challenge present in controlling hydrogel degradation exists in that the material properties determining degradation rate within a clinically relevant setting may also determine other facets necessary for success of gelation and biocompatibility, including elasticity, compressibility, viscoelastic behavior, tensile strength and failure strain of the material in question. Hydrogels may be constructed from both synthetic and natural materials, and engineered to exhibit similar mechanical properties and behaviors to those of natural living tissues. Due to such abilities, hydrogels as well as methods of manipulation, will continue to hold promise, particularly in the fields of tissue engineering and regenerative medicine.

References

1. J. Zhu and R. E. Marchant, Design properties of hydrogel tissue-engineering scaffolds. *Expert. Rev. Med. Devic.*, **8**(5), 607–626 (2011).
2. A. Sannino, C. Demitri, and M. Madaghiele, Biodegradable cellulose-based hydrogels: Design and applications. *Mater.*, **2**(2), 353–373 (2009).

3. J. L. Drury and D. J. Mooney, Hydrogels for tissue engineering: Scaffold design variables and applications. *Biomaterials*, **24**(24), 4337–4351 (2003).
4. Y. Qiu and K. Park, Environment-sensitive hydrogels for drug delivery. *Adv. Drug Deliver. Rev.*, (2012).
5. N. A. Peppas, P. Bures, W. Leobandung, and H. Ichikawa, Hydrogels in pharmaceutical formulations. *Eur. J. Pharm. Biopharm.*, **50**(1), 27–46 (2000).
6. G. Pitarresi, F. S. Palumbo, G. Giammona, M. A. Casadei, and F. Micheletti Moracci, Biodegradable hydrogels obtained by photocross-linking of dextran and polyaspartamide derivatives. *Biomaterials*, **24**(23), 4301–4313 (2003).
7. G. D. Nicodemus and S. J. Bryant, Cell encapsulation in biodegradable hydrogels for tissue engineering applications. *Tissue Eng. Part B: Rev.*, **14**(2), 149–165 (2008).
8. M. A. Rice and K. S. Anseth, Controlling cartilaginous matrix evolution in hydrogels with degradation triggered by exogenous addition of an enzyme. *Tissue Eng.*, **13**(4), 683–691 (2007).
9. H. Tan and K. G. Marra, Injectable, biodegradable hydrogels for tissue engineering applications. *Mater.*, **3**(3), 1746–1767 (2010).
10. P. van de Wetering, A. T. Metters, R. G. Schoenmakers, and J. A. Hubbell, Poly(ethylene glycol) hydrogels formed by conjugate addition with controllable swelling, degradation, and release of pharmaceutically active proteins. *J. Control. Release*, **102**(3) 619–627 (2005).
11. X. Z. Shu, S. Ahmad, Y. Liu, and G. D. Prestwich, Synthesis and evaluation of injectable, *in situ* cross-linkable synthetic extracellular matrices for tissue engineering. *J. Biomed. Mater. Res. Part A*, **79**(4), 902–912 (2006).
12. T. Boontheekul, H. J. Kong, and D. J. Mooney, Controlling alginate gel degradation utilizing partial oxidation and bimodal molecular weight distribution. *Biomaterials*, **26**(15), 2455–2465 (2005).
13. K. H. Bouhadir, K. Y. Lee, E. Alsberg, K. L. Damm, K. W. Anderson, and D. J. Mooney, Degradation of partially oxidized alginate and its potential application for tissue engineering. *Biotechnol. Progr.*, **17**(5), 945–950 (2001).
14. O. Jeon, C. Powell, S. M. Ahmed, and E. Alsberg, Biodegradable, photocross-linked alginate hydrogels with independently tailorable physical properties and cell adhesivity. *Tissue Eng. Part A*, **16**(9), 2915–2925 (2010).
15. H. J. Kong, D. Kaigler, K. Kim, and D. J. Mooney, Controlling rigidity and degradation of alginate hydrogels via molecular weight distribution. *Biomacromolecules*, **5**(5), 1720–1727 (2004).
16. P. Markland, Y. Zhang, G. L. Amidon, and V. C. Yang, A pH-and ionic strength-responsive polypeptide hydrogel: Synthesis, characterization, and preliminary protein release studies. *J. Biomed. Mater. Res.*, **47**(4), 595–602 (1999).
17. E. O. Akala, P. Kopečková, and J. Kopeček, Novel pH-sensitive hydrogels with adjustable swelling kinetics. *Biomaterials*, **19**(11), 1037–1047 (1998).
18. E. Catıker, M. Gümüşderelioğlu, and A. Güner, Degradation of PLA, PLGA homo- and copolymers in the presence of serum albumin: A spectroscopic investigation. *Polym. Int.*, **49**(7), 728–734 (2000).

19. Y. Kurono, T. Maki, T. Yotsuyanagi, and K. Ikeda, Esterase-like activity of human serum albumin: Structure-activity relationships for the reactions with phenyl acetates and p-nitrophenyl esters. *Chem. Pharm. Bull.*, **27**(11), 2781–2786 (1979).
20. T. R. Hoare and D. S. Kohane, Hydrogels in drug delivery: Progress and challenges. *Polymer*, **49**(8), 1993–2007 (2008).
21. B. Jeong and A. Gutowska, Lessons from nature: Stimuli-responsive polymers and their biomedical applications. *Trends Biotechnol.*, **20**(7), 305–311 (2002).
22. C. Wachiralarpphaithoon, Y. Iwasaki, and K. Akiyoshi, Enzyme-degradable phosphorylcholine porous hydrogels cross-linked with polyphosphoesters for cell matrices. *Biomaterials*, **28**(6), 984–993 (2007).
23. B. Jeong, Y. H. Bae, and S. W. Kim, Drug release from biodegradable injectable thermosensitive hydrogel of PEG–PLGA–PEG triblock copolymers. *J. control. release*, **63**(1), 155–163 (2000).
24. H. J. Chung, Y. Lee, and T. G. Park, Thermo-sensitive and biodegradable hydrogels based on stereocomplexed Pluronic multi-block copolymers for controlled protein delivery. *J. control. release*, **127**(1), 22–30 (2008).
25. V. Bulmus, Z. Ding, C. J. Long, P. S. Stayton, and A. S. Hoffman, Site-specific polymer-streptavidin bioconjugate for pH-controlled binding and triggered release of biotin. *Bioconjugate chem.*, **11**(1), 78–83 (2000).
26. H. Lee and T. G. Park, Conjugation of trypsin by temperature-sensitive polymers containing a carbohydrate moiety: Thermal modulation of enzyme activity. *Biotechnol. Progr.*, **14**(3), 508–516 (1998).
27. H. K. Kim and T. G. Park, Synthesis and characterization of thermally reversible bioconjugates composed of α-chymotrypsin and poly(N-isopropylacrylamide-co-acrylamido-2-deoxy-D-glucose). *Enzyme Microb. Techn.*, **25**(1), 31–37 (1999).
28. T. Shimizu, M. Yamato, A. Kikuchi, and T. Okano, Two-dimensional manipulation of cardiac myocyte sheets utilizing temperature-responsive culture dishes augments the pulsatile amplitude. *Tissue Eng.*, **7**(2), 141–151 (2001).
29. B. Vernon, S. W. Kim, and Y. H. Bae, Insulin release from islets of Langerhans entrapped in a poly(N-isopropylacrylamide-co-acrylic acid) polymer gel. *J. Biomat. Sci- Polym. E.*, **10**(2), 183–198 (1999).
30. T. Oya, T. Enoki, A. Y. Grosberg, S. Masamune, T. Sakiyama, Y. Takeoka, K. Tanaka, G. Wang, Y. Yilmaz, and M.S. Feld, Reversible molecular adsorption based on multiple-point interaction by shrinkable gels. *Sci.*, **286**(5444), 1543–1545 (1999).
31. Y. H. Bae, T. Okano, and S.W. Kim, "On–off" thermocontrol of solute transport. I. temperature dependence of swelling of N-isopropylacrylamide networks modified with hydrophobic components in water. *Pharm. Res.*, **8**(4), 531–537 (1991).
32. Y. H. Bae, T. Okano, and S. W. Kirn, "On–off" thermocontrol of solute transport. ii. solute release from thermosensitive hydrogels. *Pharm. Res.*, **8**(5), 624–628 (1991).
33. T. Okano, Y. Bae, H. Jacobs, and S. Kim, Thermally on-off switching polymers for drug permeation and release. *J. Control. Release*, **11**(1), 255–265 (1990).

34. X. Huang and T. L. Lowe, Biodegradable thermoresponsive hydrogels for aqueous encapsulation and controlled release of hydrophilic model drugs. *Biomacromolecules*, **6**(4), 2131–2139 (2005).
35. X. Zhang, D. Wu, and C.-C. Chu, Synthesis and characterization of partially biodegradable, temperature and pH sensitive Dex–MA/PNIPAAm hydrogels. *Biomaterials*, **25**(19), 4719–4730 (2004).
36. H. Schild, Poly(N-isopropylacrylamide): Experiment, theory and application. *Prog. Polym. Sci.*, **17**(2), 163–249 (1992).
37. X. Huang, B. R. Nayak, and T. L. Lowe, Synthesis and characterization of novel thermoresponsive-co-biodegradable hydrogels composed of N-isopropylacrylamide, poly(L-lactic acid), and dextran. *J. Polym. Sci. Pol. Chem.*, **42**(20), 5054–5066 (2004).
38. C. Y. Gong, S. Shi, P. W. Dong, B. Yang, X. R. Qi, G. Guo, Y. C. Gu, X. Zhao, Y. Q. Wei, and Z. Y. Qian, Biodegradable *in situ* gel-forming controlled drug delivery system based on thermosensitive PCL–PEG–PCL hydrogel: Part 1 — synthesis, characterization, and acute toxicity evaluation. *J. Pharm. Sci.*, **98**(12), 4684–4694 (2009).
39. Z. Li, W. Ning, J. Wang, A. Choi, P. -Y. Lee, P. Tyagi, and L. Huang, Controlled gene delivery system based on thermosensitive biodegradable hydrogel. *Pharm. Res.*, **20**(6), 884–888 (2003).
40. S. R. van Tomme, G. Storm, and W. E. Hennink, *In situ* gelling hydrogels for pharmaceutical and biomedical applications. *Int. J. Pharm.*, **355**(1), 1–18 (2008).
41. H. K. Kim, W. S. Shim, S. E. Kim, K.-H. Lee, E. Kang, J.-H. Kim, K. Kim, I. C. Kwon, and D. S. Lee, Injectable *in situ* — forming pH/thermo-sensitive hydrogel for bone tissue engineering. *Tissue Eng. Part A*, **15**(4), 923–933 (2008).
42. C. Zhao, X. Zhuang, P. He, C. Xiao, C. He, J. Sun, X. Chen, and X. Jing, Synthesis of biodegradable thermo-and pH-responsive hydrogels for controlled drug release. *Polymer*, **50**(18), 4308–4316 (2009).
43. J. Feijen, Biodegradable hydrogel matrices for the controlled release of pharmacologically active agents, (1991).
44. T. Coviello, P. Matricardi, C. Marianecci, and F. Alhaique, Polysaccharide hydrogels for modified release formulations. *J. Control. Release*, **119**(1), 5–24 (2007).
45. A. D'Emanuele and J. N. Staniforth, Feedback controlled drug delivery using an electro-diffusion pump. *J. Control. Release*, **23**(2), 97–104 (1993).
46. M. A. LeRoux, F. Guilak, and L. A. Setton, Compressive and shear properties of alginate gel: Effects of sodium ions and alginate concentration. *J. Biomed. Mater. Res.*, **47**(1), 46–53 (1999).
47. Y. Osada, Conversion of chemical into mechanical energy by synthetic polymers(chemomechanical systems). In *Polymer Physics*. Springer, 1–46 (1987).
48. E. Edelman, J. Kost, H. Bobeck, and R. Langer, Regulation of drug release from polymer matrices by oscillating magnetic fields. *J. Biomed. Mater. Res.*, **19**(1), 67–83 (1985).
49. J. Kost, R. Noecker, E. Kunica, and R. Langer, Magnetically controlled release systems: Effect of polymer composition. *J. Biomed. Mater. Res.*, **19**(8), 935–940 (1985).

50. J. Kost, J. Wolfrum, and R. Langer, Magnetically enhanced insulin release in diabetic rats. *J. Biomed. Mater. Res.*, **21**(12), 1367–1373 (1987).
51. J. Kost, K. Leong, and R. Langer, Ultrasound-enhanced polymer degradation and release of incorporated substances. *Proc. Natl. Acad. Sci.*, **86**(20), 7663–7666 (1989).
52. C. S. Kwok, P. D. Mourad, L. A. Crum, and B. D. Ratner, Surface modification of polymers with self-assembled molecular structures: Multitechnique surface characterization. *Biomacromolecules*, **1**(1), 139–148 (2000).
53. C. S. Kwok, P. D. Mourad, L. A. Crum, and B. D. Ratner, Self-assembled molecular structures as ultrasonically — responsive barrier membranes for pulsatile drug delivery. *J. Biomed. Mater. Res.*, **57**(2), 151–164 (2001).
54. T. Miyata, N. Asami, and T. Uragami, A reversibly antigen-responsive hydrogel. *Nature*, **399**(6738), 766–769 (1999).
55. T. Miyata, N. Asami, and T. Uragami, Preparation of an antigen-sensitive hydrogel using antigen-antibody bindings. *Macromolecules*, **32**(6), 2082–2084 (1999).
56. Y. Nobuhiko, O. Teruo, and S. Yasuhisa, Inflammation responsive degradation of cross-linked hyaluronic acid gels. *J. Control. Release*, **22**(2), 105–116 (1992).
57. N. Yui, J. Nihira, T. Okano, and Y. Sakurai, Regulated release of drug microspheres from inflammation responsive degradable matrices of cross-linked hyaluronic acid. *J. Control. Release*, **25**(1–2), 133–143 (1993).
58. S. J. Bryant, K. L. Durand, and K. S. Anseth, Manipulations in hydrogel chemistry control photoencapsulated chondrocyte behavior and their extracellular matrix production. *J. Biomed. Mater. Res. A*, **67**(4), 1430–1436 (2003).
59. A. S. Sawhney, C. P. Pathak, and J. A. Hubbell, Bioerodible hydrogels based on photopolymerized poly(ethylene glycol)-co-poly(alpha-hydroxy acid) diacrylate macromers. *Macromolecules*, **26**(4), 581–587 (1993).
60. M. Martina and D. W. Hutmacher, Biodegradable polymers applied in tissue engineering research: A review. *Polym. Int.*, **56**(2), 145–157 (2007).
61. G. Chan and D. J. Mooney, New materials for tissue engineering: Towards greater control over the biological response. *Trends Biotechnol.*, **26**(7), 382–392 (2008).
62. M. K. Nguyen and D. S. Lee, Injectable biodegradable hydrogels. *Macromol. Biosci.*, **10**(6), 563–579 (2010).
63. J. Kim, K.-W. Lee, T. E. Hefferan, B. L. Currier, M. J. Yaszemski, and L. Lu, Synthesis and evaluation of novel biodegradable hydrogels based on poly(ethylene glycol) and sebacic acid as tissue engineering scaffolds. *Biomacromolecules*, **9**(1), 149–157 (2007).
64. Y. Wang, G. A. Ameer, B. J. Sheppard, and R. Langer, A tough biodegradable elastomer. *Nat. Biotechnol.*, **20**(6), 602–606 (2002).
65. A. Metters, K. Anseth, and C. Bowman, Fundamental studies of a novel, biodegradable PEG-b-PLA hydrogel. *Polymer* **41**(11), 3993–4004 (2000).
66. A. T. Metters, C. N. Bowman, and K. S. Anseth, A statistical kinetic model for the bulk degradation of PLA-b-PEG-b-PLA hydrogel networks. *J. Phys. Chem. B*, **104**(30), 7043–7049 (2000).

67. S. J. Bryant, R. J. Bender, K. L. Durand, and K. S. Anseth, Encapsulating chondrocytes in degrading PEG hydrogels with high modulus: Engineering gel structural changes to facilitate cartilaginous tissue production. *Biotechnol. Bioeng.*, **86**(7), 747–755 (2004).
68. T. Ichi, J. Watanabe, T. Ooya, and N. Yui, Controllable erosion time and profile in poly(ethylene glycol) hydrogels by supramolecular structure of hydrolyzable polyrotaxane. *Biomacromolecules*, **2**(1), 204–210, (2001).
69. H. Tan, C. R. Chu, K. A. Payne, and K. G. Marra, Injectable *in situ* forming biodegradable chitosan–hyaluronic acid-based hydrogels for cartilage tissue engineering. *Biomaterials*, **30**(13), 2499–2506 (2009).
70. M. Changez, V. Koul, B. Krishna, A. K. Dinda, and V. Choudhary, Studies on biodegradation and release of gentamicin sulphate from interpenetrating network hydrogels based on poly(acrylic acid) and gelatin: *In vitro* and *in vivo*. *Biomaterials*, **25**(1), 139–146 (2004).
71. K. C. Khemani and C. Scholz, *Degradable polymers and materials*. American Chemical Society (2006).
72. S. K. Teo, W. A. Colburn, W. G. Tracewell, K. A. Kook, D. I. Stirling, M. S. Jaworsky, M. A. Scheffler, S. D. Thomas, and O.L. Laskin, Clinical pharmacokinetics of thalidomide. *Clin. Pharmacokinet.*, **43**(5), 311–327 (2004).
73. S. de Jong, B. Van Eerdenbrugh, C. V. van Nostrum, J. Kettenes-van den Bosch, and W. Hennink, Physically cross-linked dextran hydrogels by stereocomplex formation of lactic acid oligomers: Degradation and protein release behavior. *J. Control Release*, **71**(3), 261–275 (2001).
74. D. W. Lim, S. H. Choi, and T. G. Park, A new class of biodegradable hydrogels stereocomplexed by enantiomeric oligo(lactide) side chains of poly(HEMA-g-OLA) s. *Macromol. Rapid Comm.*, **21**(8), 464–471 (2000).
75. C. F. van Nostrum, T. F. Veldhuis, G. W. Bos, and W. E. Hennink, Tuning the Degradation Rate of Poly(2-hydroxypropyl methacrylamide)-g raft-oligo(lactic acid) Stereocomplex Hydrogels. *Macromolecules*, **37**(6), 2113–2118 (2004).
76. C. Hiemstra, W. Zhou, Z. Zhong, M. Wouters, and J. Feijen, Rapidly *in situ* forming biodegradable robust hydrogels by combining stereocomplexation and photopolymerization. *J. Am. Chem. Soc.*, **129**(32), 9918–9926 (2007).
77. J. E. Oh, Y. S. Nam, K. H. Lee, and T. G. Park, Conjugation of drug to poly(D, L-lactic-co-glycolic acid) for controlled release from biodegradable microspheres. *J. Control. Release*, **57**(3), 269–280 (1999).
78. T. G. Park, Degradation of poly(D, L-lactic acid) microspheres: Effect of molecular weight. *J. Control. Release*, **30**(2), 161–173 (1994).
79. A. T. Metters, K. S. Anseth, and C. N. Bowman, Fundamental studies of a novel, biodegradable PEG-b-PLA hydrogel. *Polymer*, **41**(11), 3993–4004 (2000).
80. J. L. West and J. A. Hubbell, Separation of the arterial wall from blood contact using hydrogel barriers reduces intimal thickening after balloon injury in the rat: The roles of medial and luminal factors in arterial healing. *Proc. Natl. Acad. Sci.*, **93**(23), 13188–13193 (1996).
81. L. Almany and D. Seliktar, Biosynthetic hydrogel scaffolds made from fibrinogen and polyethylene glycol for 3D cell cultures. *Biomaterials*, **26**(15), 2467–2477 (2005).

82. H. J. Kong, E. Alsberg, D. Kaigler, K. Y. Lee, and D. J. Mooney, Controlling degradation of hydrogels via the size of cross-linked junctions. *Adv. Mater.*, **16**(21), 1917–1921 (2004).
83. A. S. Hoffman, Hydrogels for biomedical applications. *Adv. Drug Deliv. Rev.*, (2012).
84. H. J. Kong, E. S. Kim, Y.-C. Huang, and D. J. Mooney, Design of biodegradable hydrogel for the local and sustained delivery of angiogenic plasmid DNA. *Pharm. Res.*, **25**(5), 1230–1238 (2008).
85. S. R. van Tomme, C. F. van Nostrum, S. C. de Smedt, and W. E. Hennink, Degradation behavior of dextran hydrogels composed of positively and negatively charged microspheres. *Biomaterials*, **27**(22), 4141–4148 (2006).
86. D. Hwang, V. Moolchandani, R. Dandu, M. Haider, J. Cappello, and H. Ghandehari, Influence of polymer structure and biodegradation on DNA release from silk-elastin-like protein polymer hydrogels. *Int. J. Pharm.*, **368**(1), 215–219 (2009).
87. O. Smidsrød, Alginate as immobilization matrix for cells. *Trends Biotechnol.*, **8**, 71–78 (1990).
88. F. A. Johnson, D. Q. Craig, and A. D. Mercer, Characterization of the block structure and molecular weight of sodium alginates. *J. Pharm Pharmacol.*, **49**(7), 639–643 (1997).
89. O. Jeon, K. H. Bouhadir, J. M. Mansour, and E. Alsberg, Photocross-linked alginate hydrogels with tunable biodegradation rates and mechanical properties. *Biomaterials*, **30**(14), 2724–2734 (2009).
90. K. Y. Lee, E. Alsberg, and D. J. Mooney, Degradable and injectable poly(aldehyde guluronate) hydrogels for bone tissue engineering. *J. Biomed. Mater. Res.*, **56**(2), 228–233 (2001).
91. P. B. Malafaya, G. A. Silva, and R. L. Reis, Natural — origin polymers as carriers and scaffolds for biomolecules and cell delivery in tissue engineering applications. *Adv. Drug Deliv. Rev.*, **59**(4), 207–233 (2007).
92. K. Y. Lee, K. H. Bouhadir, and D. J. Mooney, Degradation behavior of covalently cross-linked poly(aldehyde guluronate) hydrogels. *Macromolecules*, **33**(1), 97–101 (2000).
93. C. Cha, R. H. Kohman, and H. Kong, Biodegradable polymer cross-linker: Independent control of stiffness, toughness, and hydrogel degradation rate. *Adv. Funct. Mater.*, **19**(19), 3056–3062 (2009).
94. S. Gerecht, S. A. Townsend, H. Pressler, H. Zhu, C. L. Nijst, J. P. Bruggeman, J. W. Nichol, and R. Langer, A porous photocurable elastomer for cell encapsulation and culture. Biomaterials, **28**(32), 4826–4835 (2007).
95. I. Martin, B. Obradovic, S. Treppo, A. Grodzinsky, R. Langer, L. Freed, and G. Vunjak-Novakovic, Modulation of the mechanical properties of tissue engineered cartilage. *Biorheology*, **37**(1), 141–147 (2000).
96. A. Khademhosseini, and R. Langer, Microengineered hydrogels for tissue engineering. *Biomaterials*, **28**(34), 5087–5092 (2007).
97. Y. Du, E. Lo, S. Ali, and A. Khademhosseini, Directed assembly of cell-laden microgels for fabrication of 3D tissue constructs. *Proc. Natl. Acad. Sci.*, **105**(28), 9522–9527 (2008).

98. A. Khademhosseini, G. Eng, J. Yeh, J. Fukuda, J. Blumling, R. Langer, and J. A. Burdick, Micromolding of photocross-linkable hyaluronic acid for cell encapsulation and entrapment. *J. Biomed. Mater. Res. A*, **79**(3), 522–532 (2006).
99. A. Khademhosseini, J. Yeh, S. Jon, G. Eng, K. Y. Suh, J. A. Burdick, and R. Langer, Molded polyethylene glycol microstructures for capturing cells within microfluidic channels. *Lab Chip*, **4**(5), 425–430 (2004).
100. J. Yeh, Y. Ling, J. M. Karp, J. Gantz, A. Chandawarkar, G. Eng, J. Blumling Iii, R. Langer, and A. Khademhosseini, Micromolding of shape-controlled, harvestable cell-laden hydrogels. *Biomaterials*, **27**(31), 5391–5398 (2006).
101. Y. Ling, J. Rubin, Y. Deng, C. Huang, U. Demirci, J. M. Karp, and A. Khademhosseini, A cell-laden microfluidic hydrogel. *Lab Chip*, **7**(6), 756–762 (2007).
102. N. Annabi, J. W. Nichol, X. Zhong, C. Ji, S. Koshy, A. Khademhosseini, and F. Dehghani, Controlling the porosity and microarchitecture of hydrogels for tissue engineering. *Tissue Eng. B Rev.*, **16**(4), 371–383 (2010).
103. D. Horák, J. Kroupová, M.Šlouf, and P. Dvořák, Poly(2-hydroxyethyl methacrylate)-based slabs as a mouse embryonic stem cell support. *Biomaterials*, **25**(22), 5249–5260 (2004).
104. L. Draghi, S. Resta, M. Pirozzolo, and M. Tanzi, Microspheres leaching for scaffold porosity control. *J. Mater. Sci. : Mater. Med.*, **16**(12), 1093–1097 (2005).
105. Y. Gong, Q. Zhou, C. Gao, and J. Shen, *In vitro* and *in vivo* degradability and cyto-compatibility of poly(L-lactic acid) scaffold fabricated by a gelatin particle leaching method. *Acta Biomater.*, **3**(4), 531–540 (2007).
106. S. W. Suh, J. Y. Shin, J. Kim, J. Kim, C. H. Beak, D.-I. Kim, H. Kim, S. S. Jeon, and I.-W. Choo, Effect of different particles on cell proliferation in polymer scaffolds using a solvent-casting and particulate leaching technique. *ASAIO J*, **48**(5), 460–464 (2002).
107. J. Zhang, L. Wu, D. Jing, and J. Ding, A comparative study of porous scaffolds with cubic and spherical macropores. *Polymer*, **46**(13), 4979–4985 (2005).
108. S. Park, JD. G. Woo, B. K. Sun, H.-M. Chung, S. J. Im, Y. M. Choi, K. Park, K. M. Huh, and K. -H. Park, *In vitro* and *in vivo* test of PEG/PCL-based hydrogel scaffold for cell delivery application. *J. Control. Release*, **124**(1), 51–59 (2007).
109. M. Dadsetan, T. E. Hefferan, J. P. Szatkowski, P. K. Mishra, S. I. Macura, L. Lu, and M. J. Yaszemski, Effect of hydrogel porosity on marrow stromal cell phenotypic expression. *Biomaterials*, **29**(14), 2193–2202 (2008).
110. J. H. Kim, S. B. Lee, S. J. Kim, and Y. M. Lee, Rapid temperature/pH response of porous alginate-g-poly(N-isopropylacrylamide) hydrogels. *Polymer*, **43**(26), 7549–7558 (2002).
111. D. Horak, H. Hlidkova, J. Hradil, M. Lapčíková, and M. Šlouf, Superporous poly(2-hydroxyethyl methacrylate) based scaffolds: preparation and characterization. *Polymer*, **49**(8), 2046–2054 (2008).
112. X. Wu, L. Black, G. Santacana-Laffitte, and C. W. Patrick, Preparation and assessment of glutaraldehyde — cross-linked collagen–chitosan hydrogels for adipose tissue engineering. *J. Biomed. Mater. Res. A*, **81**(1), 59–65 (2007).

113. M.-H. Ho, P.-Y. Kuo, H.-J. Hsieh, T.-Y. Hsien, L.-T. Hou, J.-Y. Lai, and D.-M. Wang, Preparation of porous scaffolds by using freeze-extraction and freeze-gelation methods. *Biomaterials*, **25**(1), 129–138 (2004).
114. K. M. Huh, N. Baek, and K. Park, Enhanced swelling rate of poly(ethylene glycol)-grafted superporous hydrogels. *J. Bioact. Compat. Pol.*, **20**(3), 231–243 (2005).
115. V. Keskar, N. W. Marion, J. J. Mao, and R. A. Gemeinhart, *In vitro* evaluation of macroporous hydrogels to facilitate stem cell infiltration, growth, and mineralization. *Tissue Eng. A*, **15**(7), 1695–1707 (2009).
116. H. A. El-Rehim, E. S. A. Hegazy, and D. Diaa, Characterization of super-absorbent material based on carboxymethylcellulose sodium salt prepared by electron beam irradiation. *J. Macromol. Sci. A: Pure. Appl. Chem.*, **43**(1), 101–113 (2006).
117. Q. P. Pham, U. Sharma, and A. G. Mikos, Electrospinning of polymeric nanofibers for tissue engineering applications: A review. *Tissue Eng.*, **12**(5), 1197–1211 (2006).
118. L. Li, and Y.-L. Hsieh, Ultra-fine polyelectrolyte hydrogel fibres from poly(acrylic acid)/poly(vinyl alcohol). *Nanotechnology*, **16**(12), 2852 (2005).
119. T. Arai, G. Freddi, R. Innocenti, and M. Tsukada, Biodegradation of Bombyx mori silk fibroin fibers and films. *J. Appl. Polym. Sci.*, **91**(4), 2383–2390 (2004).
120. R. L. Horan, K. Antle, A. L. Collette, Y. Wang, J. Huang, J. E. Moreau, V. Volloch, D. L. Kaplan, and G. H. Altman, *In vitro* degradation of silk fibroin. *Biomaterials*, **26**(17), 3385–3393 (2005).
121. A. Kurioka, M. Yamazaki, and H. Hirano, Primary structure and possible functions of a trypsin inhibitor of Bombyx mori. *Eur. J. Biochem.*, **259**(1–2), 120–126 (1999).
122. C. Vepari, and D. L. Kaplan, Silk as a biomaterial. *Prog. Polym. Sci.*, **32**(8), 991–1007 (2007).
123. T. C. Laurent, *The Chemistry, Biology And Medical Applications Of Hyaluronan And Its Derivatives.* Portland Press, **72**, (1998).
124. J. Baier Leach, K. A. Bivens, C. W. Patrick Jr, and C. E. Schmidt, Photocross-linked hyaluronic acid hydrogels: Natural, biodegradable tissue engineering scaffolds. *Biotechnol. Bioeng.*, **82**(5), 578–589 (2003).
125. H. Tan, C. M. Ramirez, N. Miljkovic, H. Li, J. P. Rubin, and K. G. Marra, Thermosensitive injectable hyaluronic acid hydrogel for adipose tissue engineering. *Biomaterials*, **30**(36), 6844–6853 (2009).
126. S. Herrick, O. Blanc-Brude, A. Gray, and G. Laurent, Fibrinogen. *Int. J. Biochem. Cell B*, **31**(7), 741–746 (1999).
127. Z. Werb, ECM and cell surface proteolysis: regulating cellular ecology. *Cell*, **91**(4), 439–442 (1997).
128. D. L. Elbert, and J. A. Hubbell, Conjugate addition reactions combined with free-radical cross-linking for the design of materials for tissue engineering. *Biomacromolecules*, **2**(2), 430–441 (2001).
129. P. Gupta, K. Vermani, and S. Garg, Hydrogels: From controlled release to pH-responsive drug delivery. *Drug Discov. Today*, **7**(10), 569–579 (2002).

130. R. H. Schmedlen, K. S. Masters, and J. L. West, Photocross-linkable polyvinyl alcohol hydrogels that can be modified with cell adhesion peptides for use in tissue engineering. *Biomaterials*, **23**(22), 4325–4332 (2002).
131. J.-Z. Du, T.-M. Sun, S.-Q. Weng, X.-S. Chen, and J. Wang, Synthesis and characterization of photo-cross-linked hydrogels based on biodegradable polyphosphoesters and poly(ethylene glycol) copolymers. *Biomacromolecules*, **8**(11), 3375–3381 (2007).
132. J. P. Fisher, D. Dean, P. S. Engel, and A. G. Mikos, Photoinitiated polymerization of biomaterials. *Ann. Rev. Mater. Res.*, **31**(1), 171–181 (2001).
133. J. L. Ifkovits and J. A. Burdick, Review: Photopolymerizable and degradable biomaterials for tissue engineering applications. *Tissue Eng.*, **13**(10), 2369–2385 (2007).
134. J. B. Lee, J. J. Yoon, D. S. Lee, and T. G. Park, Photo-cross-linkable, thermo-sensitive and biodegradable Pluronic hydrogels for sustained release of protein. *J. Biomater Sci- Polym E.*, **15**(12), 1571–1583 (2004).
135. Q. Li, J. Wang, S. Shahani, D. D. N. Sun, B. Sharma, J. H. Elisseeff, and K. W. Leong, Biodegradable and photocross-linkable polyphosphoester hydrogel. *Biomaterials*, **27**(7), 1027–1034 (2006).
136. D. L. Nettles, T. P. Vail, M. T. Morgan, M. W. Grinstaff, and L. A. Setton, *Photocross-linkable hyaluronan as a scaffold for articular cartilage repair. Ann. Biomed. Eng.*, **32**(3), 391–397 (2004).
137. K. T. Nguyen and J. L. West, Photopolymerizable hydrogels for tissue engineering applications. *Biomaterials*, **23**(22), 4307–4314 (2002).
138. K. A. Smeds and M. W. Grinstaff, Photocross-linkable polysaccharides for *in situ* hydrogel formation. *J. Biomed. Mater. Res.*, **54**(1), 115–121 (2001).
139. A. Ganiyu Jimoh, D. L. Wise, J. D. Gresser, and D. J. Trantolo, Pulsed FSH release from an implantable capsule system. *J. Control. Release*, **34**(2), 87–95 (1995).
140. P. Kibat, Y. Igari, M. Wheatley, H. Eisen, and R. Langer, Enzymatically activated microencapsulated liposomes can provide pulsatile drug release. *FASEB J.*, **4**(8), 2533–2539 (1990).
141. I. Yasutaka, P. G. Kibat, and R. Langer, Optimization of a microencapsulated liposome system for enzymatically controlled release of macromolecules. *J. Control. Release*, **14**(3), 263–267 (1990).
142. J. Heller, S. Pangburn, and K. Roskos, Development of enzymatically degradable protective coatings for use in triggered drug delivery systems: Derivatized starch hydrogels. *Biomaterials*, **11**(5), 345–350 (1990).
143. J. Tefft, K. Roskos, and J. Heller, The effect of lipase on the release of naltrexone from triglyceride–coated cellulose acetate phthalate microspheres. *J. Biomed. Mater. Res.*, **26**(6), 713–724 (1992).
144. K. Moriyama, T. Ooya, and N. Yui, Pulsatile peptide release from multi-layered hydrogel formulations consisting of poly(ethylene glycol)-grafted and ungrafted dextrans. *J. Biomater. Sci-Polym E.*, **10**(12), 1251–1264 (1999).
145. K. Moriyama, T. Ooya, and N. Yui, Hyaluronic acid grafted with poly(ethylene glycol) as a novel peptide formulation. *J. Control. Release*, **59**(1), 77–86 (1999).

146. C. Gong, S. Shi, L. Wu, M. Gou, Q. Yin, Q. Guo, P. Dong, F. Zhang, F. Luo, and X. Zhao, Biodegradable *in situ* gel-forming controlled drug delivery system based on thermosensitive PCL–PEG–PCL hydrogel. Part 2: Sol–gel–sol transition and drug delivery behavior. *Acta Biomater.*, **5**(9), 3358–3370 (2009).
147. W. S. Shim, J.-H. Kim, H. Park, K. Kim, I. Chan Kwon, and D. S. Lee, Biodegradability and biocompatibility of a pH-and thermo-sensitive hydrogel formed from a sulfonamide-modified poly(ε-caprolactone-co-lactide)–poly(ethylene glycol)–poly(ε-caprolactone-co-lactide) block copolymer. *Biomaterials*, **27**(30), 5178–5185 (2006).
148. S. Murdan, *Electro-responsive drug delivery from hydrogels. J. Control. Release*, **92**(1), 1–17 (2003).
149. M. B. Delgado-Charro and R. H. Guy, Transdermal reverse iontophoresis of valproate: a noninvasive method for therapeutic drug monitoring. *Pharm. Res.*, **20**(9), 1508–1513 (2003).
150. J. E. Riviere and M. C. Heit, Electrically-assisted transdermal drug delivery. *Pharm. Res.*, **14**(6), 687–697 (1997).
151. R. Vanbever and V. Preat, *In vivo* efficacy and safety of skin electroporation. *Adv. Drug Deliv. Rev.*, **35**(1), 77–88 (1999).
152. T. Budtova, I. Suleimenov, and S. Frenkel, Electrokinetics of the contraction of a polyelectrolyte hydrogel under the influence of constant electric current. *Polym. Gels Netw.*, **3**(3), 387–393 (1995).
153. J. Gong, T. Nitta, and Y. Osada, Electrokinetic modeling of the contractile phenomena of polyelectrolyte gels. One-dimensional capillary model. *J. Phys. Chem.*, **98**(38), 9583–9587 (1994).
154. Y. Yang, and J. B. Engberts, Stimuli response of polysoap hydrogels in aqueous solution and DC electric fields. *Colloids Surf A Physicochem. Eng. Asp.*, **169**(1), 85–94 (2000).
155. R. D. Leavitt and L. Z. Avila, *Method Of Local Radiotherapy By Polymerizing A Material In Vivo To Form A Hydrogel*, (1999).
156. A. Kikuchi, and T. Okano, Pulsatile drug release control using hydrogels. *Adv. Drug Deliv. Rev.*, **54**(1), 53–77 (2002).
157. Y. Wang, D. D. Rudym, A. Walsh, L. Abrahamsen, H.-J. Kim, H. S. Kim, C. Kirker-Head, and D. L. Kaplan, *In vivo* degradation of three-dimensional silk fibroin scaffolds. *Biomaterials*, **29**(24), 3415–3428 (2008).
158. T. Miyata, T. Uragami, and K. Nakamae, Biomolecule-sensitive hydrogels. *Adv. Drug Deliv. Rev.*, **54**(1), 79–98 (2002).

Chapter 7

Tailoring Hydrogel Adhesiveness to Cells, Proteins, and Bacteria

Silviya Petrova Zustiak
Department of Biomedical Engineering, Saint Louis University
3507 Lindell Blvd, St Louis, MO 13603
szustiak@slu.edu

In many applications, such as biosensors or biomedical implants and devices, protein adsorption could lead to inflammation, heightened foreign body response, and ultimately device failure. Bacterial contamination and infection is also a critical issue in multiple biotechnology and medical applications. On the other hand, eliciting and controlling protein and cell adhesion is a desirable and important aspect of tissue engineering. Therefore, tailoring hydrogel adhesiveness to cells, proteins, and bacteria has tremendous clinical and industrial implications. This chapter will focus on strategies to control hydrogel adhesiveness, including the incorporation of peptides and proteins to elicit cell attachment and facilitate cell sheet engineering, development of polymer brushes and zwitterionic materials for the prevention of protein and bacterial adhesion, as well as design of media-responsive coatings.

1. Tailoring Hydrogel Cell Adhesiveness

1.1. Introduction

Hydrogels are receiving increasing interest as cell culture substrates and cell scaffolds for various tissue engineering applications due to their mimicry of the natural cell microenvironment. Since most cells depend on attachment to the extracellular matrix (ECM) to survive and proliferate, building and tailoring cell adhesiveness of hydrogels is becoming increasingly important. While natural hydrogels could be inherently biocompatible and cell adhesive, synthetic hydrogels typically require cell adhesive sites to be added independently and many chemistries have been developed to do so. This section will address strategies for tailoring cell adhesiveness of both natural and synthetic hydrogels by utilizing either whole proteins or short peptide motifs. For excellent detailed reviews on the specific chemistries utilized, the readers are referred to the following recent articles describing protein-hydrogel interactions,[1] designing adhesive materials to direct stem cell fate,[2] synthetic materials to direct morphogenesis,[3] and adhesive hydrogels as cell scaffolds.[4]

1.2. Tailoring cell adhesiveness is achievable for both natural and synthetic hydrogels

Both natural hydrogels, such as collagen, laminin, or fibrinogen, and synthetic, such as polyethylene glycol (PEG), polyvinyl alcohol (PVA), polycaprolactone (PCL), or poly(2-hydroxyethyl methacrylate) (pHEMA) hydrogels could be used as cell scaffolds. Natural hydrogels, often composed of ECM proteins, are inherently cell adhesive as they possess specific amino acid sequence domains that are readily recognized by cells. While inherently biocompatible, tailoring of cell adhesiveness for these hydrogels is very limited. Minimal tunability might be achieved by manipulating the hydrogel precursor concentration which in turn is associated with alteration in the physical and mechanical hydrogel properties.[5] Techniques to target independent manipulation of mechanical and biochemical properties as well as improve scaffold integrity, include addition of crosslinkers such as glutaraldehyde,[6] riboflavin combined with UV irradiation,[7] or genipin.[8–10] Such crosslinkers, hence the name suggests, increase the number of crosslinks in the hydrogel, thus improving mechanical compliance and decreasing pore size, without significant alteration in the overall number of cell adhesive domains. A greater tunability of cell adhesiveness as well as independent tuning of mechanical and biochemical hydrogel properties is typically offered by synthetic hydrogels where synthetic hydrogels provide the backbone to which adhesive moieties are added independently. Such adhesive moieties might be in the form of whole ECM proteins or small peptide sequences.

1.3. Tailoring cell adhesiveness by incorporation of whole proteins

Proteins, naturally present in the ECM, such as collagen,[11] fibrinogen,[12,13] fibronectin.[14–16] or laminin[17] are typically chosen to impart cell adhesiveness. To functionalize hydrogels with proteins, reaction conditions which sustain protein structure and activity must be considered (Fig. 1).[1] For example, chemical immobilization

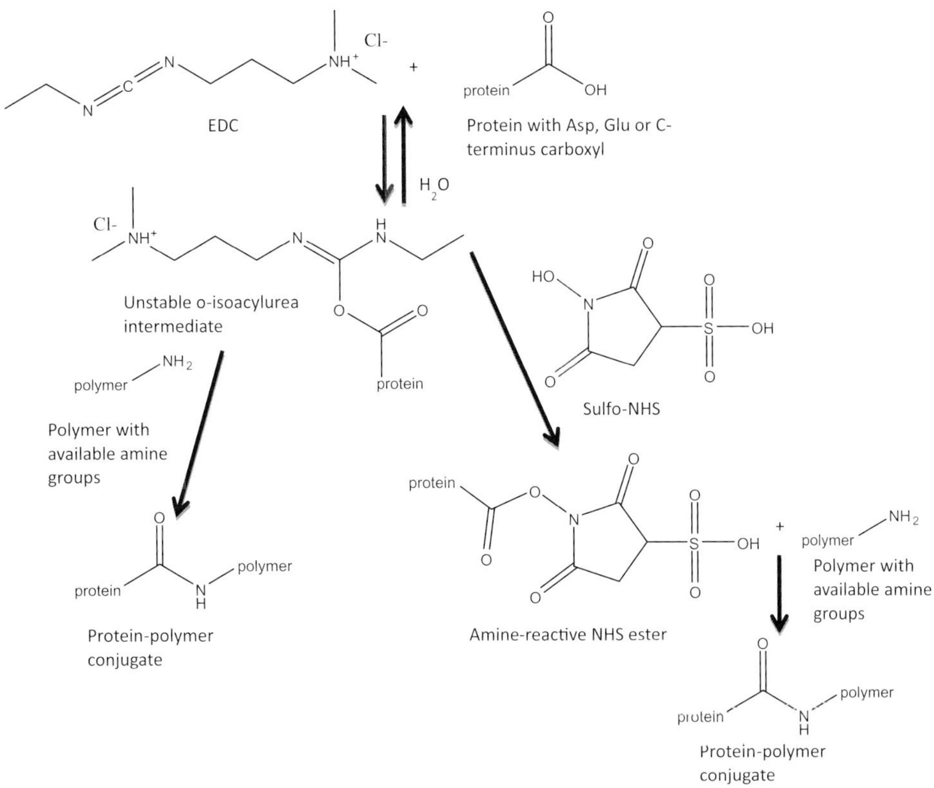

Fig. 1. Schematic representation of EDC/sulfo–NHS chemistry, which is the most commonly used chemistry to covalently conjugate proteins to synthetic polymers. In this example, a stable amide bond is formed between the carboxylate group of a protein and the amine groups of a polymer, but due to the modular nature of the reaction, protein amide groups could also be reacted with polymer amides. Sulfo–NHS is added to improve reaction yield by forming a semi-stable reaction intermediate.[1]

reactions require aqueous conditions since organic solvents may cause denaturation and degradation of the protein. Further, many protein chemistries are non-specific in that they target amines (e.g., N-terminus, Lys), carboxyls (e.g., C-terminus, Asp, Glu), thiols (Cys), or hydroxyls (e.g., Ser, Thr, Tyr). The presence of multiple available residues for modification makes chemical interactions attractive for a wide range of applications but could lead to heterogeneous and poorly reproducible substrates. In addition, random modifications could reduce protein activity either by causing change in protein conformation or by sterically blocking the protein active sites.[1]

Typical strategies for incorporating cell adhesive biomolecules to hydrogels include covalent tethering,[11,18] affinity immobilization,[19] adsorption,[20] or physical entrapment.[15] Adsorption of proteins onto hydrogels to impart cell adhesiveness has been studied extensively.[21,22] However, protein adsorption is associated with many challenges *in vivo* due to desorption and exchange with physiological fluid. Other drawbacks of adsorptive hydrogels include the potential to cause long term inflammation *in vivo*,[23] while some other inert hydrogels such as PEG or PVA are inherently resistant to protein adsorption. Another strategy for tailoring cell adhesiveness is by using affinity interactions in order to incorporate functionalized biomolecules into the hydrogel structure. One of the most commonly used affinity molecule — heparin sulfate, a sulphated glycosaminoglycan, has been used to assemble non-covalent three-dimensional (3D) networks for enhancing cellular affinity[24,25] and for inducing stem cell differentiation.[19] Heparin and other affinity molecules, such as hyaluronic acid (HA) and alginate,[26] typically bind biomolecules via electrostatic interactions. Covalent interactions are generally most stable and provide greater control over protein presentation than any other method.[27] PEGylation of proteins into hydrogels has also been utilized successfully in pharmaceuticals and more recently in biomaterials to produce cell adhesive and instructive hydrogels, where it has been shown that the protein bioactivity is preserved despite the chemical modifications.[28] For a detailed discussion on the various chemistries to incorporate whole proteins into synthetic or natural polymers, the readers are referred to a recent comprehensive review on the subject.[1]

1.4. Tailoring cell adhesiveness by incorporation of short peptide motifs

While efficient, incorporation of whole proteins is not always practical or desirable, since whole proteins could significantly alter not only the biochemical but also the mechanical properties of the hydrogel. For example, Scott *et al.* demonstrated that the addition of covalently crosslinked collagen to synthetic PEG hydrogels, lead to decrease in storage modulus,[11] while Millon *et al.* observed an increase in PVA modulus upon covalent incorporation of fibronectin.[29]

Addition of short cell adhesive peptide motifs is an excellent alternative strategy to whole proteins.[30] Despite the fact that cell adhesive ligands retain only 10% to 30% of their biological activity as compared to the whole protein,[31,32] chemical conjugation of polymers with short peptides has several advantages: (1) higher stability against conformational change; (2) control of ligand density; (3) control of ligand orientation to possibly provide more favorable ligand–receptor interactions and cell adhesion; (4) benefits in terms of minimizing immune response and infection; (5) higher stability during sterilization; (6) easier storage and characterization; and (7) cost effectiveness.[33] Various chemistries have been developed for the chemical immobilization of peptide sequences typically utilizing the amine groups of Lys, carboxylic groups of Asp and Glu, thiols of Cys, and hydroxyls of Ser, Thr, and Tyr. Excellent detailed discussions on peptide incorporation into hydrogels have been described elsewhere.[33,34]

Adhesion motifs can be incorporated into hydrogels either directly[35,36] or via a spacer arm composed of repeating neutral amino acids[37] or a short polymer chain such as a PEG spacer.[38] Spacer arms aid integrin–ligand interactions by increasing the mobility of the peptide and alleviating steric hindrance from the polymer backbone. In general, it has been shown that a cell adhesive ligand, such as arginine-glycine-aspartic acid (RGD), should be at least 11–32Å from a material surface to allow for integrin-mediated binding of cells.[39] By using different PEG spacers, Wilson *et al.* observed a correlation between spacer length and epithelial hTCEpi cell behavior; as spacer length increased, the RGD concentration required to support cell viability and spreading decreased.[40] Furthermore, in the presence of soluble RGD, which is a cell attachment inhibitor, more cells remained attached on the RGD functionalized hydrogels via the longest spacers, alluding to the tenacity of cell adhesiveness.[40] In addition, spacer arms could be used to emulate the native presentation of adhesive motifs. For example, the RGD domain of fibronectin is presented to the cells via a loop-like extension from the fibronectin protein.[41,42] Salinas and Anseth *et al.* have demonstrated that native loop-like presentation of RGD is equally important as adding a spacer arm for achieving high human Mesenchymal Stem Cells (hMSCs) attachment and viability.[37] Further, Zhu *et al.* demonstrated that the loop-like cyclic presentation of RGD, which the authors termed cRGD, facilitated better endothelial cell adhesion and spreading in comparison to linear RGD-modified hydrogels[43] (Fig. 2). Lastly, the charge of neighboring amino acids in the spacer arm can be utilized as a means for tailoring peptide motif reaction kinetics and incorporation efficiency.[44]

Common cell adhesion motifs include, but are not limited to RGD, IKVAV, YIGSR, LGTIPG, PDGSR, LRE, LRGDN, and IKLLI which originate from laminin; DGEA and RGD from collagen Type I; and KQAGDV, REDV, and PHSRN from fibronectin.[45] The collagen-, fibronectin, and laminin-derived ligand RGD is one of the most commonly incorporated ligands to elicit cell adhesiveness, where both concentration and presentation affect the fate of anchorage-dependent cells, including cell proliferation, viability, and spreading.[33] For example, using inert PEG hydrogels with covalently incorporated RGD, it has been demonstrated that even nanomolar ligand concentration can support cell survival, but that a threshold at micromolar ligand concentration exists where further increase in RGD concentration does not increase cell viability further.[46,47] In addition to cell viability and proliferation, RGD concentration also correlated well with cell spreading area as demonstrated by Schmedlen *et al.* with fibroblasts seeded onto RGD-functionalized PVA hydrogels.[48] In another recent study, Ali *et al.* incorporated YIGSR and IKVAV in addition to RGD in PEG hydrogels to induce endothelial cell tubulogenesis.[49]

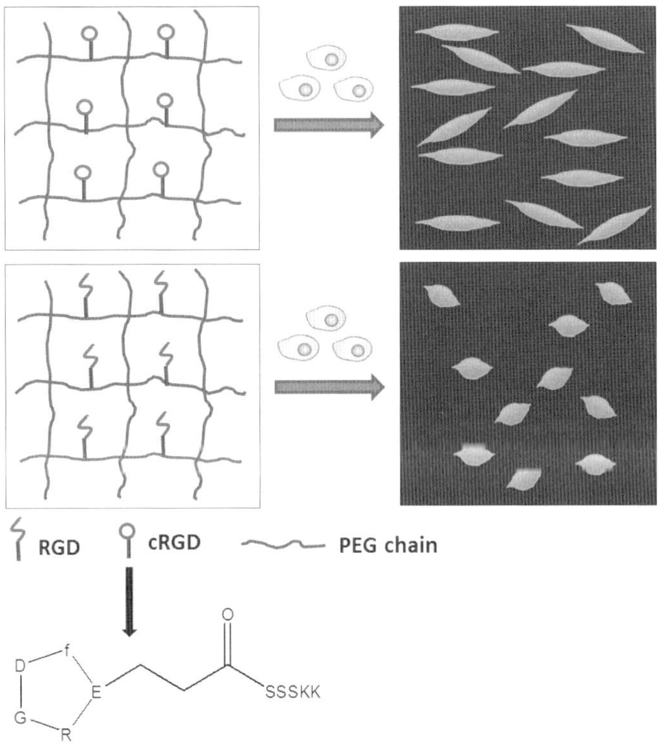

Fig. 2. The authors describe a novel type of PEGDA macromers designed with a cRGD peptide attached in the middle of the PEGDA chain which can be photopolymerized to form 3D hydrogel networks with uniform cRGD distribution. *Top*: Higher cell proliferation and spreading is observed on the cRGD compared to linear RGD gels. *Bottom*: Chemical structure of the designed cyclic RGD peptide, c[RGDfE(SSSKK-NH_2] with a tail of SSSKK, which consists of a spacer with three serine residues and a linker with two lysine residues for further conjugation to other molecules. The arrow shows the direction of the amino acid sequence from N-terminus to C-terminus prior to cyclization of the linear peptide.[43]

The authors were able to show that while each ligand induced tubule formation, the combination of YIGSR and RGD promoted the largest tubule diameters and volumes as well as the largest amount of ECM proteins produced.[49] YIGSR, IKVAV, and RGD alone and in combination have also been shown to promote neurite outgrowth of PC12 cells in PEG hydrogels,[46,50] and adhesion and viability of preadipocytes in PEG hydrogels.[51] Further, ligand-tethering to hydrogels is gaining increasing interest in other related areas such as cryopreservation of cells and tissues. For example, it has been shown that tethering of alginate with RGD cell adhesive motif improves the cryopreservation of insulin-secreting C2C12 cells.[52]

In addition to type and concentration, ligand presentation, such as homogeneous versus a clustered or a gradient presentation also affects cell adhesiveness.

For example, RGD gradients onto PEG hydrogels have been shown to affect chondrocyte cell number and phenotype[53] and spacing of RGD islands have been shown to affect MC3T3-E1 pre-osteoblasts spreading, where increase in cell spreading correlated with decrease in island spacing.[54] Clustering of RGD into 3D HA hydrogels was also shown to affect cell spreading and integrin expression of MSCs,[53] ligand clustering was required to support cell locomotion of NR6 cells,[55] and ligand cluster size and density correlated with NR6 cell adhesion.[56] Further, patterning of single-cell islands of adhesive ligands or proteins onto otherwise inert substrates has revealed that cells would conform to the pattern geometry.[57,58] Even though patterning of biochemical signals onto hydrogels is challenging, some techniques involving microprinting, lithography and microfluidics, have been developed.[54,59] Examples include microcontact printing of anchoring points followed by a microfluidic device to create an RGD gradient,[60] combination of microfluidics and photopolymerization to produce RGD gradients on PEG-diacrylate (PEGDA) hydrogels,[61] two-photon laser-scanning lithography to produce RGD patterns in two-dimensional (2D) and 3D PEG hydrogels,[62] and photolithography for micropatterning of adhesive ligands onto polyacrylamide hydrogels.[58]

1.5. Tailoring cell adhesiveness for cell sheet engineering

Perhaps one of the areas where tailoring of cell adhesiveness is most intriguing is "cell sheet engineering" which is now an established tissue reconstruction technology.[63] The efficiency of this technology is strongly dependent on precise control of cell adhesiveness to the substrates. In addition, due to the popularity and large array of applications for cell sheet engineering, "on-demand" design of cell adhesiveness is required since the various cell types show individual cell adhesion and detachment behaviors.[64] Cell sheet engineering technology involves mainly a thermo-responsive hydrogel, such as poly(N-isopropylacrylamide) (pNIPAM), which enables reversible cell adhesion due to the controllable hydrophobicity of the surface (Fig. 3).[65] PNIPAM is a thermoresponsive polymer with a lower critical solution temperature (LCST) of 32°C.[66] Above this temperature, the polymer is hydrophobic allowing protein adsorption, such as fibronectin, and consequent cell attachment. Below this temperature, the polymer becomes hydrophilic, releasing the adsorbed proteins in conjunction with the cells attached to them. Thus, in this approach cell sheets can be harvested by simply reducing the temperature once cell confluency is achieved Thermoresponsive surfaces can be prepared by a variety of polymer grafting methods, including electron beam-induced graft polymerization,[67] surface-initiated atom transfer radical polymerization (ATRP),[68] and other techniques.

Control of pNIPAM cell adhesiveness is of great interest for a variety of applications, as mentioned earlier, and therefore many tuning strategies have been

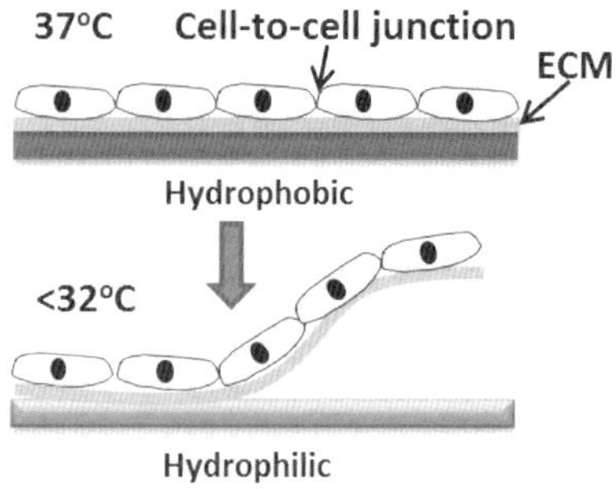

Fig. 3. Schematic of cell sheet technology utilizing temperature responsive culture dishes.[65]

attempted. The most common one is by adjusting polymer content, which results in alteration of surface hydrophobicity and therefore alteration of cell adhesion strength to the substrate.[68,69] For example, using pNIPAM grafted brush surfaces, Mizutani *et al.* showed that by increasing brush thickness, i.e., brush chain length, surface hydrophobicity decreased leading to a decrease in cell attachment strength.[68] The authors attributed this effect to the increased mobility of the longer chains as opposed to the more dense and tightly packed shorter chains.[68] In a separate study, a nominal brush thickness that supports cell adhesion was found to be less than 30 nm.[69] A major drawback of decreasing polymer content is that this method leads to poor thermally-induced detachment during the cell sheet harvesting. Several approaches have been adopted to overcome this "dilemma". For example, Haraguchi *et al.* used a composite hydrogel prepared of inorganic nanocomposite clay (NC) and pNIPAM and showed that in this novel hydrogel system, cell adhesion and harvesting were unaffected by pNIPAM gel thickness.[70] Another strategy described by Takahashi *et al.* is to chemically modify the terminal groups of pNIPAM brushes.[71] For example, the authors demonstrated that terminal carboxylation lead to both acceleration of cell adhesion and rapid harvest of cell sheets.[71] Other field advancements include micropatterning to create sheets of aligned cells[72] or to create substrates for single cell studies.[57] One drawback of the thermoresponsive hydrogels is that cell harvesting at low temperature might take up to 60 min.[73] Alternative approaches that focus on fast cell detachment include the use of quinone ester and O-silyl hydroquinone electroactive groups that release adhesive ligand and cell sheets selectively via application of reductive or oxidative potentials.[74] Such electrochemical approaches are further advantageous because they allow cell detachment not only from flat surfaces but from various other types such as rod shaped or patterned surfaces.[75,76] For more details of cell sheet engineering technologies and applications, the readers are referred to several reviews on the subject.[63,64,77,78]

1.6. Additional considerations in tailoring cell adhesiveness

A few issues need to be taken into account when utilizing protein or peptide-modified hydrogels to tailor cell adhesiveness. First, not only whole proteins but also short peptide sequences have the potential to alter overall hydrogel physical and mechanical properties. For example, Zustiak *et al.* has demonstrated that incorporation of YIGSR peptide into inert PEG hydrogels lead to increase in storage modulus and decrease in hydrogel swelling due to hydrogen bonding between the hydroxyl hydrogen of the Y residue and the ether oxygen of the PEG backbone.[79] Since in many applications it is desirable to decouple ligand presentation and hydrogel mechanical properties, multiple approaches have been tested: (1) carefully monitoring and adjusting mechanical properties when ligand concentration is increased,[80] (2) using modular PEG hydrogels assembled from PEG microgels and collagen, where compacting PEG microgels into a PEG modugels allows for independent control of stiffness and collagen presentation,[81] or (3) using interpenetrating networks (IPNs).[82] Another alternative method to elicit cell adhesiveness without altering bulk material properties was considered by Ino *et al.* where the authors used plasma functionalization of PVA to render only the hydrogel surface cell adhesive without influencing interactions within the hydrogel.[83]

In addition to alternative conjugation strategies, alternative cell binding motifs are also being tested. For example, Zhang *et al.* showed that fibronectin cell binding domain III_{9-10} elicited higher cell adhesion and spreading on PEG hydrogels than the tripeptide RGD.[84] Further, it has to be noted that charged hydrogels will stimulate protein adsorption from the media, typically fibronectin, which in turn will render them cell adhesive where cell adhesiveness could be tailored by manipulating overall hydrogel charge.[85] Lastly, laboratory sterilization protocols prior to *in vivo* experiments need careful consideration. For example, Huebsch *et al.* have shown that UV irradiation, a low-cost commonly used sterilization procedure does not fully prevent bacterial growth and could also lead to progressive peptide degradation, thus leaving ethanol sterilization as the more viable option.[86]

2. Tailoring Protein and Bacteria Adhesiveness of Hydrogels

2.1. Introduction

While adsorption of proteins is often desired in order to elicit cell adhesion to various synthetic hydrogels, in many applications, such as biosensors or biomedical implants and devices, protein adsorption, could be undesirable.[87,88] Importantly, bacterial contamination and infection is a critical issue in multiple biotechnology and medical applications.[89–92] In addition, controlling bacterial adherence to various coatings could be used not only as a biofilm and contamination prevention, but also for collecting, analyzing, and cleaning bacterial contamination.[93,94] Thus, non-fouling surfaces that can resist protein, cell, or bacterial adhesion over extended periods of time are actively being developed. Key strategies to tailor adhesiveness to proteins and bacteria include functionalization of surfaces with solvated polymers such as PEG, chemical conjugation of antimicrobial peptides,[95] as well as release of bactericidal agents such as antibiotics, enzymes, silver, etc. The focus of this review is on the polymer design, structure, and functionality associated with adhesion resistance. On strategies to incorporate and/or release bactericidal agents into the polymer networks, the readers are referred to an excellent recent review on the subject.[96] On approaches for the design and preparation of surfaces based on antifouling materials, the readers are referred to the following review.[97]

2.2. Polymer brushes

Non-fouling surfaces could be provided by hydrogel networks, employing naturally inert hydrogels such as PEG,[98] but most often polymer brushes, i.e., polymer chains tethered to a surface, are used. Tethering of polymer brushes is achieved by various strategies such as UV irradiation,[99] ATRP, reversible addition fragmentation transfer polymerization (RAFT),[100] plasma treatment,[101] or gamma-irradiation.[102] For more details on brush synthesis, as well as grafting and patterning methods, the readers are referred to some excellent reviews on the topic.[103–105]

Solvated polymer brushes made of polymers such as PEG and Pluronics, are one of the most common strategies to tailor or inhibit protein and bacterial adhesion.[106,107] The key properties that contribute to the bio-adhesion resistance of such surfaces are: (1) a polymer that is naturally inert — neutral, hydrophilic, well-hydrated, and hydrogen-bond accepting;[108] and (2) the physical design of the brush — a height exceeding the range of electrostatic and van der Waals attractions, and a density sufficient to avoid penetration by small proteins.[109,110] Overall, considerable attention have been focused on developing strategies to attain high brush densities and optimal brush length.[96] Interestingly, Fang *et al.* have shown that brush age could also affect bacterial adhesion.[111] The finite decrease in protein adhesiveness was attributed to polymer relaxation and dissipation of interfacial defects with brush aging.[111] Lastly, hydrogel geometry can be used to tune adhesion, such as the natural adhesiveness of gecko lizards,[112] its synthetic equivalents,[113] as well as sharklet micropatterned surfaces.[114] Building on that concept, Synytska *et al.* have shown that patterning brushes on surfaces of different roughness would influence their adhesiveness, with smoother surfaces proving more adhesive (Fig. 4).[115]

While most developed brushes are predominantly linear,[97] comb-like brushes have also shown to be highly effective in reducing protein adsorption. Examples

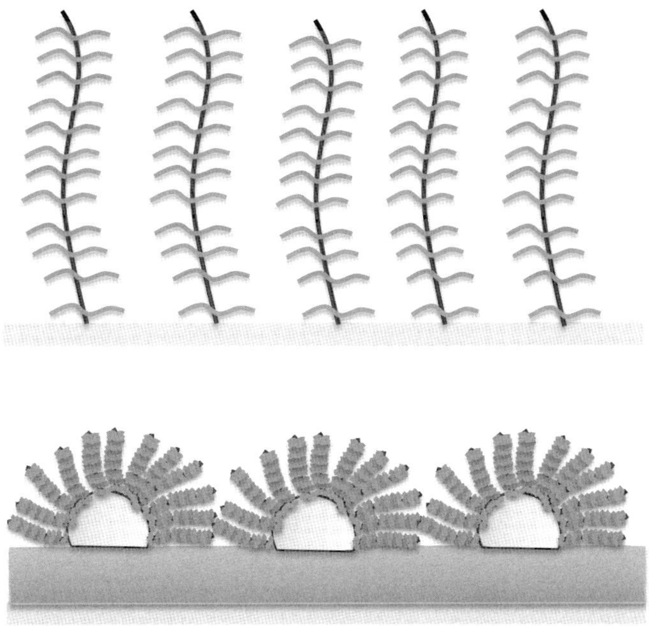

Fig. 4. Schematic representation of polymer brushes grafted on a flat or a rough substrate. The authors were able to show that due to decrease in overall contact area, the grafted rough surface were less adhesive than the smooth ones.[115]

include PEG chains grafted onto a poly(L-lysine) (PLL) backbone,[116,117] carbohydrates such as dextran grafted onto PLL backbone,[118] as well as other glycopolymers.[99] PEG brushes have been largely successful,[119] even though PEG degradation could occur in some instances[120] and specific protein interactions with PEG, even though rare, are still possible.[121] Alternative materials, such as bioactive peptide mimics, "peptoids", have also been used as anti-fouling brushes.[122] In contrast to peptides, peptoid side chains are attached to the backbone nitrogen to form tertiary amide bonds.[123] This shift in the side chain position is perceived responsible for the ability of peptoids to resist protease degradation and possess anti-fouling properties.[124] For example, surface-grafted polysarcosine brushes used as an anti-fouling surface showed resistance to cell attachment and some clinically relevant bacterial strength for over a 7 week period.[125] Inhibition of protein adsorption and cell attachment was further inhibited by tuning chain density and length and was attributed to the highly hydrophilic nature of the peptoid.[125]

Despite the large array of polymer brushes developed, it has to be noted that even well designed brushes that resist protein and bacterial adhesion *in vitro*, still fail to inhibit protein and bacterial adhesion *in vivo*.[106] One explanation for this inconsistency between *in vitro* and *in vivo* performance is that no brush is "perfect".

Consistent grafting of polymer chains is hard to implement and impurities on the surface can create flaws and heterogeneities in the brush as small as tens of nanometers. Such sports could become locally less repulsive or even attractive and compromise the effectiveness of the brush. For example, Gon and Santore created a patchy PEG brush, where <10 nm large adhesive islands were incorporated into the brush.[126] Using fibrinogen as a model protein, the authors demonstrated that protein adsorption occurred when the adsorbing protein could make multiple surface contacts with the adhesives patches and thus depended on island spacing.[126] In addition, protein adhesion was strongly and inversely influenced by brush height.[127] In a separate study, the authors also showed that the patchy brushes were more protein than bacteria resistant, due to the tendency of the bacteria to compress large brush areas in order to interact with the patches.[128] Thus, in comparison to protein resistance, bacterial resistance was found proportional not to the tether length and spacing, but to the overall PEG mass and the resulting osmotic pressure of the brush.[128]

2.3. Media-responsive non-fouling materials

Specially designed low-adhesive surfaces could be used to improve device performance in changeable environments, such as air and water. Fabrication of environment-responsive coatings with low interfacial energy in variable media is of interest for many applications including micro-electromechanical systems (MEMS), microfluidic devices, biomedical equipment, anti-fouling coatings, and many others.[96,129] In air, adhesion to polar substrates mostly occurs as a result of capillary forces because of the condensation of water vapors.[130] In water, interactions are typically more complex with various forces playing a role.

Thus, surface modification by responsive polymer coatings, where changing of the hydrophilic/hydrophobic properties of the medium results in spontaneous reconstruction of the polymer coatings and switching of the interfacial energy, are desired. Some strategies to engineer such coatings have been developed, including the assembly of block copolymer nanostructured layers,[131] incorporation of carbon nanotubes into amphiphilic block copolymers,[132] application of segmented polyurethanes,[133] and synthesis of mixed polymer brushes.[115,134] For example, in mixed polymer brushes two different polymers, a hydrophobic and a hydrophilic one, are grafted onto the same substrate.[134] They tend to segregate macroscopically, where the size of the two phases correlates with the end-to-end distance of the polymer chain. The hydrophobic component, which becomes exposed in air, minimizes capillary condensation and therefore adhesion.[135] However, in water, hydrophobic interactions enhance the attraction between non-polar moieties of proteins and the coating, thus enhancing protein adhesiveness.[136] Thus, in an aqueous

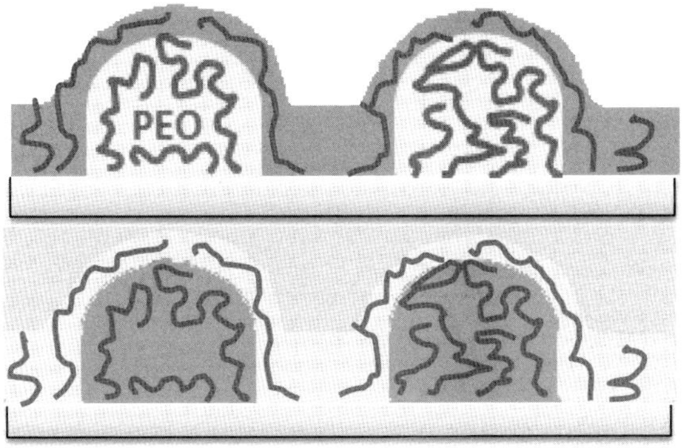

Fig. 5. Schematic of PDMS–PEO brushes in air and in water. To minimize interfacial energy, the hydrophobic PDMS phase is exposed in air, and the hydrophilic PEO phase is exposed in water.[134]

environment, hydrophilic polymers, which reduce polymer–water interfacial energy, are used to render anti-fouling properties. An example of a mixed polymer brush composed of PEO and polydimethylsiloxane (PDMS) polymer chains is presented in Fig. 5.[134] Similar strategies are described by Synytska *et al.*, where the authors used comb-like polymer brushes composed of PDMS and PEG to create an adaptive anti-fouling coating[115] as well as by Sheparovich *et al.*, where the authors used hydrophobic nanoparticles and hydrophilic polymer chains tethered to a surface.[137] For more details on linear chain polymer brushes, the readers are referred to an excellent review.[103]

2.4. Zwitterionic non-fouling materials

Zwitterionic polymers, containing both positive and negative charges, are gaining increasing popularity as non-fouling surfaces.[138,139] Some of the most common zwitterionic polymers include poly(carboxybetaine methacrylate) (pCBMA), poly(N,N-dimethyl-N-(*p*-vinylbenyl)-N-(3-sulfopropyl) ammonium) (PDMVSA), poly (2-methacryloyloxyethyl) ethyl-dimethyl-(3-sulfopropyl)-ammonium) (PDMMSA), poly(2-methacryloyloxyethyl pshophorylcholine) (PMPC),[140] and poly(sulfobetaine methacrylate (pSBMA)[139] among others. In examining several different polymers, Ladd *et al.* demonstrated zwitterionic polymers to be a viable alternative to more traditional PEG-based polymer brushes.[141] The authors attributed this anti-fouling effect of zwitterionic polymers to a high surface packing density as well as steric repulsion from the flexible polymer brush surfaces.[141] Further, Cheng *et al.* showed that zwitterionic pCBMA grafted from glass surfaces is strongly protein resistant regardless of temperature and is also resistant to several bacterial strains up to 192 h, an improvement over traditional PEG-based brushes.[142] Zwitterionic oligopeptides, containing an alternating sequence of positively and negatively charged amino acids are another promising material for non-fouling surfaces. For example, Kakegawa *et al.* demonstrated that using a short oligopeptide GGGG–KEKEKEK, a protein resistant zwitterionic peptide with a GGGG linker, and a cell adhesive peptide of the same sequence but an added RGD, protein and cell adhesive domains can be efficiently micropatterned.[143] The authors further showed that cell density can be controlled by manipulating the ratio of the two oligopeptides.[143] Other exciting advancements of the field include the modification of zwiterrionic polymers with adhesive biomimetic groups for selective manipulation of surface adhesiveness. For example, pCBMA conjugated with an adhesive antibody 3, 4-dihydroxy-phenylalanine (DOPA) enabled the detection of a cancer biomarker ALCAM directly from human serum, implicating its usefulness for diagnostics and nano-scale biosensor development.[144]

Extension of the zwitterionic approach is to use mixtures of positively charged and negatively charged monomers, while keeping the overall charge neutral. For example, it has been shown that a mixture of positively charged [2-(methacryoloxy) ethyl] trimethyl ammonium chloride (TM) and negatively-charged 3-sulfopropyl methacrylate potassium salt (SA) monomers show similar non-fouling properties as zwitterionic surface coatings.[145,146] An interesting example on the use of mixed-charge pH responsive copolymers for selective bacterial adhesion and release was demonstrated by Mi *et al.* implicating their usefulness for surface decontamination.[94] Using mixed-charge copolymer surface composed of positively charged ([2-(acryloyloxy)ethyl] trimethyl ammonium chloride (TMA) and negatively charged carboxylic acid (2-carboxy ethyl acrylate) (CAA) monomers, the authors showed that the polymers had an overall neutral charge under neutral and basic pH, but were positively charged at acidic pH due to deprotonation of the carboxylic group.[94] Since most bacterial strains have an isoelectric point in the pH range of 1.5–4.5[147] and above it they are negatively charged and thus attracted to cationic materials,[148] bacterial cells adhered to the polymer brushes in physiologic media but were efficiently rinsed at a low pH.[94]

Summary and Future Directions

In many applications, such as biosensors or biomedical implants and devices, protein adsorption could lead to inflammation, heightened foreign body response, and ultimately device failure. Bacterial contamination and infection is also a critical issue in multiple biotechnology and medical applications. On the other hand, eliciting and controlling protein and cell adhesion is a desirable and important aspect of tissue engineering. Thus, new strategies for tailoring hydrogel adhesiveness to cells, bacteria, and proteins are constantly being developed. Recent advancements include targeting physiologically relevant representation of cell adhesive ligands, such as the cyclic RGD described earlier,[43] development of new chemistries for the incorporation of both peptides and proteins,[149] or the design of novel non-fouling surfaces.[150] One illustrative novel concept is the use of chirality to tailor protein adsorption and cell adhesiveness,[151] where Wang *et al.* has demonstrated that cells would adhere differentially on enantiomers of the same polymer.[152] Areas where non-fouling surfaces need further improvement include extending the longevity of the surfaces and thus achieving long term protein and bacterial resistance, new strategies for tight control of non-fouling surface properties to minimize "imperfections", and correlating *in vitro* to *in vivo* surface performance. Along with advancements in experimental techniques, development of theories for an *a priori* prediction of surface performance would also be beneficial.[153]

References

1. S. P. Zustiak, Y. Wei, and J. B. Leach, Protein–hydrogel interactions in tissue engineering: Mechanisms and applications. *Tissue Eng. Part B: Rev.*, **19**, 160–171 (2013).
2. M. P. Lutolf, P. M. Gilbert, and H. M. Blau Designing materials to direct stem-cell fate. *Nature*, **462**, 433–441 (2009).
3. M. P. Lutolf and J. A. Hubbell, Synthetic biomaterials as instructive extracellular microenvironments for morphogenesis in tissue engineering. *Nat. Biotechnol.*, **23**, 47–55 (2005).
4. D. Seliktar, Designing cell-compatible hydrogels for biomedical applications. *Science*, **336**, 1124–1128 (2012).
5. L. G. Griffith and M. A. Swartz Capturing complex 3D tissue physiology *in vitro*. *Nat. Rev. Mol. Cell Bio.*, **7**, 211–224 (2006).
6. P. L. Chandran, D. C. Paik, and J. W. Holmes, Structural mechanism for alteration of collagen gel mechanics by glutaraldehyde crosslinking. *Connect. Tissue Res.*, **53**, 285–297 (2012).
7. Y. S. Chiang, Y. L. Chen, S. F. Chuang, C. M. Wu, P. J. Wei, C. F. Han *et al.*, Riboflavin-ultraviolet-A-induced collagen cross-linking treatments in improving dentin bonding. *Dent. Mater.*, **29**, 682–692 (2013).
8. S. Fiejdasz, K. Szczubialka, J. Lewandowska-Lancucka, A. M. Osyczka, and M. Nowakowska, Biopolymer-based hydrogels as injectable materials for tissue repair scaffolds. *Biomed. Mater.*, **8**, 035013 (2013).
9. D. J. Macaya, K. Hayakawa, K. Arai, and M. Spector, Astrocyte infiltration into injectable collagen-based hydrogels containing FGF-2 to treat spinal cord injury. *Biomater.*, **34**, 3591–3602 (2013).
10. Y. C. Kuo and I. N. Ku, Effects of gel concentration, human fibronectin, and cation supplement on the tissue-engineered cartilage. *Biotechnol. Progr.*, **23**, 238–245 (2007).

11. R. Scott, L. Marquardt, and R. K. Willits, Characterization of poly (ethylene glycol) gels with added collagen for neural tissue engineering. *J. Biomed. Mater. Res. Part A*, **93**, 817–823 (2010).
12. C. Fuoco, M. L. Salvatori, A. Biondo, K. Shapira-Schweitzer, S. Santoleri, S. Antonini *et al.*, Injectable polyethylene glycol-fibrinogen hydrogel adjuvant improves survival and differentiation of transplanted mesoangioblasts in acute and chronic skeletal-muscle degeneration. *Skeletal Muscle*, **2**, 24 (2012).
13. M. Gonen-Wadmany, L. Oss-Ronen, and D. Seliktar, Protein-polymer conjugates for forming photopolymerizable biomimetic hydrogels for tissue engineering. *Biomaterials*, **28**, 3876–3886 (2007).
14. V. Kuzmenko, S. Samfors, D. Hagg, and P. Gatenholm Universal method for protein bioconjugation with nanocellulose scaffolds for increased cell adhesion. *Mater. Sci. Eng. C*, **33**, 4599–4607 (2013).
15. S. Ravi, J. M. Caves, A. W. Martinez, C. A. Haller, and E. L. Chaikof, Incorporation of fibronectin to enhance cytocompatibility in multilayer elastin-like protein scaffolds for tissue engineering. *J. Biomed. Mater. Res. Part A*, **101**, 1915–1925 (2013).
16. C. R. Nuttelman, D. J. Mortisen, S. M. Henry, and K. S. Anseth, Attachment of fibronectin to poly (vinyl alcohol) hydrogels promotes NIH3T3 cell adhesion, proliferation, and migration. *J. Biomed. Mater. Res.*, **57**, 217–223 (2001).
17. A. T. Francisco, R. J. Mancino, R. D. Bowles, J. M. Brunger, D. M. Tainter, Y. T. Chen *et al.*, Injectable laminin-functionalized hydrogel for nucleus pulposus regeneration. *Biomaterials*, **34**, 7381–7388 (2013).
18. O. Sarig-Nadir and D. Seliktar Compositional alterations of fibrin-based materials for regulating *in vitro* neural outgrowth. *Tissue Eng. Part A*, **14**, 401–411 (2008).
19. H. Tan, Q. Zhou, H. Qi, D. Zhu, X. Ma, and D. Xiong, Heparin interacting protein mediated assembly of nano-fibrous hydrogel scaffolds for guided stem cell differentiation. *Macromol. Biosci.*, **12**, 621–627 (2012).
20. N. R. Gandavarapu, P. D. Mariner, M. P. Schwartz, and K. S. Anseth, Extracellular matrix protein adsorption to phosphate-functionalized gels from serum promotes osteogenic differentiation of human mesenchymal stem cells. *Acta Biomater.*, **9**, 4525–4534 (2013).
21. T. Yan, R. Sun, C. Li, B. Tan, X. Mao, and N. Ao Immobilization of type-I collagen and basic fibroblast growth factor (bFGF) onto poly (HEMA-co-MMA) hydrogel surface and its cytotoxicity study. *J. Mater. Sci- Mater. M*, **21**, 2425–2433 (2010).
22. E. Brynda, M. Houska, J. Kysilka, M. Pradny, P. Lesny, P. Jendelova *et al.*, Surface modification of hydrogels based on poly (2-hydroxyethyl methacrylate) with extra-cellular matrix proteins. *J. Mater. Sci- Mater. M*, **20**, 909–915 (2009).
23. J. M. Morais, F. Papadimitrakopoulos, and D. J. Burgess, Biomaterials/tissue interactions: Possible solutions to overcome foreign body response. *AAPS J.*, **12**, 188–196 (2010).
24. J. Lee, J. J. Yoo, A. Atala, and S. J. Lee, Controlled heparin conjugation on electrospun poly (epsilon-caprolactone)/gelatin fibers for morphology-dependent protein delivery and enhanced cellular affinity. *Acta Biomater.*, **8**, 2549–2558 (2012).

25. J. Lee, J. J. Yoo, A. Atala, and S. J. Lee, The effect of controlled release of PDGF–BB from heparin-conjugated electrospun PCL/gelatin scaffolds on cellular bioactivity and infiltration. *Biomaterials*, **33**, 6709–6720 (2012).
26. I. Freeman and S. Cohen, The influence of the sequential delivery of angiogenic factors from affinity-binding alginate scaffolds on vascularization. *Biomaterials*, **30**, 2122–2131 (2009).
27. K. J. Jeong and A. Panitch, Interplay between covalent and physical interactions within environment sensitive hydrogels. *Biomacromolecules*, **10**, 1090–1099 (2009).
28. M. Gonen-Wadmany, R. Goldshmid, and D. Seliktar, Biological and mechanical implications of PEGylating proteins into hydrogel biomaterials. *Biomaterials*, **32**, 6025–6033 (2011).
29. L. E. Millon, D. T. Padavan, A. M. Hamilton, D. R. Boughner, and W.Wan, Exploring cell compatibility of a fibronectin-functionalized physically crosslinked poly (vinyl alcohol) hydrogel. *J. Biomed. Mater. Res. B*, **100**, 1–10 (2012).
30. D. L. Hern and J. A. Hubbell, Incorporation of adhesion peptides into nonadhesive hydrogels useful for tissue resurfacing. *J. Biomed. Mater. Res.*, **39**, 266–276 (1998).
31. A. Hautanen, J. Gailit, D. M. Mann, and E. Ruoslahti, Effects of modifications of the RGD sequence and its context on recognition by the fibronectin receptor. *J Biol Chem.*, **264**, 1437–1442 (1989).
32. E. Ruoslahti, RGD and other recognition sequences for integrins. *Annu Rev Cell Dev Biol.*, **12**, 697–715 (1996).
33. U. Hersel, C. Dahmen, and H. Kessler, RGD modified polymers: Biomaterials for stimulated cell adhesion and beyond. *Biomaterials*, **24**, 4385–4415 (2003).
34. H. Shin, S. Jo, and A. G. Mikos, Biomimetic materials for tissue engineering. *Biomaterials*, **24**, 4353–4364 (2003).
35. M. P. Lutolf and J. A. Hubbell, Synthesis and physicochemical characterization of end-linked poly (ethylene glycol)-co-peptide hydrogels formed by Michael-type addition. *Biomacromolecules*, **4**, 713–722 (2003).
36. S. P. Zustiak and J. B. Leach, Hydrolytically degradable poly (ethylene glycol) hydrogel scaffolds with tunable degradation and mechanical properties. *Biomacromolecules*, **11**, 1348–1357 (2010).
37. C. N. Salinas and K. S. Anseth, The influence of the RGD peptide motif and its contextual presentation in PEG gels on human mesenchymal stem cell viability. *J. Tissue Eng. Regen. Med.*, **2**, 296–304 (2008).
38. K. H. Park, M. H. Kim, S. H. Park, H. J. Lee, I. K. Kim, and H. M. Chung, Synthesis of Arg-Gly-Asp (RGD) sequence conjugated thermo-reversible gel via the PEG spacer arm as an extracellular matrix for a pheochromocytoma cell (PC12) culture. *Biosci. Biotechnol. Bioch.*, **68**, 2224–2229 (2004).
39. J. H. Beer, K. T. Springer, and B. S. Coller, Immobilized Arg-Gly-Asp (RGD) peptides of varying lengths as structural probes of the platelet glycoprotein IIb/IIIa receptor. *Blood*, **79**, 117–128 (1992).

40. M. J. Wilson, S. J. Liliensiek, C. J. Murphy, W. L. Murphy, and P. F. Nealey, Hydrogels with well-defined peptide-hydrogel spacing and concentration: Impact on epithelial cell behavior. *Soft Matter*, **8**, 390–398 (2012).
41. M. D. Pierschbacher and E. Ruoslahti, Cell attachment activity of fibronectin can be duplicated by small synthetic fragments of the molecule. *Nature*, **309**, 30–33 (1984).
42. M. D. Pierschbacher and E. Ruoslahti, Variants of the cell recognition site of fibronectin that retain attachment-promoting activity. *Proc. Natl. Acad. Sci. USA*, **81**, 5985–5988 (1984).
43. J. Zhu, C. Tang, K. Kottke-Marchant, and R. E. Marchant, Design and synthesis of biomimetic hydrogel scaffolds with controlled organization of cyclic RGD peptides. *Bioconjugate Chem.*, **20**, 333–339 (2009).
44. M. P. Lutolf, N. Tirelli, S. Cerritelli, L. Cavalli, and J. A. Hubbell, Systematic modulation of Michael-type reactivity of thiols through the use of charged amino acids. *Bioconjugate Chem.*, **12**, 1051–1056 (2001).
45. K. Vats, D. S. Benoit, Dynamic manipulation of hydrogels to control cell behavior: A review. *Tissue Eng. Part B: Rev.*, **19**, 455–469 (2013).
46. S. P. Zustiak, S. Pubill, A. Ribeiro, J. B. Leach, Hydrolytically degradable poly (ethylene glycol) hydrogel scaffolds as a cell delivery vehicle: characterization of PC12 cell response. *Biotechnol. Progr.*, **29**, 1255–1264 (2013).
47. L. Lin, J. Zhu, K. Kottke-Marchant, R. E. Marchant, Biomimetic-engineered poly(ethylene glycol) hydrogel for smooth muscle cell migration. *Tissue Eng. Part A*, **20**, 864–873 (2014).
48. R. H. Schmedlen, K. S. Masters, and J. L. West, Photocrosslinkable polyvinyl alcohol hydrogels that can be modified with cell adhesion peptides for use in tissue engineering. *Biomaterials*, **23**, 4325–4332 (2002).
49. S. Ali, J. E. Saik, D. J. Gould, M. E. Dickinson, and J. L. West, Immobilization of cell-adhesive laminin peptides in degradable pegda hydrogels influences endothelial cell tubulogenesis. *Biores. Open Access*, **2**, 241–249 (2013).
50. J. W. Gunn, S. D. Turner, and B. K. Mann, Adhesive and mechanical properties of hydrogels influence neurite extension. *J. Biomed. Mater. Res. Part A*, **72**, 91–97 (2005).
51. P. N. Patel, A. S. Gobin, J. L. West, and C. W. Patrick, Poly (ethylene glycol) hydrogel system supports preadipocyte viability, adhesion, and proliferation. *Tissue Eng.*, **11**, 1498–1505 (2005).
52. H. F. Ahmad and A. Sambanis, Cryopreservation effects on recombinant myoblasts encapsulated in adhesive alginate hydrogels. *Acta Biomater.* **9**, 6814–6822 (2013).
53. L. A. Smith Callahan, E. P. Childers, S. L. Bernard, S. D. Weiner, and M. L. Becker, Maximizing phenotype constraint and extracellular matrix production in primary human chondrocytes using arginine-glycine-aspartate concentration gradient hydrogels. *Acta Biomater.*, **9**, 7420–7428 (2013).
54. W. A. Comisar, N. H. Kazmers, D. J. Mooney, and J. J. Linderman, Engineering RGD nanopatterned hydrogels to control preosteoblast behavior: A combined computational and experimental approach. *Biomaterials*, **28**, 4409–4417 (2007).

55. G. Maheshwari, G. Brown, D. A. Lauffenburger, A. Wells, L. G. Griffith, Cell adhesion and motility depend on nanoscale RGD clustering. *J. Cell Sci.*, **113** (Pt 10), 1677–1686 (2000).
56. L. Y. Koo, D. J. Irvine, A. M. Mayes, D. A. Lauffenburger, and L. G. Griffith, Co-regulation of cell adhesion by nanoscale RGD organization and mechanical stimulus. *J. Cell Sci.*, **115**, 1423–1433 (2002).
57. K. Mandal, M. Balland, and L. Bureau, Thermoresponsive micropatterned substrates for single cell studies. *Plos One*, **7**, e37548 (2012).
58. J. Zhang, W. H. Guo, A. Rape, and Y. L. Wang, Micropatterning cell adhesion on polyacrylamide hydrogels. *Method. Mol. Biol.*, **1066**, 147–156 (2013).
59. D. Aydin, I. Louban, N. Perschmann, J. Blummel, T. Lohmuller, E. A. Cavalcanti-Adam *et al.*, Polymeric substrates with tunable elasticity and nanoscopically controlled biomolecule presentation. *Langmuir*, **26**, 15472–15480 (2010).
60. S. H. Ngalim, A. Magenau, Y. Zhu, L. Tonnesen, Z. Fairjones, J. J. Gooding T. Bocking, K. Gaus, Creating adhesive and soluble gradients for imaging cell migration with fluorescence microscopy. *JoVE*, (2013).
61. Z. Liu, L. Xiao, B. Xu, Y. Zhang, A. F. Mak, Y. Li, *et al.*, Covalently immobilized biomolecule gradient on hydrogel surface using a gradient generating microfluidic device for a quantitative mesenchymal stem cell study. *Biomicrofluids*, **6**, 24111–2411112 (2012).
62. J. C. Hoffmann and J. L. West, Three-dimensional photolithographic micropatterning: A novel tool to probe the complexities of cell migration. *Integr. Biol.* (*Camb*), **5**, 817–827 (2013).
63. J. Yang, M. Yamato, C. Kohno, A. Nishimoto, H. Sekine, F. Fukai *et al.*, Cell sheet engineering: Recreating tissues without biodegradable scaffolds. *Biomaterials*, 26, 6415–6422 (2005).
64. A. Kikuchi and T. Okano, Nanostructured designs of biomedical materials: Applications of cell sheet engineering to functional regenerative tissues and organs. *J. Control Release*, **101**, 69–84 (2005).
65. N. Matsuda, T. Shimizu, M. Yamato, and T. Okano, Tissue Engineering Based on Cell Sheet Technology. *Adv. Mater.*, **19**, 3089–3099 (2007).
66. Z. Ding, G. Chen, and A. S. Hoffman, Synthesis and purification of thermally sensitive oligomer–enzyme conjugates of poly (N-isopropylacrylamide)–trypsin. *Bioconjugate Chem.*, **7**, 121–125 (1996).
67. Y. Tsuda, A. Kikuchi, M. Yamato, A. Nakao, Y. Sakurai, M. Umezu *et al.*, The use of patterned dual thermoresponsive surfaces for the collective recovery as co-cultured cell sheets. *Biomaterials*, **26**, 1885–1893 (2005).
68. A. Mizutani, A. Kikuchi, M. Yamato, H. Kanazawa, and T. Okano, Preparation of thermoresponsive polymer brush surfaces and their interaction with cells. *Biomaterials*, **29**, 2073–2081 (2008).
69. Y. Akiyama, A. Kikuchi, M. Yamato, and T. Okano, Ultrathin poly (N-isopropylacrylamide) grafted layer on polystyrene surfaces for cell adhesion/detachment control. Langmuir, **20**, 5506–5511 (2004).

70. K. Haraguchi, T. Takehisa, and M. Ebato, Control of cell cultivation and cell sheet detachment on the surface of polymer/clay nanocomposite hydrogels. *Biomacromolecules*, **7**, 3267–3275 (2006).
71. H. Takahashi, N. Matsuzaka, M. Nakayama, A. Kikuchi, M. Yamato, and T. Okano, Terminally functionalized thermoresponsive polymer brushes for simultaneously promoting cell adhesion and cell sheet harvest. *Biomacromolecules*, **13**, 253–260 (2011).
72. B. C. Isenberg, Y. Tsuda, C. Williams, T. Shimizu, M. Yamato, T. Okano *et al.*, A thermoresponsive, microtextured substrate for cell sheet engineering with defined structural organization. *Biomaterials*, **29**, 2565–2572 (2008).
73. Z. Tang, Y. Akiyama, M. Yamato, and T. Okano, Comb-type grafted poly (<i> N</i>-isopropylacrylamide) gel modified surfaces for rapid detachment of cell sheet. *Biomaterials*, **31**, 7435–7443 (2010).
74. W. -S. Yeo and M. Mrksich, Electroactive self-assembled monolayers that permit orthogonal control over the adhesion of cells to patterned substrates. *Langmuir*, **22**, 10816–10820 (2006).
75. J. Fukuda, Y. Kameoka, and H. Suzuki, Spatio-temporal detachment of single cells using microarrayed transparent electrodes. *Biomaterials*, **32**, 6663–6669 (2011).
76. N. Sadr, M. Zhu, T. Osaki, T. Kakegawa, Y. Yang, M. Moretti *et al.*, SAM-based cell transfer to photopatterned hydrogels for microengineering vascular-like structures. *Biomaterials*, **32**, 7479–7490 (2011).
77. S Masuda, T. Shimizu, M. Yamato, and T. Okano, Cell sheet engineering for heart tissue repair. *Adv Drug Deliv. Rev.*, **60**, 277–285 (2008).
78. J. Yang, M. Yamato, T. Shimizu, H. Sekine, K. Ohashi, M. Kanzaki *et al.*, Reconstruction of functional tissues with cell sheet engineering. *Biomaterials*, **28**, 5033–5043 (2007).
79. S. P. Zustiak, R. Durbal, and J. B. Leach, Influence of cell-adhesive peptide ligands on poly (ethylene glycol) hydrogel physical, mechanical and transport properties. *Acta Biomater.*, **6**, 3404–3414 (2010).
80. J. B. Leach, X. Q. Brown, J. G. Jacot, P. A. Dimilla, and J. Y. Wong, Neurite outgrowth and branching of PC12 cells on very soft substrates sharply decreases below a threshold of substrate rigidity. *J. Neural Eng.*, **4**, 26–34 (2007).
81. R. A. Scott, D. L. Elbert, and R. K. Willits, Modular poly (ethylene glycol) scaffolds provide the ability to decouple the effects of stiffness and protein concentration on PC12 cells. *Acta Biomater.*, **7**, 3841–3849 (2011).
82. K. Saha, A. J. Keung, E. F. Irwin, Y. Li, L. Little, D. V. Schaffer *et al.*, Substrate modulus directs neural stem cell behavior. *Biophys. J.*, **95**, 4426–4438 (2008).
83. J. M. Ino, P. Chevallier, D. Letourneur, D. Mantovani, and C. Le Visage, Plasma functionalization of poly (vinyl alcohol) hydrogel for cell adhesion enhancement. *Biomatter*, **3** (2013), e25414.
84. C. Zhang, S. Hekmatfer, and N. W. Karuri, A comparative study of polyethylene glycol hydrogels derivatized with the RGD peptide and the cell-binding domain of fibronectin. *J. Biomed. Mater. Res. Part A*, **102**, 170–179 (2013).

85. Y. Cheng, C. He, C. Xiao, J. Ding, H. Cui, X. Zhuang *et al.*, Versatile biofunctionalization of polypeptide-based thermosensitive hydrogels via click chemistry. *Biomacromolecules*, **14**, 468–475 (2014).
86. N. Huebsch, M. Gilbert, and KE. Healy, Analysis of sterilization protocols for peptide-modified hydrogels. *J. Biomed. Mater. Res. Part B*, **74**, 440–447 (2005).
87. S. Sharma, R. W. Johnson, and T. A. Desai, XPS and AFM analysis of antifouling PEG interfaces for microfabricated silicon biosensors. *Biosens. Bioelectron.*, **20**, 227–239 (2004).
88. S. Vaddiraju, I. Tomazos, D. J. Burgess, F. C. Jain, and F. Papadimitrakopoulos, Emerging synergy between nanotechnology and implantable biosensors: A review. *Biosens. Bioelectron.*, **25**, 1553–1565 (2010).
89. J. Costerton, P. S. Stewart, and E. Greenberg. Bacterial biofilms: A common cause of persistent infections. *Science*, **284**, 1318–1322 (1999).
90. L. Hall-Stoodley, J. W. Costerton, and P. Stoodley, Bacterial biofilms: From the natural environment to infectious diseases. *Nat. Rev. Microbiol.*, **2**, 95–108 (2004).
91. K. M. Bischoff, S. Liu, T. D. Leathers, R. E. Worthington, J. O. Rich, Modeling bacterial contamination of fuel ethanol fermentation. *Biotechnol. Bioeng.*, **103**, 117–122 (2009).
92. W. Senaratne, L. Andruzzi, and C. K. Ober, Self-assembled monolayers and polymer brushes in biotechnology: Current applications and future perspectives. *Biomacromolecules*, **6**, 2427–2448 (2005).
93. I. P. Parkin and R. G. Palgrave, Self-cleaning coatings. *J. Mater Chem.*, **15**, 1689–1695 (2005).
94. L. Mi, M. T. Bernards, G. Cheng, Q. Yu, and S. Jiang, pH responsive properties of non-fouling mixed-charge polymer brushes based on quaternary amine and carboxylic acid monomers. *Biomaterials*, **31**, 2919–2925 (2010).
95. K. Glinel, A. M. Jonas, T. Jouenne, J. Leprince, L. Galas, and W. T. Huck, Antibacterial and antifouling polymer brushes incorporating antimicrobial peptide. *Bioconjugate Chem.*, **20**, 71–77 (2008).
96. I. Banerjee, R. C. Pangule, and R. S. Kane, Antifouling coatings: Recent developments in the design of surfaces that prevent fouling by proteins, bacteria, and marine organisms. *Adv. Mater.*, **23**, 690–718 (2011).
97. Q. Yu, Y. Zhang, H. Wang, J. Brash, and H. Chen, Anti-fouling bioactive surfaces. *Acta Biomater.*, **7**, 1550–1557 (2011).
98. A. S. Sawhney, C. P. Pathak, J. J. van Rensburg, R. C. Dunn, and J. A. Hubbell, Optimization of photopolymerized bioerodible hydrogel properties for adhesion prevention. *J. Biomed. Mater. Res.*, **28**, 831–838 (1994).
99. Q. Yang, J. Tian, M.-X. Hu, Z.-K. Xu, Construction of a comb-like glycosylated membrane surface by a combination of UV-induced graft polymerization and surface-initiated ATRP. *Langmuir*, **23**, 6684–6690 (2007).
100. S. G. Boyes, A. M. Granville, M. Baum, B. Akgun, B. K. Mirous, and W. J. Brittain, Polymer brushes — surface immobilized polymers. *Surface Science*, **570**, 1–12 (2004).

101. B. Gupta, C. Plummer, I. Bisson, P. Frey, and J. Hilborn, Plasma-induced graft polymerization of acrylic acid onto poly (ethylene terephthalate) films: Characterization and human smooth muscle cell growth on grafted films. *Biomaterials*, **23**, 863–871 (2002).
102. K. Kato, E. Uchida, E. T. Kang, Y. Uyama, and Y. Ikada, Polymer surface with graft chains. *Progr. Polym. Sci.*, **28**, 209–259 (2003).
103. B. Zhao and W. J. Brittain, Polymer brushes: Surface-immobilized macromolecules. *Progr. Polym. Sci.*, **25**, 677–710 (2000).
104. R. Barbey, L. Lavanant, D. Paripovic, N. Schüwer, C. Sugnaux, S. Tugulu *et al.*, Polymer brushes via surface-initiated controlled radical polymerization: Synthesis, characterization, properties, and applications. *Chem. Rev.*, **109**, 5437–527 (2009).
105. P. Uhlmann, H. Merlitz, Sommer, and M. Stamm, Polymer Brushes for Surface Tuning. *Macromol. Rapid Comm.*, **30**, 732–740 (2009).
106. B. D. Ratner and S. J. Bryant, Biomaterials: Where we have been and where we are going. *Annu Rev Biomed Eng.*, **6**, 41–75 (2004).
107. A. K. Muszanska, H. J. Busscher, A. Herrmann, H. C. van der Mei, and W. Norde, Pluronic–lysozyme conjugates as anti-adhesive and antibacterial bifunctional polymers for surface coating. *Biomaterials*, **32**, 6333–6341 (2011).
108. E. Ostuni, R. G. Chapman, R. E. Holmlin, S. Takayama, and G. M. Whitesides, A survey of structure–property relationships of surfaces that resist the adsorption of protein. *Langmuir*, **17**, 5605–5620 (2001).
109. R. Michel, S. Pasche, M. Textor, and D. G. Castner, Influence of PEG architecture on protein adsorption and conformation. *Langmuir*, **21**, 12327–12332 (2005).
110. S. Pasche, M. Textor, L. Meagher, N. D. Spencer, and H. J. Griesser, Relationship between interfacial forces measured by colloid-probe atomic force microscopy and protein resistance of poly (ethylene glycol)-grafted poly (L-lysine) adlayers on niobia surfaces. *Langmuir*, **21**, 6508–65020 (2005).
111. B. Fang, S. Gon, M. Park, K.-N. Kumar, V. M. Rotello, K. Nusslein *et al.*, Bacterial adhesion on hybrid cationic nanoparticle-polymer brush surfaces: Ionic strength tunes capture from monovalent to multivalent binding. *Colloid Surface B*, **87**, 109–115 (2011).
112. S. Reddy, E. Arzt, and A. del Campo, Bioinspired surfaces with switchable adhesion. *Adv. Mater.*, **19**, 3833–3837 (2007).
113. D. Paretkar, M. Kamperman, A. S. Schneider, D. Martina, C. Creton, and E. Arzt, Bioinspired pressure actuated adhesive system. *Mat. Sci. Eng. C*, **31**, 1152–1159 (2011).
114. S. T. Reddy, K. K. Chung, C. J. McDaniel, R. O. Darouiche, J. Landman, A. B. Brennan, Micropatterned surfaces for reducing the risk of catheter-associated urinary tract infection: An *in vitro* study on the effect of sharklet micropatterned surfaces to inhibit bacterial colonization and migration of uropathogenic *Escherichia coli*. *J. Endourol.*, **25**, 1547–1552 (2011).
115. A. Synytska, E. Svetushkina, D. Martina, C. Bellmann, F. Simon, L. Ionov *et al.*, Intelligent materials with adaptive adhesion properties based on comb-like polymer brushes. *Langmuir*, **28**, 16444–16454 (2012).

116. M. Müller, S. Lee, H. A. Spikes, and N. D. Spencer, The influence of molecular architecture on the macroscopic lubrication properties of the brush-like co-polyelectrolyte poly (L-lysine)-g-poly (ethylene glycol) (PLL-g-PEG) adsorbed on oxide surfaces. *Tribol. Lett.*, **15**, 395–405 (2003).
117. S. Lee and N. D. Spencer, Adsorption properties of poly (L-lysine)-graft-poly (ethylene glycol) (PLL-g-PEG) at a hydrophobic interface: Influence of tribological stress, pH, salt concentration, and polymer molecular weight. *Langmuir*, **24**, 9479–9488 (2008).
118. C. Perrino, S. Lee, S. W. Choi, A. Maruyama, and N. D. Spencer, A biomimetic alternative to poly (ethylene glycol) as an antifouling coating: Resistance to nonspecific protein adsorption of poly (L-lysine)-graft-dextran. *Langmuir*, **24**, 8850–8856 (2008).
119. Y. Zou, N. A. Rossi, J. N. Kizhakkedathu, and D. E. Brooks, Barrier capacity of hydrophilic polymer brushes to prevent hydrophobic interactions: Effect of graft density and hydrophilicity. *Macromolecules*, **42**, 4817–4828 (2009).
120. S. Han, C. Kim, and D. Kwon, Thermal/oxidative degradation and stabilization of polyethylene glycol. *Polymer*, **38**, 317–323 (1997).
121. A. Halperin, G. Fragneto, A. Schollier, M. Sferrazza, Primary versus ternary adsorption of proteins onto PEG brushes. *Langmuir*, **23**, 10603–10617 (2007).
122. K. H. A. Lau, Peptoids for biomaterials science. *Biomater. Sci.*, **2**, 627–633 (2014).
123. W. S. Horne, Peptide and peptoid foldamers in medicinal chemistry. *Expert opin. Drug Discov.*, **6**, 1247–1262 (2011).
124. Q. Sui, D. Borchardt, and D. L. Rabenstein, Kinetics and equilibria of cis/trans isomerization of backbone amide bonds in peptoids. *J. Am. Chem. Soc.*, **129**, 12042–12048 (2007).
125. K. H. A. Lau, C. Ren, T. S. Sileika, S. H. Park, I. Szleifer, and P. B. Messersmith, Surface-grafted polysarcosine as a peptoid antifouling polymer brush. *Langmuir*, **28**, 16099–16107 (2012).
126. S. Gon, M. Bendersky, J. L. Ross, and M. M. Santore, Manipulating protein adsorption using a patchy protein-resistant brush. *Langmuir*, **26**, 12147–12154 (2010).
127. S. Gon and M. M. Santore, Sensitivity of protein adsorption to architectural variations in a protein-resistant polymer brush containing engineered nanoscale adhesive sites. *Langmuir*, **27**, 15083–15091 (2011).
128. B. Fang, S. Gon, M. H. Park, K. N. Kumar, V. M. Rotello, K. Nusslein *et al.*, Using flow to switch the valency of bacterial capture on engineered surfaces containing immobilized nanoparticles. *Langmuir*, **28**, 7803–7810 (2012).
129. F. W. Delrio, M. P. de Boer, J. A. Knapp, E. Jr. David Reedy, P. J. Clews, and M. L. Dunn, The role of van der Waals forces in adhesion of micromachined surfaces. *Nat. Mater.*, **4**, 629–634 (2005).
130. B. Bhushan, Adhesion and stiction: Mechanisms, measurement techniques, and methods for reduction. *J. Vac. Sci. Technol. B*, **21**, 2262–2296.
131. C. J. Weinman, J. A. Finlay, D. Park, M. Y. Paik, S. Krishnan, H. S. Sundaram *et al.*, ABC triblock surface active block copolymer with grafted ethoxylated fluoroalkyl amphiphilic side chains for marine antifouling/fouling-release applications. *Langmuir*, **25**, 12266–12274 (2009).

132. E. Martinelli, M. Suffredini, G. Galli, A. Glisenti, M. E. Pettitt, M. E. Callow *et al.*, Amphiphilic block copolymer/poly (dimethylsiloxane) (PDMS) blends and nanocomposites for improved fouling-release. *Biofouling*, **27**, 529–541 (2011).
133. I. Francolini, F. Crisante, A. Martinelli, L. D'Ilario, and A. Piozzi, Synthesis of biomimetic segmented polyurethanes as antifouling biomaterials. *Acta Biomater.*, **8**, 549–558 (2012).
134. R. Sheparovych, M. Motornov, and S. Minko. Adapting low-adhesive thin films from mixed polymer brushes. *Langmuir*, **24**, 13828–13832 (2008).
135. Z. Burton and B. Bhushan, Hydrophobicity, adhesion, and friction properties of nanopatterned polymers and scale dependence for micro-and nanoelectromechanical systems. *Nano lett.*, **5**, 1607–1613 (2005).
136. D. Chandler, Interfaces and the driving force of hydrophobic assembly. *Nature*, **437**, 640–647 (2005).
137. R. Sheparovych, M. Motornov, and S. Minko, Low adhesive surfaces that adapt to changing environments. *Adv. Mater.*, **21**, 1840–1844 (2009).
138. G. Li, G. Cheng, H. Xue, S. Chen, F. Zhang, and S. Jiang, Ultra low fouling zwitterionic polymers with a biomimetic adhesive group. *Biomaterials*, **29**, 4592–4597 (2008).
139. Y. -H. Zhao, K. -H. Wee, and R. Bai, Highly hydrophilic and low-protein-fouling polypropylene membrane prepared by surface modification with sulfobetaine-based zwitterionic polymer through a combined surface polymerization method. *J. Membrane Sci.*, **362**, 326–333 (2010).
140. P. -S. Liu, Q. Chen, S. -S. Wu, J. Shen, and S. -C. Lin, Surface modification of cellulose membranes with zwitterionic polymers for resistance to protein adsorption and platelet adhesion. *J. Membrane Sci.*, **350**, 387–394 (2010).
141. J. Ladd, Z. Zhang, S. Chen, J. C. Hower, and S. Jiang, Zwitterionic polymers exhibiting high resistance to nonspecific protein adsorption from human serum and plasma. *Biomacromolecules*, **9**, 1357–1361 (2008).
142. G. Cheng, G. Li, H. Xue, S. Chen, J. D. Bryers, and S. Jiang, Zwitterionic carboxybetaine polymer surfaces and their resistance to long-term biofilm formation. *Biomaterials*, **30**, 5234–5240 (2009).
143. T. Kakegawa, N. Mochizuki, N. Sadr, H. Suzuki, and J. Fukuda, Cell-Adhesive and cell-repulsive zwitterionic oligopeptides for micropatterning and rapid electrochemical detachment of cells. *Tissue Eng. Part A*, **19**, 290–298 (2012).
144. N. D. Brault, C. Gao, Xue H, Piliarik M, Homola J, Jiang S *et al.*, Ultra-low fouling and functionalizable zwitterionic coatings grafted onto SiO2 via a biomimetic adhesive group for sensing and detection in complex media. *Biosens. Bioelectron.*, **25**, 2276–2282 (2010).
145. S. Chen and S. Jiang, An new avenue to nonfouling materials. *Adv. Mater.*, **20**, 335–338 (2008).
146. M. T. Bernards, G. Cheng, Z. Zhang, S. Chen, and S. Jiang, Nonfouling polymer brushes via surface-initiated, two-component atom transfer radical polymerization. *Macromolecules*, **41**, 4216–4219 (2008).

147. V. P. Harden and J. O. Harris, The isoelectric point of bacterial cells. *J. Bacteriol.*, **65**, 198–202 (1953).
148. S. Rose, S. Okere, G. Hanlon, A. Lloyd, and A. Lewis, Bacterial adhesion to phosphorylcholine-based polymers with varying cationic charge and the effect of heparin pre-adsorption. *J. Mater. Sci.- Mater. M.*, **16**, 1003–1015 (2005).
149. C. A. DeForest, B. D. Polizzotti, and K. S. Anseth, Sequential click reactions for synthesizing and patterning three-dimensional cell microenvironments. *Nat. Mater.*, **8**, 659–664 (2009).
150. O. Pop-Georgievski, C. Rodriguez-Emmenegger, A. de los Santos Pereira, V. Proks, E. Brynda, and F. Rypacek, Biomimetic non-fouling surfaces: Extending the concepts. *J. Mater. Chem. Part B*, **1**, 2859–2867 (2013).
151. X. Wang, H. Gan, and T. Sun, Chiral design for polymeric biointerface: The influence of surface chirality on protein adsorption. *Adv. Funct. Mater.*, **21**, 3276–3281 (2011).
152. X. Wang, H. Gan, M. Zhang, and T. Sun, Modulating cell behaviors on chiral polymer brush films with different hydrophobic side groups. *Langmuir*, **28**, 2791–2798 (2012).
153. K. A. Lau, C. Ren, S. H. Park, I. Szleifer, and P. B. Messersmith, An experimental — theoretical analysis of protein adsorption on peptidomimetic polymer brushes. *Langmuir*, **28**, 2288–2298 (2011).

Chapter 8

Photo-Crosslinking Methods to Design Hydrogels

Brian Amsden
Department of Chemical Engineering
Queen's University
Kingston, Ontario, Canada

Hydrogel formation using photo-initiated crosslinking has gained increased interest in multiple biomedical fields, including regenerative medicine, tissue engineering, and drug delivery. A wide variety of approaches have been developed, including those based on free radical polymerization, nitrene reactions and cycloaddition reactions. Each of these approaches has advantages and disadvantages when considering application to different applications. This chapter provides an overview of the materials, chemistries, and applications of each of these approaches in the formation of hydrogel biomaterials.

1. Introduction

Visible or UV light along with light-sensitive compounds to generate covalent crosslinks for the formation of hydrogel biomaterials was first explored in the early 1990s,[1–3] and since then interest in this approach has expanded and encompassed a wide variety of starting materials. This interest is a result of the potential advantages provided by this approach, which include the ability to form networks at ambient temperature under relatively mild conditions, the rapid kinetics of gel formation, and the ability to tailor the network properties by controlling the conditions of the crosslinking reaction.[4] These advantages make this method of forming hydrogels particularly well suited for direct application *in vivo*,[5–8] for the encapsulation of viable cells for tissue engineering and regenerative medicine strategies,[3,9–12] as well as for controlled drug release applications.[13–18] This chapter will outline the various methods that have been examined for the preparation of hydrogel biomaterials though photo-crosslinking.

The general strategy utilized for the formation of hydrogels via photo-crosslinking is to employ either: (i) multifunctional water soluble monomers or (ii) water soluble polymers and then functionalize them either along the backbone or at their termini with reactive groups capable of undergoing covalent linking upon exposure to light energy of the appropriate wavelength. However, the former approach often yields inhomogeneous networks,[19,20] and cannot be done in the presence of cells due to the cytotoxicity of the monomers typically used. Thus, most strategies involve the preparation of water-soluble polymers functionalized with photo reactive groups. A variety of different water soluble polymers have been examined, including synthetics such as poly(ethylene glycol) (PEG) (linear and star configurations) and poly(vinyl alcohol) (PVA), as well as naturally derived polymers such as hyaluronic acid (HA), chondroitin sulfate, chitosan, dextran, and alginate (Fig. 1). The photo-reactive approaches taken can be classified into three categories: free radical polymerizations, nitrene reactions, and cycloaddition reactions.

2. Free-Radical Polymerization

This approach to the formation of hydrogels involves the conjugation of unsaturated groups either at polymer termini or along the polymer backbone. Typically used unsaturated groups are the (meth)acrylates, because the double bonded carbon in these groups are highly reactive, leading to rapid gelation kinetics.[21] A number of chemical strategies have been employed for grafting (meth)acrylates to water soluble polymers, exploiting the available amine, hydroxyl, and carboxylic acid groups; free amine and hydroxyl groups are readily functionalized with (meth)acrylate derivatized molecules such as glycidyl methacrylate,[10,22,23] 2-isocyanatoethyl methacrylate,[24] methacrylic anhydride,[25,26] and (meth)acryloyl chloride,[10] while the carboxylic acid groups can be reacted with primary amine derivatized (meth)acrylates such as N-(3-aminopropyl) methacrylamide[27] or 2-aminoethyl (meth)acrylate[28] in the presence of N-hydroxysuccinimide and 1-ethyl-3-(3-dimethylaminopropyl)-carbodiimide hydrochloride. Some examples of water-soluble polymers that have been functionalized with (meth)acrylate groups include: PEG (linear and multi-arm star configurations),[29,30] PVA,[31] dextran,[32] HA,[26] chondroitin sulfate,[10] glycol chitosan,[23] and alginate.[25] Representative structures of some of these polymers manner are given in Fig. 2.

Hydrogel formation by photo-crosslinking via a free radical chain-growth polymerization approach typically relies on the use of a cytocompatible

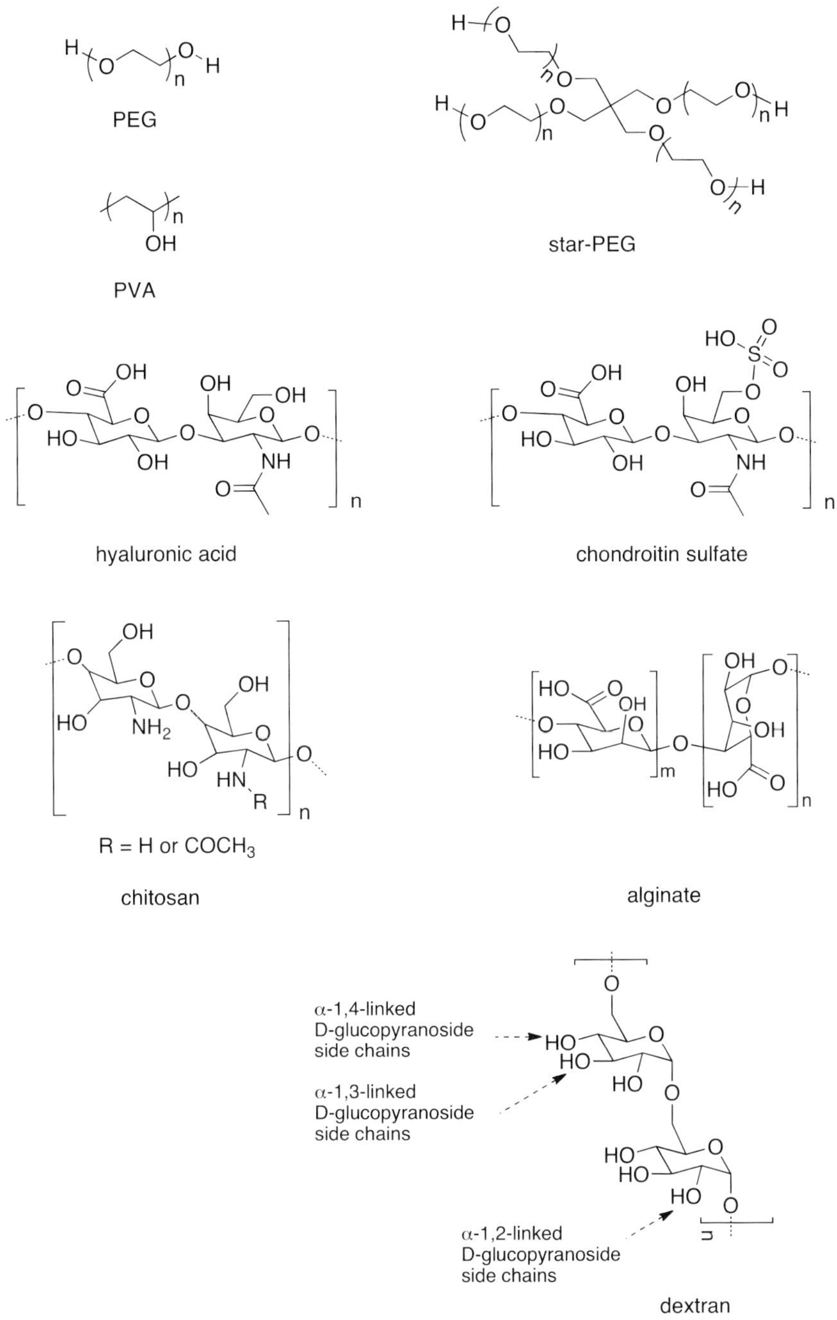

Fig. 1. Structures of representative polymers that have been used to form photo-crosslinked hydrogels.

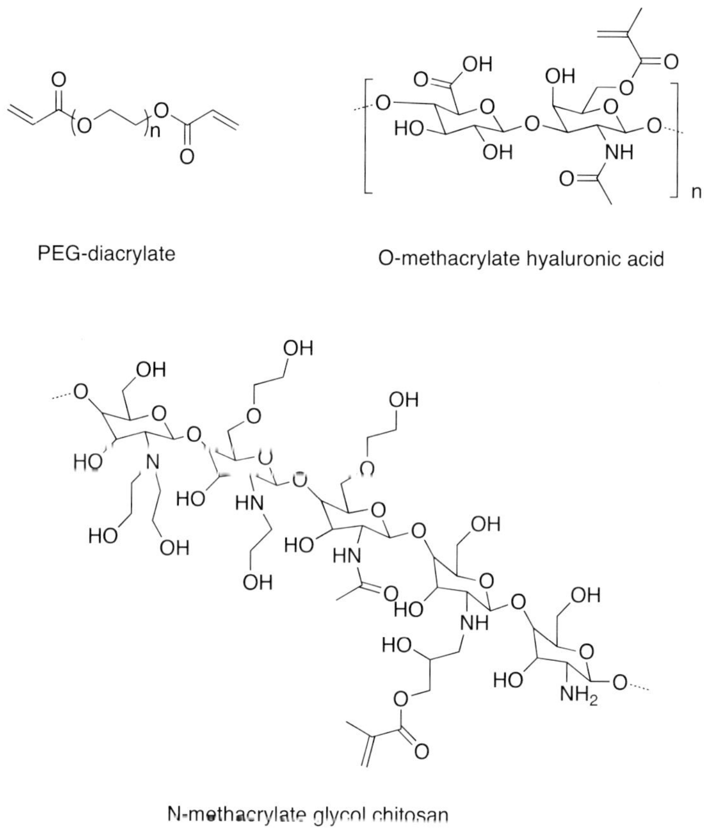

Fig. 2. Examples of water-soluble polymers that have been functionalized with (meth)acrylate groups.

photoinitiator that absorbs sufficiently at a specific wavelength of light and either decomposes (Type I) or abstracts hydrogen from a donor molecule (Type II) to form radical initiating species.[4] The initiator radicals react with the unsaturated groups on the polymer, leading to radical propagation and the formation of short kinetic chains linking the water-soluble polymers together in a network. Polymerization of a kinetic chain is halted either by radical termination or chain transfer.[21]

Gelation kinetics are controlled by both reaction and diffusion controlled mechanisms. Initially, the polymerization rate increases with conversion of the double bonds. As the crosslinked network begins to form, the mobility of the terminating macroradicals is restricted, resulting in an accumulation of radicals in the system, and the rate of polymerization increases. At some point, continued propagation of macroradicals is limited by diffusion restriction.[21] For highly concentrated systems, complete double bond conversion is difficult to achieve. As residual acrylate groups have been implicated with cytotoxicity and poor gel mechanical properties, it is important to achieve nearly complete double bond conversion. By forming hydrogels using pre-polymers functionalized with moieties containing double bonds and dissolved in aqueous media, high double bond conversion can be obtained as a result of the high mobility of the polymer chains in solution.[33]

When choosing a photoinitiator, water solubility, radical generation efficiency, absorbance within the long-wave or visible region, as well as cytocompatibility need to be considered. Type II initiators, such as eosin Y, camphorquinone, or riboflavin, can be initiated with visible (blue region) light. However, they require a coinitiator such as a tertiary amine (e.g., triethanolamine), and often an accelerant such as N-vinylpyrrolidone to induce effective photo-gelation.[34] For this reason, type I initiators are more often used. Of the available commercial type I initiators, 2-hydroxy-1-[4-(hydroxyethoxy)phenyl]-2-methyl-1-propanone (or Irgacure 2959, Fig. 3) is the most commonly employed due to its reasonable water solubility, its ability to absorb and decompose to generate radicals when exposed to long-wave UV (320–380 nm), as well as its demonstrated cytocompatibility with a number of cell types.[34–36] Nevertheless, as pointed out by Fairbanks *et al.*,[37] Irgacure 2959 absorbs poorly (4 M^{-1} cm^{-1}) at the long-wave UV wavelengths

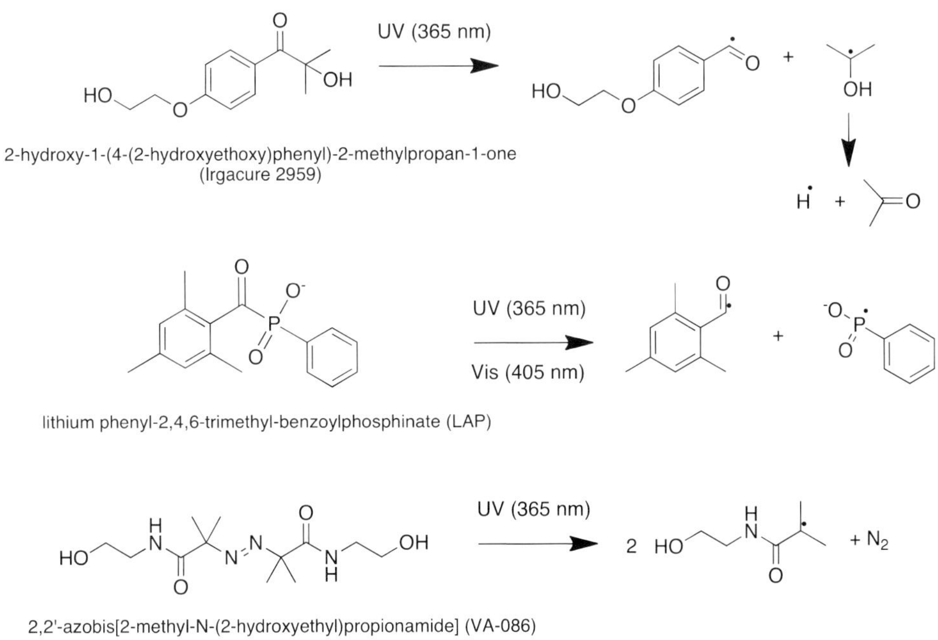

Fig. 3. Chemical structures of photoinitiators with demonstrated cytocompatibility, and the free radical species formed upon their photodissociation.

(~ 365 nm) commonly used. These researchers have demonstrated the potential of lithium phenyl-2,4,6-trimethyl-benzoylphosphinate (LAP) (Fig. 3), a photoinitiator developed by Majima *et al.*[38] as a suitable substitute for Irgacure 2959. LAP was capable of initiating photogelation within an order of magnitude of time faster than Irgacure 2959 at the same conditions of concentration (2.2 mM), wavelength (365 nm) and UV intensity (10 mW/cm^2). It was also able to induce gelation within 5 min at a concentration 10 times less than that of Irgacure 2959 (0.22 mM) when used at a wavelength of 365 nm and 10 mw/cm^2. Moreover, LAP effectively absorbs within the blue light (405 nm) region and was as effective as Irgacure at 365 nm at photogelation, when tested at the same concentration.[39] Recently, Rouillard *et al.* have examined the effectiveness of 2,2′-azobis[2-methyl-N-(2-hydroxyethyl)propionamide] (VA-086) (Fig. 2) as a photoinitiator in comparison to Irgacure 2959.[36] These authors demonstrated that VA-086 could effectively initiate the photo-crosslinking of O-methacrylate alginate using a UV intensity of 2 W/cm^2, VA-086 solution concentrations of from 0.1–1.5% w/v, and exposure times of up to 10 min.

When using long-wave UV irradiation to initiate crosslinking, the intensity of the irradiation employed is an important parameter to consider. Sufficient intensity is required to initiate the polymerization, and increased intensity will result in an increase in photoinitiation. Nevertheless, a 100-fold increase in light intensity will only result in a 10 fold increase in photoinitiation.[21] However, too high an intensity can cause UV induced polymer degradation[23] as well as localized heating, which may generate local gel inhomogeneities.[21] A survey of the literature shows that UV intensities between 4 and 20 mW/cm^2 are commonly used, yielding gel formation times typically ranging from 1–5 min.[10,23,34–37,40,41] Furthermore, it is important to consider potential light attenuation when crosslinking thick samples. This issue arises as a result of light absorption by the photoinitiator.[42] This problem can be overcome through the use of photo-bleaching initiators or dual initiators. With photo-bleaching initiators, the initiator radical absorbs light at a different wavelength than the initiator molecule and for dual initiator systems, photoinitiation causes a temperature increase sufficiently large that thermal initiation is possible.[33]

Although highly effective at forming hydrogels through photoinitiation, chain-growth free radical polymerization of (meth)acrylated water-soluble polymers results in heterogeneous network structures consisting of dense poly(meth)acrylate kinetic chains between the water-soluble polymer.[43] Moreover, the poly(meth)acrylate chains are non-degradable, a feature commonly desirable for drug delivery and regenerative medicine approaches, and must be excreted from the body through the kidneys. One approach to overcome these issues would be to utilize polymerization of solutions of co-monomers possessing complementary reactive groups, such as thiol-acrylates/enes. An additional advantage of this strategy is that the networks formed in this fashion are more homogeneous and possess greater tensile strength and increased strain at break, than chain-growth networks of similar crosslink density.[44] In thiol-acrylate/ene polymerization, the photoinitiator radical abstracts a hydrogen atom from a thiol, forming a thiyl radical. The thiyl radical attacks the carbon–carbon double bond, forming a carbon-centred radical. This radical then abstracts a proton from another thiol, creating a thioether bond and regenerating the thiyl radical. The coupling of any two radical species will terminate the reaction[21] (Eq. 1). These thiol-acrylate/ene photopolymerizations can occur rapidly, with low light intensity.[45,46] A further potential advantage of this approach is that they can also be done in the absence of a photoinitiator, thereby allowing curing to greater depths as a result of lack of light intensity attenuation due to the photoinititator.[45]

$$\begin{aligned}
&\text{Photoinitiator} \xrightarrow{h\nu} I^{\bullet}, \\
&I^{\bullet} + RSH \rightarrow IH + RS^{\bullet}, \\
&RS^{\bullet} + CH_2 = CH - R' \rightarrow RS - CH_2 - \dot{C}H - R', \\
&RS - CH_2 - \dot{C}H - R' + RSH \rightarrow RS - CH_2 - CH_2 - R' + RS^{\bullet}.
\end{aligned} \tag{1}$$

To form hydrogels through this approach requires the use of crosslinking agents with two or more thiol groups reacting with water-soluble polymers containing two or more acrylate or ene groups, or a crosslinking agent possessing two or more acrylate or ene groups reacting with a water-soluble polymer possessing two or more thiol groups. An example of such reactants are given in Fig. 4. A potential issue when utilizing thiol-acrylate photopolymerization is that, not only will radical polymerization occur, but also a competing Michael-type addition reaction between the thiol and acrylates, resulting in mixed-mode polymerization.[45,47] A potential advantage of such mixed-mode polymerizations is that hydrogel properties such as network structure, degradation rate, and

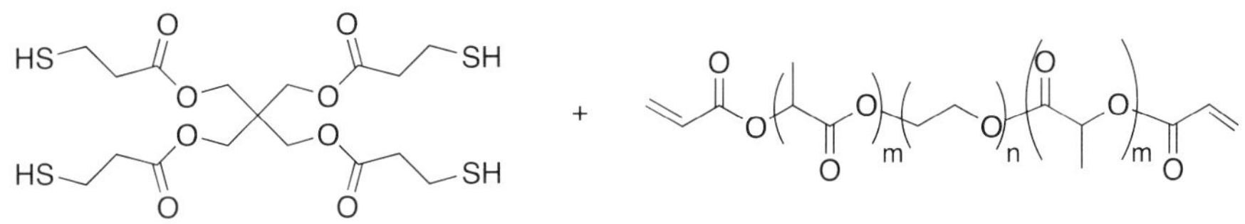

Fig. 4. Examples of reactants that will undergo thiol-acrylate photopolymerization.

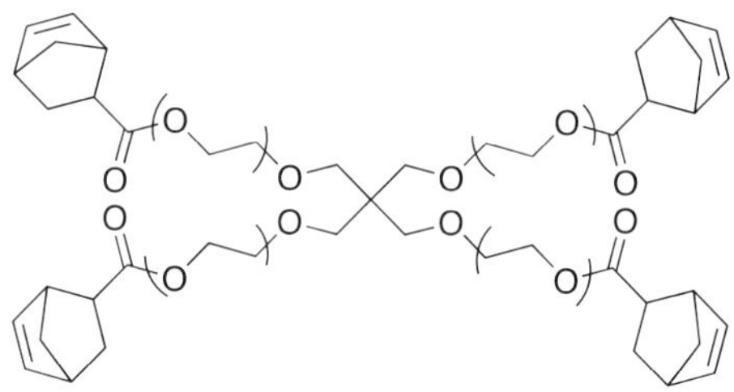

Fig. 5. Norbornene-terminated 4-armed PEG.

degradation product molecular weight, can be controlled by adjusting the thiol:acrylate ratio.[45] Furthermore, if multifunctional thiol monomers are utilized, residual thiol groups remain following polymerization, which can be utilized to functionalize the hydrogel post-polymerization.[48] However, the occurrence of Michael addition reactions can occur before photoinitiation, reducing the ability to control gelation in a time and spatial manner. This problem can be overcome by replacing the acrylate groups with norbornenes (Fig. 5).[49] The norbornene group is unreactive towards thiols in solution, providing the ability to control gel formation spatially and temporally, while resulting in a homogeneous network.

3. Photodimerization

Photodimerization is a bimolecular reaction involving an electronically excited unsaturated molecule that undergoes an addition reaction with an unexcited molecule of the same species. The resulting reaction forms a dimer. Photodimerization can be achieved with a number of chemical groups that contain alkene moieties, including: coumarins, cinnamates, thymine, anthracenes, stilbene, chalcone, and dimethylmaleimide (DMMI) (Fig. 6). Irradiation with light of an appropriate wavelength generally generates a [2+2] cycloaddition forming a cross link consisting of a cyclobutane. The exception is anthracenes, which undergo a [4+4] cycloaddition. The first report of the utilization of photodimerization to form hydrogels was by Chujo *et al.*, 1990, who prepared polyoxazoline bearing pendant coumarin moieties.[1] Since then, a number of different photodimerization approaches have been reported, including cinnamate, coumarin and thymine conjugated HA and chondroitin sulfate,[2] cinnamate conjugated poly(N,N-dimethylacrylamide),[50] 4-armed PEG bearing terminal cinnamate groups,[51] nitrocinnamate groups[52] or anthracene groups,[53] PEG with terminal coumarin groups[54], HA with pendant cinnamate groups,[55] gelatin with pendant nitrocinnamate,[56] PVA with pendant coumarin groups,[53] anthracene conjugated alginate and HA,[57] and poly(acrylamide) bearing pendant DMMI.[58]

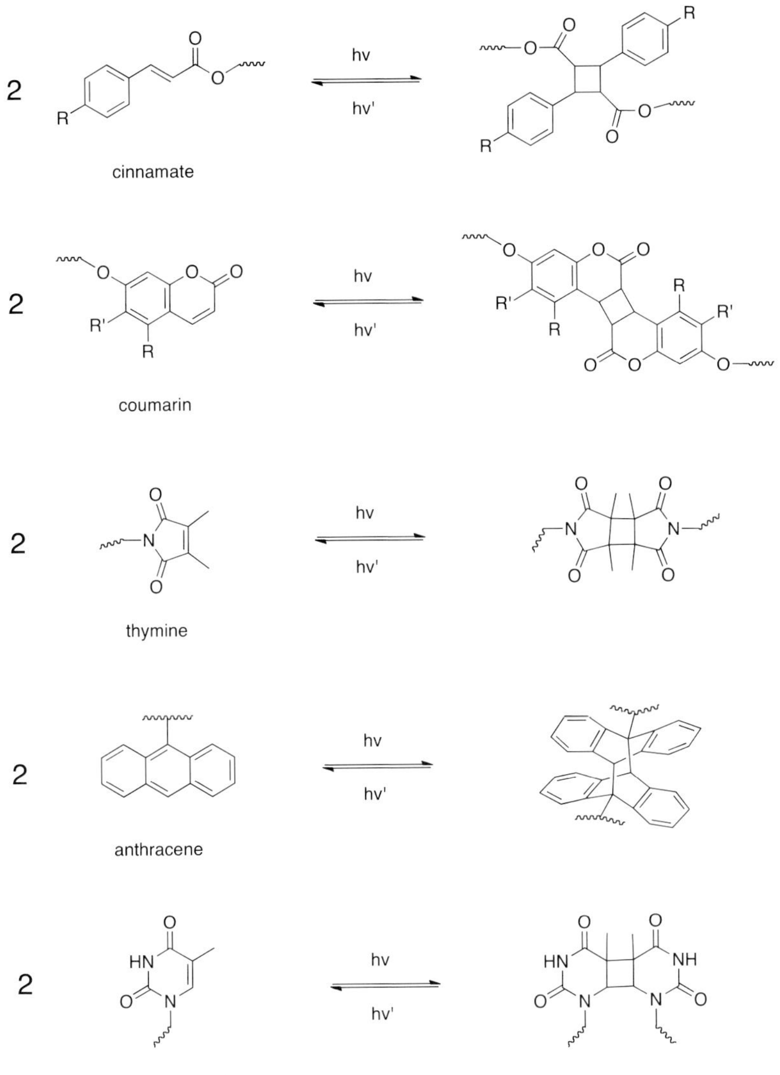

Fig. 6. Examples of photodimerizable groups and the dimers formed upon their excitation. The reverse reaction represents photoscission.

When considering this approach, the photo reactivity of the chosen photosensitive moiety should be considered. The absorption maxima and reactivity of cinnamates and coumarins may be changed by conjugating substituents on the phenyl ring. For example nitrocinnamate is 350 times more photo reactive than cinnamylidene[39] and a methyl substitution at position 4 on coumarin results in a 200 time increase in dimerization rate over that of unmodified coumarin.[59] Nevertheless, the absorption maxima always remain within the UV region.

One drawback of using cinnamates as the cross linking moiety is the potential for photochemically induced cis/trans isomerization, which decreases the quantum yield of the photo-crosslinking reaction.[39] Moreover, cinnamates are also acceptors in Michael additions, and thus may take part in side reactions depending on the nature/composition of the reacting medium.[58] In contrast, coumarins and DMMIs do not have these limitations. DMMI has the added advantage of being more water-soluble than cinnamates or coumarins. However, direct excitation of DMMI requires shortwave UV, which may also cause unwanted degradation of the polymer backbone. It is therefore advantageous to use a sensitizer, such as an aromatic ketone (e.g., thioxanthone disulfonate) to shift the cross linking conditions to a longer wavelength (>310 nm).[58]

As a crosslinking strategy, photodimerization provides the advantage of not requiring an initiator or catalyst. Nevertheless, direct photodimerization can require high energy input (Table 1) to achieve effective crosslinking. The UV intensity and time for gelation can be reduced in a number of ways. Incorporating a greater number of photodimerizable groups onto the pre-polymer will increase the likelihood of a crosslink being formed. For example, conjugating multiple photodimerizable moieties along the polymer backbone or at the termini of star-polymers as opposed to solely at the termini of a linear polymer yields faster gelation with lower intensities. The use of a water-soluble sensitizer, such as thioxanthone disulfate, can reduce the energy input, as was demonstrated by Seiffert *et al.* who prepared gels using DMMI grafted poly(acrylamide) at long-wave UV intensity of 15 mW/cm^2 within[3] min.[58] Moreover, the gelation time can also be adjusted in a sensitizer concentration dependent manner (i.e., higher concentrations of sensitizer result in reduced gelation times).[58]

A potential advantage of photodimerization as a cross linking strategy is the reversibility of the dimerization that can be afforded under the appropriate wavelength (Fig. 6). The reverse reaction, or photoscission, typically requires higher energy UV light (wavelengths <260 nm). Thus, hydrogels can be photo

Table 1. Representative photogelation conditions using various photodimerizable groups.

Polymer	Long-wave UV intensity	Durations	References
Linear PEG terminated with cinnamate	150 (W/cm^2)	5–10 (min)	51
8-arm star-PEG terminated with nitrocinnamate	4 (W/cm^2)	1 (min)	52
PVA with pendant coumarin	400 (W/cm^2)	60 (min)	53
Alginate/HA with pendant anthracene	10 (W/cm^2)	30–60 (min)	57
Poly(acrylamide) with pendant DMMI*	15 (W/cm^2)	3 (min)	58

*The solution contained 1 mM thioxanthone disulfate as a photosensitizer.

de-crosslinked, causing swelling and yielding more porous networks. This capability may be useful in the control of the release of a therapeutic agent triggered by light.[51,53,54,57] When considering a photo reactive group for the preparation of a photoscissible polymer in this manner, anthracenes are more appropriate if the process must undergo repeatable cycles of reversible photo-dimerization. This is because anthracenes do not undergo isomerization or hydrolysis reactions caused by light, and radical polymerization, to which cinnamates are susceptible, can be avoided by blocking positions 9 and 10 on the anthracene.[60]

4. Aryl Azide Photolysis

Exposure of an aryl azide to UV light of wavelengths between 250 and 365 nm results in the formation of a nitrene group (Fig. 7). The nitrene group can then rapidly undergo addition reactions with double bonds and insertion into carbon–hydrogen or nitrogen–hydrogen groups. The nitrene group can also undergo ring expansion, reacting as a nucleophile with primary amines, a reaction that predominates in the presence of primary amines.[61] This latter characteristic has been utilized to form hydrogels based on 4-azidobenzoic acid (Az) conjugated to chitosan[62] (Fig. 8).

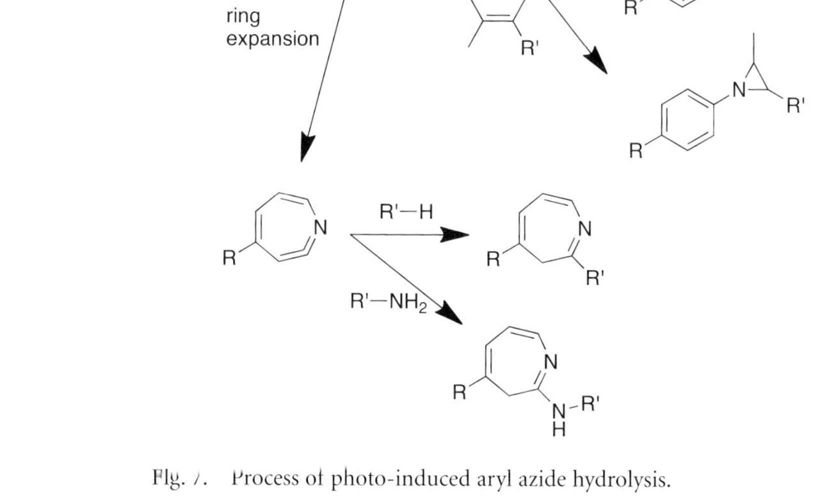

Fig. 7. Process of photo-induced aryl azide hydrolysis.

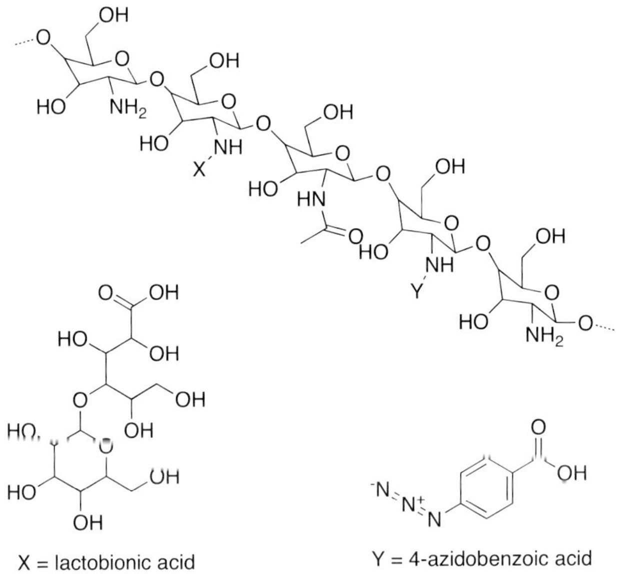

Fig. 8. Structure of Az-chitosan-LA.

Chitosan is particularly well suited to this approach, as it possesses numerous pendant primary amine groups, depending on its degree of deacetylation.[63] As chitosan is only soluble in low pH media,[64] to be effective as a hydrogel biomaterial, chitosan must also be modified so as to be water soluble at physiologic pH. Thus, (Az) was not only conjugated to chitosan to provide UV induced crosslinking, but also lactobionic acid (LA) to provide improved aqueous solubility. Initially, the polymer was crosslinked by exposure to 254 nm UV light of high intensity (4 W/cm^2), forming a gel within 60s. However, it has more recently been demonstrated that higher (365 nm) wavelengths and reduced intensities (1 mW/cm^2) can be utilized to form a gel with this pre-polymer within 5 min.[65]

The use of polymer bearing pendant primary amines along with pendant aryl azides has the advantages of having a relatively low energy of activation, which is optimal in the long-wave UV region, and there is no need for a photoinitiator. In comparison to photodimerizations, which also do not require a photoinitiator, the crosslinking reaction proceeds more quickly.[66] Preliminary investigation with the Az–chitosan–LA has also indicated that crosslinking the pre-polymer *in vivo* yields an acceptable tissue response.[67,68] However, the aryl azides will react quickly with sulfydryl groups, which will reduce the azide functional group to an amine, reducing the efficiency of the photo-activation. Moreover, the pre-polymer should be crosslinked in amine-free buffers, and the non-specific interaction of the generated nitrenes with resident proteins may restrict the utility of this gelation approach when used in the presence of loaded peptide or protein groups.

5. Cell Encapsulation

As the highly swollen aqueous environment of hydrogels is similar to water content of the extracellular matrix (ECM) of many tissues, allowing for efficient transport of nutrients and metabolites while also typically eliciting a mild host response upon implantation, a principal biomedical application of hydrogels is as cell delivery vehicles. Given the respective crosslinking conditions of the approaches described to date, free-radical polymerization gelation has shown to be the most effective for cell encapsulation given the fast gelation kinetics and low energy input levels required to induce gelation. For these approaches to be effective, the cells must remain viable within the highly reactive environment. Sources of toxicity for the cells include the photoinitiator, the wavelength of light utilized, and the free radicals themselves.

The most often utilized photoinitiator is Irgacure 2959. This is because it has a reasonable water solubility, is effective at low concentrations (typically 0.050–0.1% w/v), and has been demonstrated to be relatively non-cytotoxic at the concentrations used for crosslinking.[34–36] More recently, other photoinitiators, such as LAP[37] and VA-086[36] have been demonstrated to be as non-cytotoxic as, or less than, Irgacure 2959.

Most often, long-wave UV light, centred around 365 nm, is used, as Irgacure 2959 demonstrated the least cytotoxicity in early studies.[34,35] Long-wave UV exposure at intensities less than 10 mW/cm^2 are well tolerated by most cell types for exposure times less than 3–5 min, providing cell viability following photo encapsulation typically greater than 90%.[34,35,69] However, the cell response to such photo encapsulation conditions is phenotype-dependent.

Due to concern over the potential issue of DNA damage following exposure to long-wave UV radiation,[70] visible light photoinitiation has recently been explored. Blue light absorbing photoinitators that have been used include camphorquinone and eosin Y (with triethanolamine),[3] LAP,[37,71] and riboflavin[72] (Fig. 9). These photoinitiators have been shown to effectively photo encapsulate various cells with

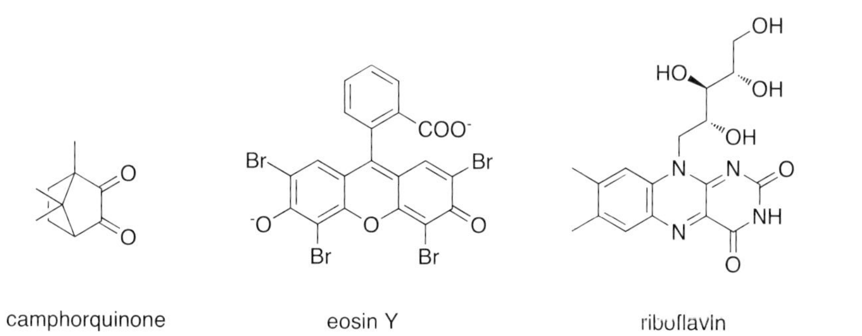

Fig. 9. Structures of commonly used, cytocompatible visible light activated photoinitiators.

high viability using multi-acrylated pre-polymers. An additional advantage of using visible light is that it is more readily transmitted through tissue, providing the ability to crosslink a pre-polymer solution following subcutaneous injection.[5]

The free radicals formed upon photoinitiation are highly reactive, and react non-specifically with other compounds within their environment, including cell membranes, proteins, and nucleic acids, potentially causing sufficient damage to induce cell death. Moreover, they can also form reactive oxygen species that can cause cellular damage.[69] Nevertheless, high cell viability, continued cell proliferation, and function are typically observed. This positive outcome is likely because most of the free radicals will react quickly with the doubly bonded carbons of the photoreactive groups on the polymer and thus be consumed before significant cell damage occurs.

The majority of the polymers discussed in this chapter do not possess the cell recognition sites present in the native ECM of tissues, which can result in poor cell retention, proliferation, and function following photo encapsulation. This issue was recognized early on,[73] and improved cell retention and proliferation within the gels following photo-crosslinking was achieved by inclusion of integrin receptor peptide ligands, such as arginine–glycine–aspartic acid (RGD), within a terpolymer consisting of N,N-dimethylacrylamide, methacrylated 7-hydroxy coumarin, and acryloxy succinimide. Following conjugation of a RGD containing peptide to this polymer backbone through reaction with the succinimide, smooth muscle cells were photo encapsulated by long-wave UV radiation induced photodimerization. Nevertheless, the UV intensities and wavelengths necessary to cause photodimerization are not conducive to high cell viability following photo encapsulation. The approach has been demonstrated to be highly effective, however, for free-radical induced photo-gelation. In these gels, peptide ligands are incorporated into the polymer network, either through direct acrylation of the peptide,[74] through attaching the peptide to one end of a linear PEG followed by acrylation of the other PEG terminus,[12,27,75,76] or by conjugating the peptide ligand directly to the polymer backbone.[11,65,77,78] Not only are peptide ligands within the gel necessary to support cell growth and function, it has been demonstrated for mesenchymal stem cells (MSCs) from the bone marrow[12] and adipose tissue,[11] that the presence of integrin receptor ligands on the pre-polymer backbone results in improved stem cell survival following photo encapsulation.

6. Degradation

Degradation of the hydrogel is desirable in many biomedical applications involving hydrogels. This can be achieved by incorporation of hydrolytically labile groups (ester, anhydride) attached to photoreactive groups. For example, hydrogels formed

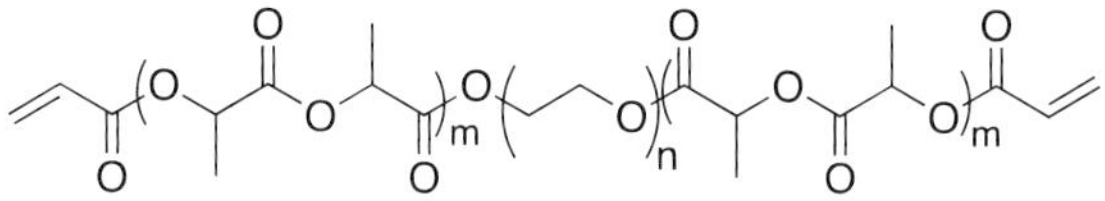

Fig. 10. Chemical structure of PEG-co-oligo(lactide) diacrylate.

from PEG–diacrylate were resistant to hydrolysis of the ester link between the PEG and the acrylate, and so the PEG was first extended with oligo(lactide) or oligo(glycolide) groups, then terminated with acrylate groups (Fig. 10).[29] Following gelation, the hydrogels degraded through the hydrolysis of the ester bonds in the oligo(α-hydroxy acid) blocks. The degradation rate of the networks in this strategy is determined by the susceptibility of the hydrolytically labile group to attack by water, as well as the hydrophobicity of the oligo(α-hydroxy acid) blocks. In a variant of this approach, hydroxyethyl methacrylate has been grafted to dextran[79] and HA[80] via an ester linkage to yield free radical polymerizable polymers that will subsequently degrade through hydrolysis of the ester link. The degradation rate of the hydrogels in these approaches is principally controlled by the number of hydroxyethyl methacrylate groups linked to the polymer backbone. To achieve further control over the hydrolysis rate of the ester groups, Jo *et al.* have demonstrated that positively charged versus negatively charged peptides linked to PEG through an ester linkage resulted in gels formed through Michael addition with varying degradation rates.[81] The positively charged peptides caused the gels to degrade 12 times faster than the gels containing the negatively charged peptide. This approach could be readily utilized in photo-crosslinkable gels utilizing a mixed-mode gelation process.

To achieve gels that degrade under cellular action, as opposed to the non-specific degradation of hydrolysis, enzyme degradable peptide regions have been included into photo-crosslinked networks.[82,83] This strategy allows control over the rate of degradation through the selection of the peptide, considering its susceptibility to cleavage by enzymes secreted by the cells of interest. Another means of forming hydrogels degradable by cellular action, is to utilize endogenous polysaccharides (e.g., HA, chondroitin sulfate), or chitosan which is degradable *in vivo* through the action of lysozyme,[84] and graft photo-reactive groups to their backbones through hydrolytically stable linkages.

References

1. Y. Chujo, K. Sada, and T. Saegusa, *Macromolecules*, **23**, 2693–2697 (1990).
2. T. Matsuda, M. Moghaddam, H. J. Mlwa, K. Sakurai, and F. Iida, *ASAIO Journal*, **38**, M154–M157 (1992).
3. C. P. Pathak, A. S. Sawhney, and J. A. Hubbell, *J. Am. Chem. Soc.*, **113**, 2548 (1993).

4. K. T. Nguyen and J. L. West, *Biomaterials*, **23**, 4307–4314 (2002).
5. A. T. Hillel, S. Unterman, Z. Nahas, B. Reid, J. M. Coburn, J. Axelman, J. J. Chae, Q. Guo, R. Trow, A. Thomas, Z. Hou, S. Lichtsteiner, D. Sutton, C. Matheson, P. Walker, N. David, S. Mori, J. M. Taube, and J. H. Elisseeff, *Sci Transl Med*, **3**, 1–12 (2011).
6. J. Elisseeff, K. Anseth, D. Sims, W. McIntosh, M. Randolph, and R. Langer, *P Natl Acad Sci USA*, **96**, 3104–3107 (1999).
7. J. West and J. Hubbell, *Biomaterials*, **16**, 1153–1156 (1995).
8. J. L. Hill-West, S. M. Chowdhury, M. J. Slepian, and J. A. Hubbell, *P Natl Acad Sci USA*, **91**, 5967–5971 (1994).
9. A. S. Sawhney, C. P. Pathak, and J. A. Hubbell, *Biomaterials*, **14**, 1008–1016 (1993).
10. Q. Li, C. G. Williams, D. D. N. Sun, J. Wang, K. Leong, and J. H. Elisseeff, *J. Biomed Mater Res A*, **68**, 28–33 (2004).
11. A. Sukarto, C. Yu, L. E. Flynn, and B. G. Amsden, *Biomacromolecules*, **13**, 2490–2502 (2012).
12. C. R. Nuttelman, M. C. Tripodi, and K. S. Anseth, *Matrix Biol.*, **24**, 208–218 (2005).
13. C. Pathak, A. Sawhney, and J. Hubbell, *Polymer Preprints*, **33**, 55–66 (1992).
14. J. West and J. Hubbell, *Reactive Polymers*, **25**, 139–147 (1995).
15. S. H. Kim and C. C. Chu, *J. Biomater. Appl.*, **15**, 23–46 (2000).
16. Y. An and J. A. Hubbell, *J. Control. Release*, **64**, 205–215 (2000).
17. O. Jeon, C. Powell, L. D. Solorio, M. D. Krebs, and E. Alsberg, *J. Control. Release*, **154**, 258–266 (2011).
18. M. Fujita, M. Ishihara, Y. Morimoto, M. Simizu, Y. Saito, H. Yura, T. Matsui, B. Takase, H. Hattori, Y. Kanatani, M. Kikuchi, and T. Maehara, *J. Surg. Res.*, **126**, 27–33 (2005).
19. S. Mallam, F. Horkay, A. M. Hecht, and E. Geissler, *Macromolecules*, **22**, 3356–3361 (1989)
20. M. Y. Kizilay and O. Okay, *Macromolecules*, **36**, 6856–6862 (2003).
21. C. Decker, *Macromol. Rapid Comm.*, **23**, 1067–1093 (2002).
22. W. Hennink, H. Talsma, J. Borchert, S. DeSmedt, and J. Demeester, *J. Control. Release*, **39**, 47–55 (1996).
23. B. G. Amsden, A. Sukarto, D. K. Knight, and S. N. Shapka, *Biomacromolecules*, **8**, 3758–3766 (2007).
24. S. Bryant, K. Davis-Arehart, N. Luo, R. Shoemaker, J. Arthur, and K. Anseth, *Macromolecules*, **37**, 6726–6733 (2004).
25. K. A. Smeds, A. Pfister-Serres, D. Miki, K. Dastgheib, M. Inoue, D. L. Hatchell, and M. W. Grinstaff, *J Biomed Mater Res*, **54**, 115–121 (2001).
26. K. A. Smeds, A. Pfister-Serres, D. L. Hatchell, and M. W. Grinstaff, *J. Macromol. Sci.*, **A36**, 981–989 (1999).
27. Y. D. Park, N. Tirelli, and J. A. Hubbell, *Biomaterials*, **24**, 893–900 (2003).
28. O. Jeon, K. H. Bouhadir, J. M. Mansour, and E. Alsberg, *Biomaterials*, **30**, 2724–2734 (2009).
29. A. Sawhney, C. Pathak, and J. Hubbell, *Macromolecules*, **26**, 581–587 (1993).
30. K. B. Keys, F. M. Andreopoulos, and N. A. Peppas, *Macromolecules*, (1998).

31. A. Muhlebach, B. Muller, C. Pharisa, M. Hofmann, B. Seiferling, and D. Guerry, *J. Polym. Sci. Pol. Chem.*, **35**, 3603–3611 (1997).
32. S. H. Kim, C. Y. Won, and C. C. Chu, *Carbohydrate Polymers*, **40**, 183–190 (1999).
33. J. L. Ifkovits and J. A. Burdick, *Tissue Engineering*, **13**, 2369–2385 (2007).
34. S. Bryant, C. Nuttelman, and K. Anseth, *J Biomat Sci-Polym E*, **11**, 439–457 (2000).
35. C. Williams, A. Malik, T. Kim, P. Manson, and J. Elisseeff, *Biomaterials*, **26**, 1211–1218 (2005).
36. A. D. Rouillard, C. M. Berglund, J. Y. Lee, W. J. Polacheck, Y. Tsui, L. J. Bonassar, and B. J. Kirby, *Tissue Eng Part C Methods*, **17**, 173–179 (2011).
37. B. D. Fairbanks, M. P. Schwartz, C. N. Bowman, and K. S. Anseth, *Biomaterials*, **30**, 6702–6707 (2009).
38. T. Majima, W. Schnabel, and W. Weber, *Die Makromolekulare Chemie*, **192**, 2307–2315 (1991).
39. F. D. Lewis, S. L. Quillen, and P. D. Hale, *J. Am. Chem. Soc.*, **110**, 1261–1267 (1988).
40. E. M. Chandler, C. M. Berglund, J. S. Lee, W. J. Polacheck, J. P. Gleghorn, B. J. Kirby, and C. Fischbach, *Biotechnology And Bioengineering*, **108**, 1683–1692 (2011).
41. J. Leach and C. Schmidt, *Biomaterials*, **26**, 125–135 (2005).
42. J. Lee, R. Prud'homme, and I. Aksay, *J. Mater. Sci.*, **16**, 3536–3544 (2001).
43. S. Lin-Gibson, R. L. Jones, and N. R. Washburn, *Macromolecules*, **38**, 2897–2902 (2005).
44. M. Malkoch, R. Vestberg, N. Gupta, L. Mespouille, P. Dubois, A. F. Mason, J. L. Hedrick, Q. Liao, C. W. Frank, K. Kingsbury, and C. J. Hawker, *Chem. Commun. (Camb.)*, 2774–2776 (2006).
45. A. Rydholm, C. Bowman, and K. Anseth, *Biomaterials*, **26**, 4495–4506 (2005).
46. N. B. Cramer and C. N. Bowman, *J Polym Sci Pol Chem*, **39**, 3311–3319 (2001).
47. C. N. Salinas and K. S. Anseth, *Macromolecules*, **41**, 6019–6026 (2008).
48. A. E. Rydholm, N. L. Held, D. S. W. Benoit, C. N. Bowman, and K. S. Anseth, *J Biomed Mater Res A*, **86A**, 23–30 (2008).
49. B. D. Fairbanks, M. P. Schwartz, and A. E. Halevi, *Adv. Mater.*, **21**, 5005–5010 (2009).
50 Y. Nakayama and T. Matsuda, *J Polym Sci Pol Chem*, **30**, 2451–2457 (1992).
51. F. M. Andreopoulos, C. R. Deible, and M. T. Stauffer, *J. Am. Chem. Soc.*, **118**, 6235–6240 (1996).
52. Y. Zheng, F. M. Andreopoulos, M. Micic, Q. Huo, S. M. Pham, and R. M. Leblanc, *Advanced Functional Materials*, **11**, 37–40 (2001).
53. M. S. Lee and J.-C. Kim, *J Appl Polym Sci*, **124**, 4339–4345 (2011).
54. M. Nagata and Y. Yamamoto, *React Funct Polym*, **68**, 915–921 (2008).
55. K. Miyamoto, M. Sasaki, Y. Minamisawa, Y. Kurahashi, H. Kano, and S.-I. Ishikawa, *J Biomed Mater Res*, **70A**, 550–559 (2004).
56. K. M. Gattás-Asfura, E. Weisman, F. M. Andreopoulos, M. Micic, B. Muller, S. Sirpal, S. M. Pham, and R. M. Leblanc, *Biomacromolecules*, **6**, 1503–1509 (2005).
57. L. A. Wells, M. A. Brook, and H. Sheardown, *Macromolecular Bioscience*, **11**, 988–998 (2011).
58. S. Seiffert, W. Oppermann, and K. Saalwächter, *Polymer*, **48**, 5599–5611 (2007).

59. Y. Chen and C. F. Chou, *J Polym Sci Pol Chem*, **33**, 2705–2714 (1995).
60. R. H. Liu, M. A. Winnik, F. Di Stefano, and J. Vanketessan, *J Polym Sci Pol Chem*, **39**, 1495–1504 (2001).
61. G. Hermanson, *Bioconjugate Techniques*, Academic Press, (1996).
62. K. Ono, Y. Saito, H. Yura, K. Ishikawa, A. Kurita, T. Akaike, and M. Ishihara, *Journal of Biomedical Materials Research*, **49**, 289–295 (2000).
63. M. Lavertu, Z. Xia, A. N. Serreqi, M. Berrada, A. Rodrigues, D. Wang, M. D. Buschmann, and A. Gupta, *J. Pharm. Biomed. Anal.*, **32**, 1149–1158 (2003).
64. N. Kubota and Y. Eguchi, *Polymer Journal*, **29**, 123–127 (1997).
65. F. Rask, S. M. Dallabrida, N. S. Ismail, Z. Amoozgar, Y. Yeo, M. A. Rupnick, and M. Radisic, *J Biomed Mater Res A*, **95A**, 105–117 (2010).
66. M. Mizutani, S. C. Arnold, and T. Matsuda, *Biomacromolecules*, **3**, 668–675 (2002).
67. M. Ishihara, K. Ono, M. Sato, K. Nakanishi, Y. Saito, H. Yura, T. Matsui, H. Hattori, M. Fujita, M. Kikuchi, and A. Kurita, *Wound Repair and Regeneration*, **9**, 513–521 (2001).
68. K. Ono, M. Ishihara, Y. Ozeki, H. Deguchi, M. Sato, and Y. Saito, *Surgery*, **130**, 844–850 (2001).
69. N. E. Fedorovich, M. H. Oudshoorn, D. van Geemen, W. E. Hennink, J. Alblas, and W. J. A. Dhert, *Biomaterials*, **30**, 344–353 (2009).
70. H. Ikehata and T. Ono, *Journal of Radiation Research*, **52**, 115–125 (2011).
71. H. Lin, D. Zhang, P. G. Alexander, G. Yang, J. Tan, A. W.-M. Cheng, and R. S. Tuan, *Biomaterials*, **34**, 331–339 (2013).
72. J. Hu, Y. Hou, H. Park, B. Choi, S. Hou, A. Chung, and M. Lee, *Acta Biomater*, **8**, 1730–1738 (2012).
73. M. J. Moghaddam and T. Matsuda, *ASAIO Trans*, **37**, M437–M438 (1991).
74. D. Hern and J. Hubbell, *J Biomed Mater Res*, **39**, 266–276 (1998).
75. B. K. Mann, A. S. Gobin, A. T. Tsai, R. H. Schmedlen, and J. L. West, *Biomaterials*, **22**, 3045–3051 (2001).
76. S. Peyton, C. Raub, V. Keschrumrus, and A. Putnam, *Biomaterials*, **27**, 4881–4893 (2006).
77. J. A. Rowley and D. J. Mooney, *Journal of Biomedical Materials Research*, **60**, 217–223 (2002).
78. X. Shu, K. Ghosh, Y. Liu, F. Palumbo, Y. Luo, R. Clark, and G. Prestwich, *J Biomed Mater Res A*, **68A**, 365–375 (2004).
79. W. N. van Dijk-Wolthuis, M. J. van Steenbergen, W. J. Underberg, and W. E. Hennink, *Journal Of Pharmaceutical Sciences*, **86**, 413–417 (1997).
80. I. E. Erickson, S. R. Kestle, K. H. Zellars, M. J. Farrell, M. Kim, J. A. Burdick, and R. L. Mauck, *Acta Biomater*, **8**, 3027–3034 (2012).
81. Y. S. Jo, J. Gantz, J. A. Hubbell, and M. P. Lutolf, *Soft Matter*, **5**, 440–446 (2009).
82. M. Kurisawa, M. Terano, and N. Yui, *J Biomat Sci-Polym E*, **8**, 691–708 (1997).
83. M. P. Lutolf, G. P. Raeber, A. H. Zisch, and N. Tirelli, *Adv. Mater.*, **15**, 888–892 (2003).
84. R. Muzzarelli, *Cell Mol Life Sci*, **53**, 131–140 (1997).

Chapter 9

Self-Assembling Hydrogels

Annada Rajbhandary and Bradley L. Nilsson*
Department of Chemistry, University of Rochester
Rochester, NY 14618, USA
**nilsson@chem.rochester.edu*

Self-assembling hydrogels are formed by the spontaneous self-assembly of monomeric components into polymer-like fibrils via non-covalent interactions and the subsequent entanglement of these fibrils into an extended network that elicits gelation of the aqueous solvent. Self-assembled hydrogels have been shown to possess advantages over covalently bonded hydrogels for utilization in biomedical applications including tissue engineering and drug delivery. The biocompatibility of self-assembled hydrogels arises, in part, due to the fact that many are composed of biological or bio-inspired molecules, including proteins, peptides, amino acids, carbohydrates, therapeutic agents, and oligonucleotides. This chapter introduces fundamental concepts in the development of self-assembled hydrogels and provides an introductory survey of the major classes of self-assembled hydrogel currently in use.

1. Introduction

Molecular self-assembly is the spontaneous self-association of molecules to form organized higher-order structures.[1–3] Nature is replete with architectures formed via molecular self-assembly, including lipid-derived cell membranes, the DNA double helix, and both functional and dysfunctional proteinaceous amyloid materials.[4,5] Materials derived from self-assembled molecules are primarily stabilized by numerous, relatively weak, non-covalent interactions as opposed to strong covalent bonds.[1] The non-covalent interactions that promote and stabilize molecular self-assembly in water include hydrogen bonding, Coulombic effects, π–π stacking, and hydrophobic and van der Waals interactions.[1] These non-covalent forces are energetically weak, providing 0.1–3.0 kcal mol^{-1} (~0.4–12.0 kJ mol^{-1}) in energetic stabilization per interaction (in comparison, the energy found in a single C–C bond is on the order of 83 kcal mol^{-1}). It is the collective energy of numerous non-covalent interactions that stabilize self-assembled materials.

Appropriately engineered self-assembled materials have been shown to exhibit emergent macromolecular hydrogel properties.[6–10] Covalent (or chemical) hydrogel networks are formed by the irreversible crosslinking of polymeric materials via the creation of covalent bonds.[11] In contrast, self-assembled (or non-covalent) hydrogels are formed by the spontaneous self-assembly of simple monomeric units into polymer-like supramolecular fibers.[12,13] When these fibers maintain appropriate solvation in water, they can effectively entangle to immobilize flow of solvent and provide three-dimensional (3D) hydrogel networks that possess similar properties to those exhibited by covalent hydrogels. In general, self-assembled hydrogels tend to be softer materials than those formed by covalently crosslinked polymers due to the weaker forces that stabilize the hydrogel network.[14,15] These weaker forces impart advantages to self-assembled hydrogels, including adaptability to environmental changes and self-healing properties.[14,16]

The relationship between self-assembly and hydrogelation phenomena is not completely understood.[6] Not all materials that self-assemble in water affect gelation of the media. Some self-assembled materials form fibers that merely precipitate from solution, presumably due to non-ideal interaction of the supramolecular network of fibers with water. For self assembled materials that do facilitate hydrogelation, the rates of assembly and the emergence of hydrogel properties are not always directly correlated. Subtle changes in the structure of the self assembling monomers can have dramatic outcomes on whether or not hydrogels form and even on the emergent properties (for example, storage (G′) and loss (G″) moduli) of the resulting hydrogels. Recent studies have indicated that the free energy of solvation of the monomeric units of self-assembling hydrogels correlates more perfectly with hydrogelation propensity of these materials than do other physicochemical properties.[17,18] A lack of information regarding molecular-scale structure of self-assembled hydrogel materials has also impeded the rational design of self-assembling hydrogels. Current study of self-assembling hydrogel materials is focused intensely on efforts to increase fundamental understanding in order span the gap between empirical and rational design of next-generation materials.

Self-assembled hydrogels have properties that have made them attractive alternatives to covalent hydrogels for sophisticated biological applications. Self-assembled, non-covalent hydrogels are inherently dynamic materials, since they lack a network of irreversible covalent bonds that effectively prevent *in situ* remodeling. As such, self-assembled hydrogels are able to assemble, disassemble, and vary their emergent characteristics in response to environment.[19–21] For example, self-assembled hydrogels have been engineered form or alter their properties in response to changes in pH, temperature, ionic strength, enzymatic activity, light, and reducing/oxidizing potential. In addition, the properties of self-assembled hydrogels can be tuned by simply modifying the structure of the rudimentary monomeric units, providing ease of synthesis and fabrication. Nearly all reported self-assembled hydrogels are derived from biologically inspired molecules or pharmaceutically active agents, imbuing these materials with inherent biocompatibility; thus, these materials can also be designed to be biodegradable. Biodegradation is also enhanced by the relative weakness of the non-covalent interactions that stabilize the self-assembled hydrogel network. Based on these properties, self-assembled hydrogels have become attractive materials for an increasing variety of biological applications. These uses include tissue engineering, drug delivery, regenerative medicine, bio-sensing and even bioelectronics.[2,22–29] This chapter provides an introductory (not comprehensive) overview of the variety of materials that have been used in self-assembling hydrogels and a description of their fundamental properties.

2. Self-Assembled Protein and Peptide Hydrogels

Proteins and engineered peptides have been extensively exploited in the design of self-assembling hydrogels. Native proteins like collagen, silk, and elastin that self-assemble to form important structural matrices in nature have been used in hydrogel formation for decades. More recently, engineered α-helical and amyloid-inspired β-sheet peptides that readily self-assemble have been utilized in the design and application of self-assembled hydrogels. The following sections describe several of the important classes of hydrogels derived from self-assembling proteins and peptides.

2.1. Hydrogels derived from native self-assembling proteins

Self-assembling proteins found in the extracellular matrix (ECM) have been widely used as hydrogelators.[30,31] The most common example is collagen, which has been isolated from animals and used for various applications for hundreds of years.[32,33] Collagen, the most abundant protein in humans, plays critical structural roles in bone and ECM.[32] The proline- and glycine-rich sequence of collagen ($(X–Y–Gly)_n$ in which X and Y are often proline (Pro) or Pro derivatives such as hydroxyproline (Hyp), see Fig. 1) enables self-assembly into stable triple helical structures.[34] Gelatin is composed primarily of heterogeneous mixtures of hydrolyzed collagen that forms temperature sensitive hydrogels.[35,36]

OGPOGPOGDOGDOGDOGDOGP**K**GP**K**GP**K**GP**K**GPOGPOGPOGPOGDOGDOGDOGDOG

GP**K**GP**K**GP**K**GP**K**GPOGPOGPOGPOGDOGDOGDOGDOGP**K**GP**K**GP**K**GP**K**GPOGPOGPO

OGPOGDOGDOGDOGDOGPKGPKGPKGPKGPOGPOGPOGPOGDOGDOGDOGDOGPKGP

Fig. 1. Representation of triple helix alignment of collagen mimetic peptides; P is proline, K is lysine, G is glycine, O is hydroxyproline, D is aspartatic acid. Positively charged K residues (in bold) and negatively charged D residue (in red) form stabilizing electrostatic interactions as indicated.

While gelatin and other collagen-based hydrogels are stabilized by both covalent crosslinking and non-covalent self-assembly, recent collagen mimetic peptides self-assemble to form triple-helical fibers that elicit hydrogelation without explicit covalent crosslinking.[32] These collagen mimetic peptides have altered X and Y positions in order to tune the self-assembly and hydrogelation processes.[31] Hartgerink and co-workers designed collagen mimetic peptides, (Pro–Lys–Gly)$_4$(Pro–Hyp–Gly)$_4$(Asp–Hyp–Gly)$_4$, that effectively self-assemble into triple-helical nanofiber networks that elicit hydrogelation (Fig. 1).[37] Lysine (Lys) and Aspartic (Asp) acid residues are incorporated in positions that enable the formation of non-covalent charge interactions across the strands of the resulting triple helix nanofibers, thus stabilizing the helices and the derivative hydrogel matrices.[37] These hydrogels were sensitive to degradation by collagenase Type IV, indicating native collagen-like structure.[37] These types of collagen-inspired hydrogel materials have great potential for use in *ex vivo* tissue engineering and *in vivo* wound healing applications.[33]

Elastin is another ECM-derived protein that has been utilized in the creation of self-assembled hydrogels.[38–40] In biological systems, elastin is expressed as a monomeric protein that undergoes self-assembly into β-sheet rich,[41,42] polymeric fibers that are ultimately stabilized by the formation of covalent crosslinks.[43] Elastin imparts the characteristic elasticity of organs and tissues that include arterial blood vessels, ligaments, skin, and lung parenchyma.[44] As such, self-assembled elastin hydrogels that are chemically crosslinked after self-assembly of the elastin fibers have been viewed as attractive biomaterials.[44]

Elastin-like polypeptides (ELPs) have also been developed, that self-assemble and form hydrogels without the need for covalent crosslinking. ELPs typically incorporate an elastin pentapeptide motif, Val–Pro–Gly–Xaa–Gly (VPGXG) that is critical for self-assembly of the monomeric units.[45] For example, Urry and co-workers, who pioneered the study of ELPs, have utilized the pentapeptide repeat sequence (VPGVG)$_m$(VPGXaaG)$_n$, in which Xaa could be any amino acid residue, for forming self-assembling hydrogels.[46,47] Hydrogels of this type exhibit "inverse temperature transition" behavior in which the elastin network becomes more ordered as the temperature of the system increases.[46–48] At low temperature, ELPs have the properties of an amorphous polymer since the hydrophobic residues are surrounded by ordered water via hydrophobic hydration. However, as the temperature is increased, the hydration shell becomes less ordered which results in the exposure of non-polar side chains, thus triggering hydrophobic collapse into a more ordered, assembled state. Tirrell and co-workers have demonstrated that temperature-dependent conformational changes from random to β-turn-like structure occur when the hydrophobic groups of the peptide are exposed to the solvent.[49] Upon hydrophobic collapse, self-assembled ELPs form mature β-spiral aggregates, composed of stacked β-sheets with intervening β-turns.[49] The temperature at which the contraction occurs is sensitive to the primary sequence of the ELP, degree of ionization, pH, salt, or ELP modifications, including phosphorylation.[46,47] Thus, ELP-derived hydrogels have the potential to be used as temperature sensors or as machines for the interconversion of energy.[46,50]

Silk fibroin has also been exploited in the creation of self-assembling hydrogels. Silk fibroin is composed primarily of hydrophobic Ala, flexible Gly, and hydrophilic Ser residues organized in recurring Gly–Ala–Gly–Ala–Gly–Ser (GAGAGS) motifs.[51,52] GAGAGS repeats self-assemble into tightly packed antiparallel β-sheets that account for the high tensile strength of silk.[51] Packing and self-assembly follows a conformational transition from random coil to β-sheet structure. The sol–gel transition of silk-derived hydrogels is dependent upon the concentration of the protein, temperature, and pH.[51] For example, at lower pH, repulsive Coulombic interactions between silk fibroin molecules are minimized, resulting in shorter gelation times. Ions such as Ca^{2+} accelerate self-assembly, possibly due to interaction with amino acids found in hydrophilic blocks at the *N*- and *C*-termini of silk proteins.

Silk elastin hybrid peptides (SELPs) that exploit the properties of both silk and elastin have been engineered to create a novel class of self-assembling hydrogel. SELPs are essentially block copolymers composed of repeated silk (GAGAGS) and elastin (GVGVP) blocks. SELPs spontaneously and irreversibly self-assemble under physiological conditions to provide non-covalent hydrogel networks. The silk-derived motif facilitates spontaneous β-sheet self-assembly and increases crosslinking while the presence of elastin-derived block increases flexibility and water solubility.[53] Changing the number and the arrangement of the silk and elastin blocks can modify the emergent properties of the resulting hydrogels. Subtle modifications to the silk/elastin sequences can also be used to tune the hydrogel properties. For example, replacement of one Val residue with glutamic acid (Glu) in the elastin motif can impart pH and temperature sensitivity to the resulting hydrogel.

Globular proteins have also been intensively studied for the formation of self-assembling hydrogels. Globular proteins can be induced to self-assemble into cross-β amyloid aggregates when heated above their denaturation temperature or upon exposure to other unfolding stimuli (pH, chemical denaturants, etc.).[54] It has been proposed that formation of amyloid fibrils is a common characteristic of all proteins.[5] The formation of hydrogel networks of these fibrils can occur under conditions where these aggregates maintain appropriate solubility in water.[54] Proteins such as β-lactoglobulin, ovalbumin and lysozymes have been used to form self-assembled hydrogels.[55] For example, β-lactoglobulin undergoes β-sheet self-assembly and hydrogelation under acidic as well as basic conditions.[54] Lysozyme derived from hen egg white undergoes α-helical to β-sheet conformational transitions leading to fibrillization and hydrogelation.[48,56] The use of globular proteins in the creation of engineered hydrogels is attractive since many of these proteins are abundant and inexpensive and the resulting hydrogel networks have been shown to be highly biocompatible, leading to applications in *ex vivo* tissue engineering.

2.2. Self-assembled β-sheet peptide hydrogels

In addition to natural protein and protein mimetic peptides, a variety of short synthetic peptides that self-assemble into amyloid like β-sheet fibrils have been engineered to form hydrogels. Amphipathic peptides composed of alternating polar and non-polar amino acids have proven to be a privileged class of self-assembling peptide in which the fibrils readily entangle to form hydrogel networks.[57,58] These amphipathic peptide sequences are prone to exist in β-strand conformations that orient the hydrophilic side chains on one face of the β-strand and hydrophilic side chains on the other. These β-strands readily assemble into β-sheets stabilized by backbone hydrogen bonding and side chain hydrophobic/aromatic/Coulombic interactions. These β-sheets assemblies are similar to amyloid "cross-β" structures that have the unique feature of forming β-sheet bilayers in which the hydrophobic groups are isolated to the interior of the β-sheet (see Fig. 2 for an example). Since only the hydrophobic side chains are highly exposed to solvent in these bilayer structures, the resulting fibrils are highly soluble in aqueous solution (in opposition to many amyloid sequences, which tend to precipitate upon self-assembly), making them ideal for the formation of hydrogel networks.

Zhang and co-workers pioneered the use of engineered β-sheet peptides to form hydrogels. They found that the AEAEAKAKAEAEAKAK (EAK16-II) sequence, derived from Zuotin in yeast, readily self-assembled and elicited hydrogelation of the solvent.[59,60] When the Glu and Lys residues of this peptide were substituted with Asp and Arg respectively, the resulting sequence, dubbed RAD16-II, exhibited even greater self-assembly and hydrogelation propensity.[59,60] Initial data suggested that these peptides assembled into fibrils with an antiparallel β-sheet packing arrangement.[58,61–63] However, recent solid state NMR analysis indicates that the related amphiphatic peptide, $(RADA)_4$ (RADA16-I), assembles into

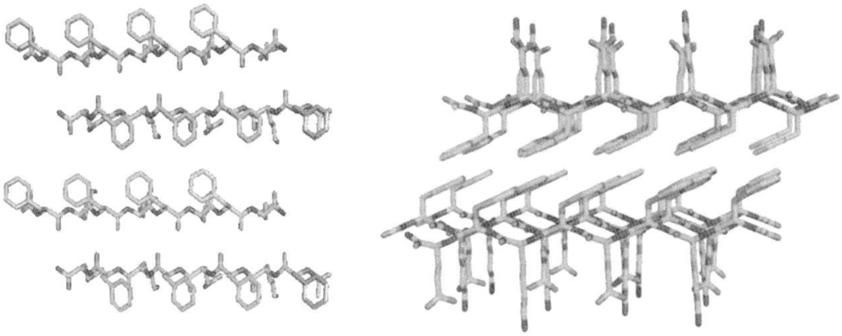

Fig. 2. (A) Antiparallel β-sheet packing arrangement of the $(FKFE)_2$ peptide; the out of register *N*-terminal Phe residue is shown in orange. (B) β-Sheet bilayer of the self-assembling $(FKFE)_2$ peptide with hydrophobic Phe side chains buried within the interior of the bilayer while the hydrophilic groups remain exposed to solvent; the bilayer is oriented with the β-sheets extending from the plane of the page.

parallel β-sheet layers.[64] The altered arrangement of charges residues may account for differing packing architectures of RAD16-I and II peptide fibrils, but additional high-resolution structural analyses are needed to assess the structure of these related peptides. Zhang's peptide-derived hydrogels have been used extensively as a model for the study of self-assembly and hydrogelation phenomena. In addition, these robust hydrogels have been applied for a variety of biomedical uses, including use as a matrix for 3D tissue culture and as a hemostat for artificial blood clotting and wound healing.[65–69]

Zhang and co-workers also discovered that changing the identity of the hydrophobic amino acid in these amphipathic peptides from Ala to other residues influences the self-assembly and hydrogelation properties of the resulting sequences.[61–63] A prominent derivative is the $(FKFE)_2$ peptide in which Ala is replaced with Phe.[61–63,70] Self-assembly and hydrogelation occurs with shorter peptide lengths (8 mers versus 16 mers) upon increasing the hydrophobicity of the non-polar residues in this class of peptide.[70] It was also observed that increasing the number of repeats of FKFE in $(FKFE)_n$ sequences increased the rigidity of the resulting gels, although not proportionally.[71] Furthermore, it was found that increased ionic strength decreased charge-to-charge repulsion between fibrils to enhance hydrogel formation.[70] Interestingly, these Phe-containing peptides formed nanotape structures that are morphologically distinct from the related Ala-containing peptides: $(FKFE)_2$ forms left-handed helical ribbons that relax to flat nanotapes over time.[61] Molecular modeling suggests that an out of register antiparallel β-sheet packing architecture most reasonably explains these morphological observations (Fig. 2(A)).[61–63] These computational studies indicate that $(FKFE)_2$ peptides must pack with one amino acid out of register, most likely the *N*-terminal Phe residue (Fig. 2(A)), in order to maintain uniform sequestration of non-polar and polar side chains on opposite faces of the β-sheet. Two of these β-sheets can laminate to form a bilayer nanoribbon in which all non-polar groups are isolated to the interior of the bilayer (Fig. 2(B)).

The $(FKFE)_2$ peptide has been widely adopted as a model to understand the underlying mechanisms of self-assembly and hydrogelation. Muller and co-workers studied the effect of swapping Phe at various positions with the Gly, Ala, Val, Leu, or Ile.[72] These substitutions influence self-assembly, but the resulting peptides still form hydrogel networks. Miller and co-workers found that the FEFK tetramer fails to effectively form hydrogels, but that reverse hydrolysis (ligation) to form $(FEFK)_n$ repeats (primarily 8 mers) initiates assembly and gelation.[73] Substitution of the polar residues (for example, Lys to Arg) is not deleterious to self-assembly and gelation when peptide charge is unchanged.[71] Charge can influence critical gelation concentration for amphipathic peptides, however, as demonstrated using VEVKVEVK, VKVKVEVK and VEVEVKVK, which have net charges of 0, +2, and −2 at neutral pH respectively. It was observed that under pH conditions where charge modulus >1, peptides were able to form hydrogels with indistinguishable structure and mechanical properties.[74]

The Nilsson group has also characterized $(XKXE)_2$ and $(XKXK)_2$ peptide self-assembly and hydrogelation as a function of the aromatic and hydrophobic character of the non-polar X residues.[75,76] Cationic $(XKXK)_2$ peptides in which Ala, Val, Leu, Ile, Phe, cyclohexylalanine (Cha), or pentafluorophenylalanine (F_5-Phe) (in order of increasing hydrophobicity) were incorporated in the X position were assessed for hydrogelation potential. It was found that hydrophobicity correlates to self-assembly propensity (as measured by the solvent ionic strength required to facilitate self-assembly) while aromaticity correlates to hydrogel rigidity. Non-aromatic Ile and Cha containing peptides formed weak hydrogels ($G' \approx 100$–200 Pa), while aromatic Phe and F_5-Phe containing peptides formed more rigid hydrogels ($G' \approx 1600$–2000 Pa). The underlying physicochemical foundation for these differing hydrogel rigidities is not understood, but there are several possible explanations. The most likely explanation is that the fibril/monomer balance is more favorable for aromatic peptides, leading to a more extensive network and thus higher rigidity. Another possible explanation is that non-covalent crosslinking is more favorable for aromatic peptides, potentially due to stabilizing π–π interactions between fibrils in the resulting network. It is significant that modification of the non-polar residues of these self-assembling peptides can be used to tune hydrogel mechanics.

Schneider and Pochan have developed self-assembling amphipathic β-hairpin peptides that form hydrogels that exhibit nearly ideal mechanical and biochemical properties for use of tissue culture scaffolds.[77] These peptides are based on a 20 amino acid sequence composed of two β-strands of alternating hydrophilic Lys and hydrophobic Val residues linked by a central type II β-turn motif (VKVKVKVK-V^{D}PPT-KVKVKVKV-NH_2, MAX1).[78] At low pH and ionic strength the peptide remains disordered and unassembled due to charge repulsion between the cationic Lys residues.[79] However, as the solvent ionic strength or pH is increased, charge repulsion is reduced either by charge screening by solution counterions or by reduction of overall position of charge and β-hairpin folding occurs, thus triggering self-assembly into β-sheet fibrils (Fig. 3(A)). These fibrils form rigid hydrogels with storage moduli from ~1,000–10,000 Pa, depending on peptide sequence and concentration.

Variants of the MAX1 peptide have provided insight into the mechanism of self-assembly/hydrogelation and on how sequence can be used to modify the emergent properties of these β-hairpin hydrogels. Replacement of the non-polar Val residues with less hydrophobic amino acids reduced the self-assembly and

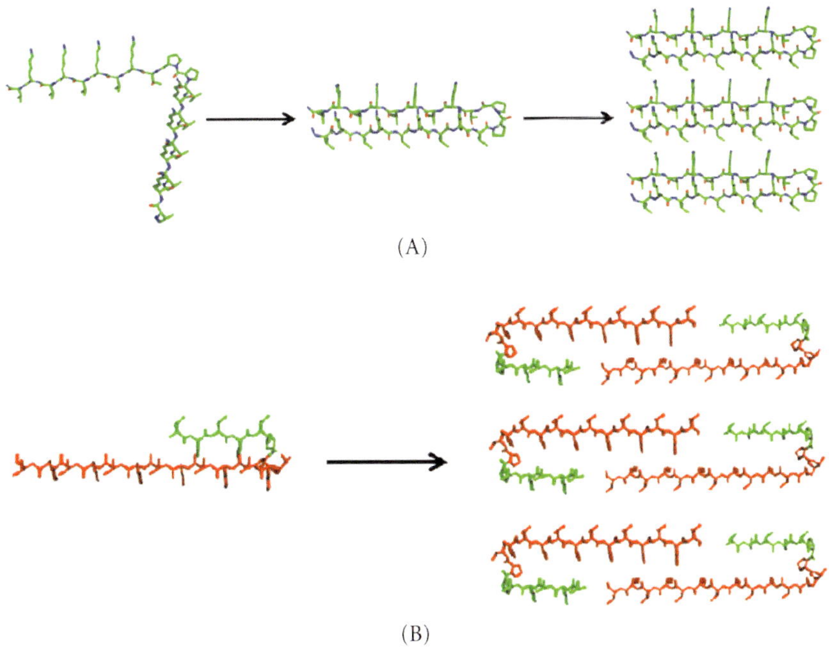

Fig. 3. (A) Self-assembling β-hairpin peptide MAX1 shown folding into a hairpin conformation and assembling into a β-sheet; these peptides also form bilayer structures, although the bilayer is not explicitly depicted in this image. (B) A designed strand-swapped β-hairpin peptide (SSP1) that assembles into β-sheet hairpin fibrils in which the overhanging β-sheet undergoes domain swapping to form unique fibrils; folding and self-assembly of these strand-swapped fibrils occurs when the peptide solutions are heated to physiological temperatures.

gelation propensity of the resulting peptides.[80–82] The selective substitution of Lys with Glu (Lys to Glu substitution in the 15th position gives the so-called MAX8 peptide) increases hydrogel rigidity and provides a hydrogel that exhibits shear thinning properties that facilitate its use as an injectable scaffold.[83] The basis for this increase in mechanical stability of the hydrogel (both in terms of storage modulus value and in self-healing of the hydrogel network after mechanical disruption) is due to the decrease of overall positive charge of the peptide. It has also been observed that universally replacing every Lys residue of the MAX1 peptide with Arg provides a peptide that self-assembles into rigid, shear thinning hydrogels that also have potent antibacterial properties.[84]

The design of self-assembled hydrogels derived from β-sheet hairpin peptides has advanced beyond simple two-stranded hairpins. Schneider and co-workers have designed three-stranded β-sheet peptides with two turn nucleation motifs; these peptides self-assemble into stable hydrogels that are responsive to changes in temperature.[85] Schneider *et al.* have also developed strand-swapped self-assembled hydrogels based on the principles of β-sheet hairpin self-assembly (Fig. 3(B)).[86] They designed several strand-swapping peptides, SSP1 and SSP2, which incorporate β-strand sequences of differing lengths. The longer length strand is denoted the exchangeable strand, while the shorter strand is non-exchangeable. Upon heating, these peptides adopt a β-hairpin conformation in which the exchangeable domain can mediate intermolecular β-sheet assembly (Fig. 3(B)), forming unique fibrils that effectively form hydrogel networks. Schneider *et al.* have also discovered that enantiomeric D- and L-β-hairpin peptides co-assemble to form hydrogels that have enhanced rigidity relative to single enantiomer self-assembled materials.[87] Recent work with related amphipathic peptides by the Nilsson group suggests that this is likely due to the formation of Pauling's predicted co-assembled "rippled" β-sheet fibrils.[58]

Hartgerink and co-workers have also conducted seminal studies in the development of self-assembled hydrogels derived from amphipathic peptides. They exploited $K_2(SL)_nK_2$ sequences that effectively self-assemble into hydrogel networks.[88,89] The flanking Lys residues impart unique length constraints on the observed fibrils. These hydrogels support the growth and proliferation of cells *ex vivo*. Second generation peptides, $K_2(SL)_3RG(SL)_3K2$, that incorporate a central motif that is sensitive to cleavage by matrix metalloproteinases form hydrogels that are readily degraded by cells as they proliferate and are replaced by the cells' own ECM deposits.[89] In another study that is instructive regarding the mechanical strengths of non-covalent self-assembled hydrogels versus covalent chemically crosslinked hydrogels, Hartgerink and coworkers were able to elicit chemical crosslinking of the hydrogel network using lysyl oxidase enzymes.[90] They found that the storage modulus of the entirely non-covalent hydrogels increased from

~500 Pa to >4,000 Pa upon treatment with lysyl oxidase. Lysyl oxidase converts Lys amines to aldehyde groups, which spontaneously form imines with neighboring amino groups.

Stupp and co-workers have developed unique peptide amphiphiles (PA) that self-assemble to provide viscoelastic hydrogels for a variety of biomedical applications.[91] Stupp's PAs are composed of linear non-polar hydrocarbons attached to short β-strand peptides (Fig. 4).[92] Additional peptide blocks that impart water solubility and biological functionality can also be appended to these PA sequences.[92] The β-sheet peptide block in the PA plays a crucial role for directing PA self-assembly into cylindrical nanofiber tubes by forming stabilizing hydrogen bonds; the non-polar hydrocarbon tail packs into the interior of these nanofiber tubes.[93] Disruption of the β-sheet block gives PAs that form spherical micelles or vesicles and not nanofiber hydrogels.[93] PAs that assemble in response to environmental conditions, including pH or ionic strength, have been designed.[94,95]

The multicomponent design of PAs makes the resulting self-assembled hydrogels amendable to application-specific modification. The earliest designs of PA hydrogels included oligo-Cys motifs that facilitated covalent stabilization of the self-assembled nanofibers via Cys thiol oxidation, an RGD cell adhesion motif for cell culture applications, and a phosphorylated Ser residue that enabled biomineralization events templated by the hydrogel scaffold.[96,97] Other variations of PAs have been utilized for therapeutic delivery, tissue regeneration, or as injectable scaffolds.[96–102]

The Stupp group has also explored strategies for co-assembly of complementary PAs to form multicomponent hydrogel networks. For example, it was found that co-assembly of reverse PAs with *C*-terminal aliphatic chains and conventional PAs bearing *N*-terminal aliphatic chains[103] form hydrogels with enhanced stability due to more efficient alignment of the antiparallel stacking of the β-sheets. They have also enforced co-assembly of PAs by exploiting complementary charge.[104] Negatively charged PAs with the IKVAV peptide (which promotes neurite outgrowth) and positively charged PAs bearing the YIGSR sequence (which is a

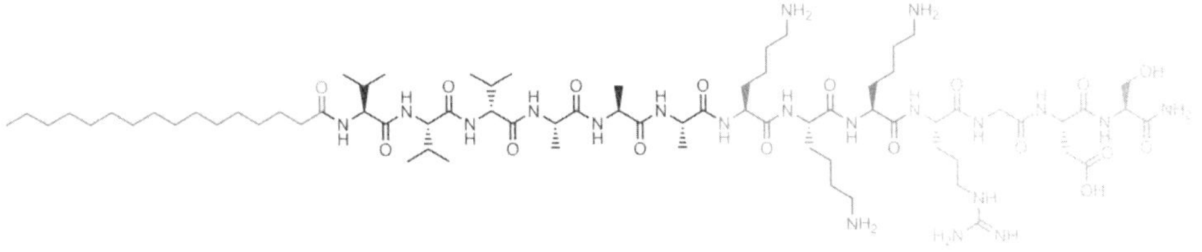

Fig. 4. Example of Stupp's peptide amphiphile: Hydrophobic hydrocarbon shown in red, β-sheet peptide block shown in black, solubilizing cationic peptide block shown in magenta, fibronectin-derived cell adhesion RGDS motif shown in green.

cellular adhesion motif) co-assemble into a multifunctional hydrogel network that promotes the growth and proliferation of neurons. These seminal studies have demonstrated elegant coupling of structure and function in the creation of self-assembled materials.

Amyloid-inspired peptides have also been exploited in the creation of functional self-assembled hydrogels. Aggeli and Boden have drawn inspiration from the amyloid-forming huntingtin protein in the creation of the Ac-QQRQQQQQEQQ–NH_2 (P_{11}-1) peptide.[105] This poly-Gln peptide assembles to form a hydrogel fibril network. Hydrogelation in response to changes in pH was made possible by substitution of key residues with aromatic, hydrophobic, or hydrophilic residues.[106–110] Collier and Messersmith have utilized the related Ac-QQKFQFQFEQQ–NH_2 (Q11) peptide for the formation of hydrogels that can be used to mimic the ECM for cell growth.[111–114] Hamley and co-workers have found that the amyloid-β (Aβ) (16–20) fragment, NH_2–KLVFF–COOH, assembles into β sheet hydrogels in phosphate buffered saline (PBS).[115] Amyloid systems are thus a rich source of inspiration in the design of novel self-assembled hydrogel systems. Interestingly, the toxicity of many amyloid proteins is likely due to pre-fibrillar aggregates; thus, mature fibril hydrogel networks derived from amyloid proteins are often entirely non-toxic to cells in culture.

2.3. Self-assembled coiled–coil peptide hydrogels

In addition to β-sheet peptides, α-helical peptides have also been utilized in the design of *de novo* hydrogel biomaterials.[116,117] α-Helical peptides have a periodicity of 3.6 amino acids per turn stabilized by hydrogen bonding of amide hydrogens with amide carbonyl groups four residues away; in coiled–coil structures the α-helices have a slightly perturbed periodicity of 3.5 residues per turn.[118] α-Helical peptides are composed of seven-amino acid repeats, denoted *abcdefg*. The heptads have an $(HPPHPPP)_n$ pattern where H represents hydrophobic residues and P represents hydrophilic residues.[118,119] α-Helical peptides often form coiled–coil quaternary structures between multiple helices stabilized by "knobs-into-holes" packing of interfacial hydrophobic side chain groups and complementary charge interactions between flanking polar residues (Fig. 5(A)).[120,121] Non-covalent coiled–coils have been engineered to form extended hydrogel networks.

Tirrell and co-workers utilized canonical "leucine (Leu) zipper" coiled–coil motifs for the formation of a hydrogel network. In a Leu zipper, the heptad incorporates Leu at the ***a*** and ***d*** positions to facilitate dimerization.[122,123] The ***e*** and ***g*** residues typically bear complementary charge.[122,123] Tirrell *et al.* placed two Leu zipper motifs at both termini of a triblock peptide linked by a central polyethylene glycol (PEG) $[(AG)3PEG]_{10}$ domain.[122,123] The non-covalent formation of Leu

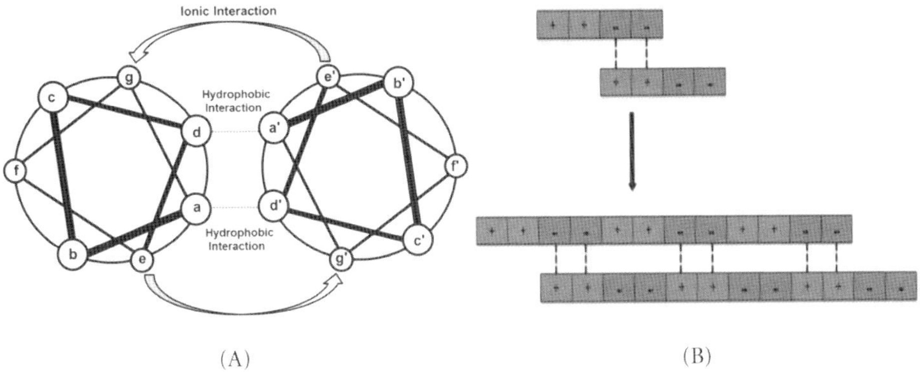

Fig. 5. (A) Sequence alignment of a typical coiled–coil structure composed of two α-helices. Hydrophobic and ionic interactions between the α-helices are indicated. (B) Extension of coiled–coil motifs into extended fibrils can be promoted by exploiting complementary charge interactions between dangling ends.

zippers creates a PEG hydrogel network.[122] Kopecek and Collier created similar hydrogels using triblock (ABA, CBA, ABC, or CBC) polypeptides.[124,125] These peptides were composed of an unstructured segment, B, linking two coiled–coil-forming motifs, A and C.[124,125] Minor manipulation of the amino acids in the A and C motifs modulated the emergent properties of the resulting hydrogels.[124,125] Both the Tirrell and Kopecek hydrogels were responsive to conditions of pH and ionic strength.[124,125]

Woolfson and co-workers have designed "sticky end" coiled–coils to promote efficient self-assembly and hydrogelation (Fig. 5(B)).[126,127] Block helical peptides were designed in which ***a*** and ***d*** were typical non-polar residues throughout the entire length of the sequence, but ***e*** and ***g*** were variably Lys (positively charged) for half of the peptide and Glu (negatively charged) for the other half.[9,127,128] These peptides formed coiled–coils in which complementary charge interaction between helices enforce dangling ends that promote extension of the coiled–coils into long, stable fibrils (Fig. 5(B)). For hydrogelation to occur, the exposed ***b***, ***c***, and ***f*** positions required combinations of Ala and Gln residues. Ala forms weak hydrophobic interactions between fibrils while glutamine forms interfibril hydrogen bonds; collectively, these interactions stabilize non-covalent crosslinking of the fibril network to elicit hydrogelation. Modification of the balance of Ala and Gln ***b***, ***c***, and ***f*** residues can alter the emergent properties of these hydrogels. For example, uniform placement of Gln at ***b***, ***c***, and ***f*** provided materials that undergo the sol–gel transition in response to increasing temperature, although weakening of the gels was observed above threshold temperatures. Uniform placement of Ala at ***b***, ***c***, and *f*, provided fibrils that were weak gels even at lower temperature but strengthened with increasing temperature and did not weaken even at very high temperatures.

While Woolfson used charge complementary sticky-ended helices to elicit coiled–coil self-assembly, Hartgerink and co-workers designed blunt-ended coiled–coils that also form stable self-assembling hydrogels.[129] Leu and Ile were employed in the ***a*** and ***d*** positions with Glu in the ***e*** and ***g*** positions to enable pH dependent assembly. The identity of amino acids incorporated into the ***b***, ***c***, and ***f*** positions determined the length and diameter of the peptide fibers formed. This work demonstrates that sticky ended coiled–coils are not a necessary pre-requisite for the self-assembly of helical peptides into functional hydrogels, expanding the design possibilities for these types of materials.

3. Self-Assembled Oligonucleotide Hydrogels

DNA biopolymers have also been used to form self-assembled hydrogels. DNA-based hydrogels exploit complementary Watson–Crick base-pairing and the principles of DNA origami to facilitate assembly of up to four strands of DNA into various geometric "monomer" structures (Fig. 6).[130,131] These monomers are designed to promote further assembly into hierarchical ordered networks that can induce gelation of aqueous solvents.[132]

Luo and co-workers pioneered the use of DNA to form hierachical DNA hydrogels.[130] Self-assembled DNA "monomer" structures composed of up to four complementary strands of DNA were created (Fig. 6).[130,133] These "monomers" were further assembled into extensive networks by enzymatically ligating the self-assembled monomers at the ends using T4 DNA ligase. These ligated networks formed weak hydrogels with storage moduli of ~5 Pa. X-, Y-, and T-shaped monomers were used to form these networks. The X monomer was utilized to form protein producing "p-gels" in which genes are included in the DNA scaffold to provide hydrogels that can express proteins in a cell-free environment at high yield.[134] Non-covalent weaving of polymerase expanded DNA chains formed hydrogels that exhibited shape memory properties, facilitating the gel's use as a water-triggered on/off circuit.[134,135]

Liu and co-workers were able to create DNA-based hydrogels that changed from gel to sol states rapidly in response to changes in environmental pH.[136] They used Y-type monomer structures that feature cytosine-rich stretches. The cytosine ends effectively non-covalently crosslink the Y-units in an "i-motif" to form the hydrogel network at acidic pH.[137] At slightly acid pH the cytosine nucleotides are partially positively charged, facilitating assembly of the Y-units by triple helix formation. At basic pH, the crosslinks are relaxed since the cytosines are uncharged and the crosslinking triple helical structures relax, resulting in loss of the hydrogel

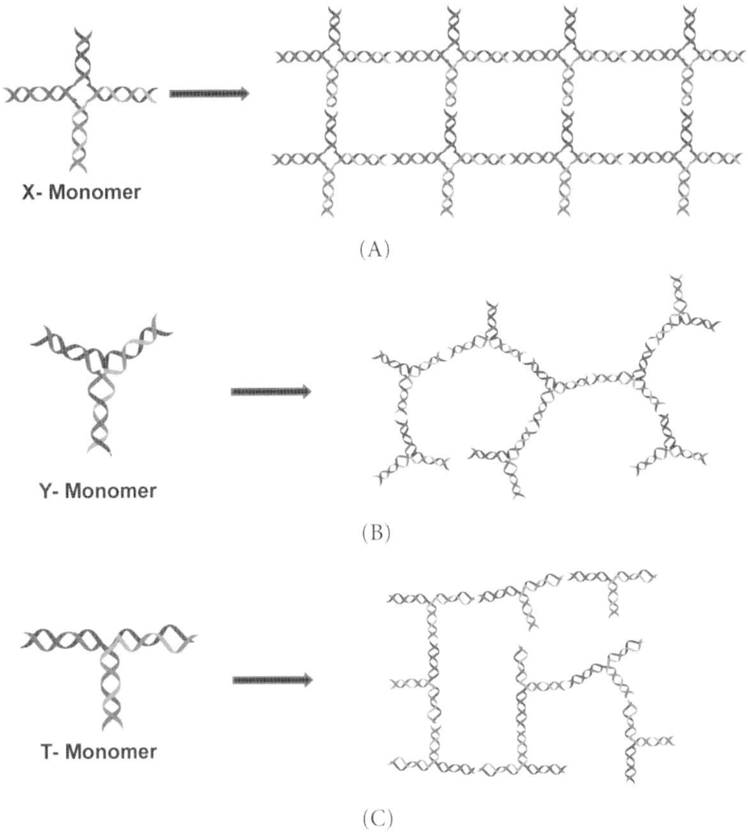

Fig. 6. Examples of DNA "monomer" structures composed of up to four complementary DNA strands that self-assemble into hierarchical hydrogel networks.

network. These sol–gel/gel–sol transitions occur very rapidly, in contrast to ligase-mediated DNA gels, which can require days to fully form. These principles have been expanded to the design of Y-monomers that reversibly assemble and disassembly in response to thermal and enzymatic stimuli.[136] The rapid responses of these next-generation, stimulus-responsive materials have great potential for biological applications, including drug delivery.

4. Low Molecular Weight Self-Assembling Hydrogelators

4.1. Amino acids and low molecular weight peptides

While biopolymers have been widely exploited in the design of self-assembled hydrogels, low molecular weight hydrogelators (LMWHs) have received significant recent attention.[6,130,133] Biopolymers, including DNA and peptides/proteins, are

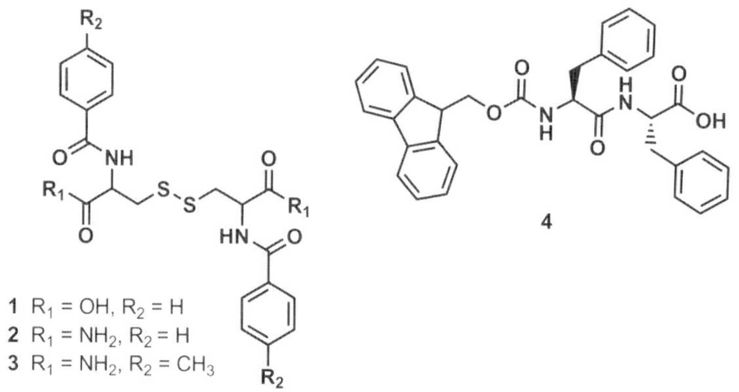

Fig. 7. Chemical structures of dibenzoylcystine derivatives (**1–3**) and Fmoc-Phe-Phe (**4**).

relatively expensive to produce at large scale. Thus, LMWHs are advantageous due to their potential as inexpensive alternatives to biopolymers for the formation of hydrogels that can be used in various biological applications. One of the earliest reports of self-assembling LMWHs appeared in 1921.[140] Gortner and Hoffman discovered that dibenzoylcystine (Fig. 7; **1**) formed a self-supporting gel in water.[140] Menger and co-workers, 74 years later, evaluated the mechanistic basis for self-assembly and hydrogelation of dibenzoylcystine derivatives in water (Fig. 7; **1–3**) and found that hydrogen bonding and π–π interactions play a critical role in stabilizing the self-assembled fibril network.[141] This work initiated the discovery of a variety of privileged scaffolds that promote self-assembly and hydrogelation of low molecular weight monomeric materials.

Fluorenylmethoxycarbonyl (Fmoc)-modified amino acids and di/tripeptides are among the most commonly reported LMWHs. Fmoc protected dipeptides such as Fmoc–Leu–Asp, Fmoc–Ala–Asp and Fmoc–Ile–Asp readily self-assemble into fibril hydrogel networks.[142] Gazit and co-workers discovered that the Phe–Phe dipeptide self-assembles into nanotubes.[143,144] Related nanotubes derived from self-assembled Fmoc–Phe–Phe (Fig. 7; **4**) formed stable hydrogels.[143] Ulijn and co-workers subsequently reported that the self-assembly of short Fmoc protected peptides, including Fmoc–Phe–Phe, is mediated by formation of antiparallel β-sheets that feature Fmoc–Fmoc π–π interactions.[145,146]

Hydrogelation of Fmoc-dipeptides is pH-dependent. At basic pH, the negative charge on the *C*-terminal carboxylic acid of Fmoc–Phe–Phe solubilizes the dipeptide, but impedes self-assembly due to charge repulsion between neighboring negative carboxlyates.[145] However, at pH <8, self-assembly and hydrogelation is promoted since the *C*-terminal carboxylic acid exists in a partial protonated state, easing charge repulsion.[146,147] The method of pH adjustment (rapid adjustment by titration with HCl versus more gradual adjustment with glucono-D-lactone (GDL) which slowly hydrolyzes to form gluconic acid) has a significant impact on Fmoc–Phe–Phe hydrogel quality.[148] Fmoc-dipeptides are typically highly hydrophobic with low inherent water solubility compared to peptide/protein and oligonucleotide biopolymers. Thus, balancing solubilizing forces with self-assembly forces is critical for LMWHs: rapid changes in pH can prevent self-assembly by instead promoting precipitation of the acidified peptide. The identity of the Fmoc-dipeptide can moderate the pH values at which self-assembly and hydrogelation occurs. For example, Fmoc-dipeptides derived of combinations of Gly, Ala, Leu, and Phe have been shown to form gels at pH 3–5.[147,148]

Co-assembly of Fmoc-dipeptides and Fmoc-amino acids has been effective for the creation of functional hydrogels at neutral pH for cell culture applications. For example, co-assembly of Fmoc–Phe–Phe and Fmoc–Lys mixtures is highly favorable since the cationic amine of the Lys forms hydrogen bonds and electrostatic interactions with the carboxylate of Fmoc–Phe–Phe and the resulting hydrogels are rigid ($G' \approx 12{,}000$ Pa).[149] In contrast, co-assembly of Fmoc–Glu and Fmoc–Phe–Phe is less effective due to charge repulsion between these molecules at neutral pH; the resulting gels are weak ($G' \approx 500$ Pa). Co-assembly of Fmoc–Ser and Fmoc–Phe–Phe is favored by side chain hydrogen bonding with the Ser OH, although complementary charge is lacking; the resulting gel is intermediate in strength ($G' \approx 3{,}500$ Pa). The gels of intermediate strength are most appropriate for the mechanical tolerances of cells in culture, illustrating the importance of exploiting non-covalent interactions to tune the emergent properties of self-assembling hydrogels.

In addition to Fmoc-dipeptides, Fmoc-protected amino acids have also proven to form robust self-assembled hydrogels. Xu and co-workers first reported the enzyme-triggered self-assembly and hydrogelation of Fmoc–Tyr (Fig. 8; **6**) by treatment of solution of Fmoc–phosphor–Tyr (Fig. 8; **5**) with phosphatase enzymes.[150] This process is an ingenious example of stimulus-responsive hydrogelation that overcomes the underlying problem of low water solubility of many LMWHs. The gradual release of Fmoc–Tyr from the phosphorylated precursor enables ordered self-assembly to occur favorably relative to simple precipitation of amorphous aggregates of Fmoc–Tyr. This strategy has also been used to promote the self-assembly and hydrogelation of other Fmoc-modified peptides that incorporate Tyr derivatives.[151,152]

Fmoc–Phe derivatives have proven to be privileged scaffolds for the formation of self-assembled hydrogels. Based on previous studies which indicated that Fmoc–Phe undergoes less efficient self-assembly than Fmoc–Tyr,[146,150] Nilsson and co-workers investigated the influence of side chain electronics and hydrophobicity on self-assembly and hydrogelation of Fmoc–Phe derivatives (Fig. 9(A)).[153] It was

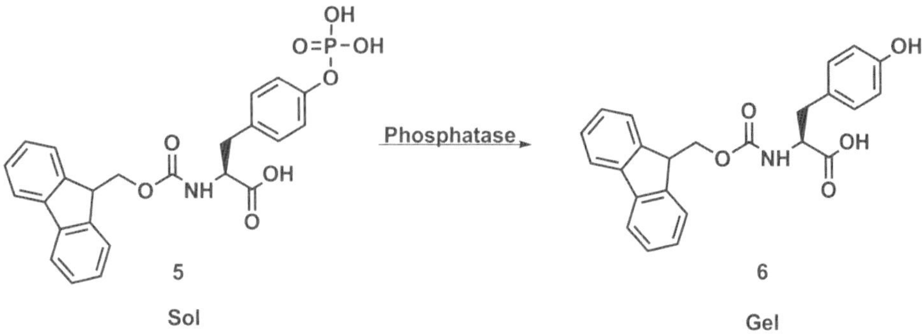

Fig. 8. Chemical structure of phosphorylated Tyr (**5**) that undergoes a sol–gel transition upon enzymatic dephosphorylation to Fmoc–Tyr (**6**).

found that Fmoc–F_5–Phe (**7**), which is significantly more hydrophobic and electron-deficient than either Fmoc–Phe or Fmoc–Tyr, undergoes more rapid gelation and forms significantly more rigid gels compared to Fmoc–Tyr (Fmoc–F_5–Phe: G' = 3000 Pa, gel time 3–5 min; Fmoc–Tyr: G′ = 1000 Pa, gel time ~30 min) under conditions where Fmoc–Phe fails to gel altogether. Fmoc–Phe derivatives are highly hydrophobic, and self-assembly and hydrogelation is most effectively promoted by dilution from an organic co-solvent (DMSO) into water (final DMSO concentration is 2% *v*/*v*). A fibril packing mode for Fmoc–Phe derivatives that involves Fmoc–Fmoc stacking and stacking of the Phe side chain groups has been proposed (Fig. 9B).[6,153] While other packing structures are possible, this fundamental packing unit is most consistent with the available spectroscopic data. The acquisition of high-resolution structure data that can confirm the packing structure of LMWH materials is necessary to facilitate a shift from empirical to rational development of next-generation LMWHs.

Additional empirical studies have provided insight into the physicochemical determinants that promote self-assembly and hydrogelation of Fmoc–Phe derivatives. Monohalogenated Fmoc–Phe derivatives (Fig. 9; **8**), including *ortho*, *meta*, and *para*-F, Cl, and Br variants all undergo efficient self-assembly and hydrogelation upon dilution from DMSO into water (2% DMSO *v*/*v* in final hydrogel solutions).[154] However, the position of the halogen substituent on the aromatic Phe side chain has a dramatic effect on self-assembly and hydrogelation rates and resulting hydrogel rigidities. In addition, whereas Fmoc–Phe does not readily self-assemble upon dilution from DMSO into water, it can co-assemble into hydrogel networks with halogenated Fmoc–Phe derivatives (**7** and **8**).[155] Thus, simple modifications to the aromatic side chain of Phe can be used to tune the self-assembly and hydrogelation properties of Fmoc–Phe derivatives.

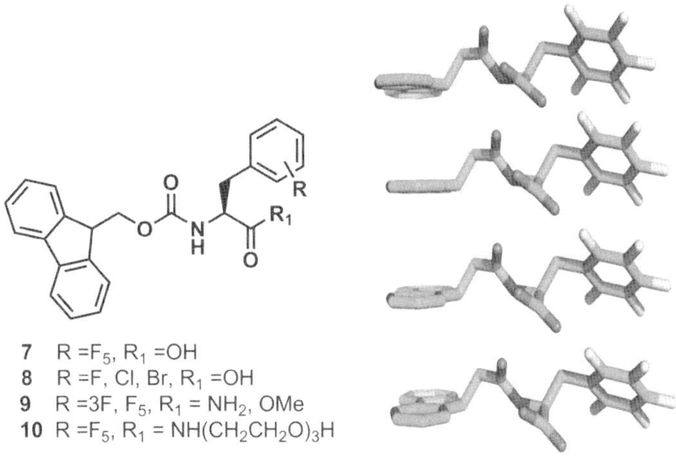

(A) (B)

Fig. 9. (A) Chemical structures of Fmoc–Phe derivatives, including F_5–Phe (**1**), monohalogenated Phe derivatives (**8**, **9**), and PEG-modified Fmoc–F_5–Phe. (B) Proposed packing structure of self-assembled Fmoc–F_5–Phe.

The effect of *C*-terminal carboxylic acid on the self-assembly and hydrogelation of Fmoc–Phe derivatives has also been examined. The self-assembly of *C*-terminal amide and *C*-terminal methyl ester Fmoc–Phe derivatives (Fig. 9; **9**) was compared to that of the parent carboxylic acid derivatives at both acidic and neutral pH.[156] It was found the carboxylate derivatives rapidly gelled at acidic pH, but at neutral pH self-assembly and hydrogel rigidity was greatly reduced. The ester derivatives failed to gel under either condition, while the amide derivatives rapidly formed relatively weak gels under both conditions. *C*-terminal functionalization of Fmoc–F_5–Phe by PEG (Fig. 9; **10**) provided stable hydrogels when co-assembled with Fmoc–F_5–Phe; the co-assembled gels exhibited shear recovery properties, making the resulting materials suitable for use as injectable tissue culture scaffolds.[157] These results indicate that hydrogen bonding capacity, charge (as a function of pH), and hydrophobicity exert profound effects on self-assembly and hydrogelation phenomena of these derivatives.

Fmoc-modification of peptides that act as cellular adhesion signals has been used to induce gelation of these peptides to create scaffolds for tissue culture applications.[158] Hamley has induced gelation of the integrin-binding RGD peptide by *N*-terminal Fmoc modification. Aromatic π-interactions involving the Fmoc group are critical for self-assembly and hydrogelation of these short peptides.[158,159] Fmoc–RGD, Fmoc–RGDS as well as scrambled Fmoc–GRD and Fmoc–GRDS sequences all formed stable hydrogels.[158,159] Gazit has also reported that related Fmoc–RGDF and Fmoc–FRGD peptides form stable β-sheet fibril hydrogels.[160]

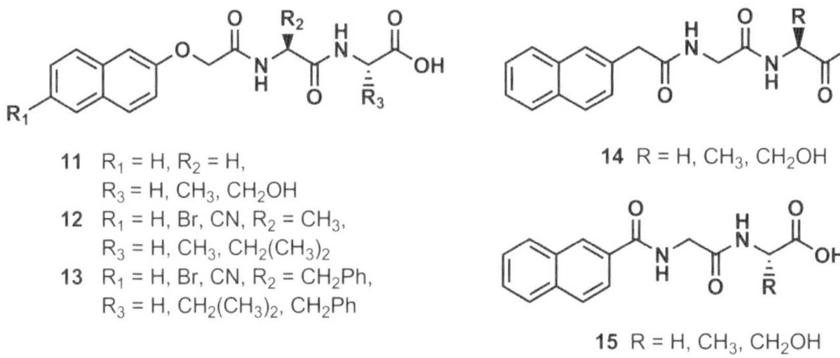

Fig. 10. Chemical structures of *N*-terminal Nap-modified peptide LMWHs.

These gel types have been shown to promote the growth and proliferation of cells in culture.

Naphthalene (Nap) modified peptides and amino acids have also proven to be privileged self-assembling LMWHs (Fig. 10). Xu and co-workers have used Nap functionalized dipeptides to form stable hydrogels.[161] In general, it has been found that hydrogels formed by Nap modified peptides are weaker than the corresponding Fmoc protected gelators.[161] The decreased surface area of Nap compared to Fmoc may impact self-assembly and hydrogelation by perturbing the stabilizing π–π interactions that occur in the assembled network. In an analysis of variously configured Nap groups (Fig. 10; **11**, **14**, **15**), it was found that only **11** peptides formed stable hydrogels while **14** and **15** failed to gel.[162] It was hypothesized that the length of the linker between the Nap derivative and the dipeptide accounts for these observations due to differences in π–π stacking geometries accessible during self-assembly. Adams and co-workers have also assessed self-assembly and hydrogelation of a library of Nap-dipeptides with varying substitution patterns on the Nap ring (Fig. 10; **12** and **13**).[6,163] A correlation between the hydrophobicity of the derivatives and self-assembly propensity was observed. Collectively, these studies reinforce the importance of hydrophobicity and π–π interactions in the design of self-assembling LMWH systems.

The development of LMWHs that self-assemble in response to biologically relevant stimuli has been a topic of intense interest.[164–166] Xu's phophastase-triggered gelation of Tyr derivatives has inspired a number of related approaches for enzyme-responsive hydrogelators. One strategy has been the enzymatic ligation of short amino acid fragments to form longer sequences that can self-assemble into hydrogel networks.[167] In one example, Ulijn and co-workers harnessed the enzymatic ligation of Fmoc–Phe and Phe–Phe to form Fmoc–Phe_3 that subsequently assembles into a transparent hydrogel network.[168] Furthermore, they have also formed stable gels via enzymatic peptide bond formation between Fmoc–Thr and the Leu methyl ester (Leu–OMe).[169] Upon saponification of the ester bond (converting Fmoc–Thr–Leu–OMe to Fmoc–Thr–Leu), a gel to solution transition occurs.[169,170] These strategies have been widely applied to a number of enzymes and LMW modified peptides with great success, demonstrating the ability to modulate gel–sol and sol–gel transitions based on response of the assembly state to environmental stimuli.[171]

Additional strategies to initiate stimulus-responsive hydrogelation of LMWHs have also been explored. For example, the Xu group has designed a photosensitive *N*-cinnamoyl-Phe hydrogel that can modulate between gel and sol states in response to UV light promoted *cis–trans*/*trans–cis* isomerization of the cinnamoyl olefin.[172] Similar strategies employing photosensitive azobenzene derivatives have also been demonstrated.[173] As discussed previously, temperature, pH, and ionic strength have all been used to induce self-assembled hydrogelation in various systems.[146,154] Self-assembled hydrogels can be modulated by the nature of added solution ions. Kosmotropes, which stabilize the interactions between water molecules and peptides, promote hydrophobic interactions that favor Fmoc–Fmoc stacking leading to hydrogelation.[174,175] In contrast, chaotropes reduce self-assembled hydrogel integrity due to the disruption of ordered assemblies in favor of less ordered aggregates. Self-assembling hydrogels have been designed by using monomer structures that incorporate disulfide bonds that induce non-assembling structures; in the presence of reducing agents, hydrogelation can be induced.[176,177] Stimulus responsive hydrogels have great potential to be exploited in biological contexts in which differences in environmental conditions can be used to dictate hydrogel structure and function in applications such as tissue engineering, wound healing, and drug delivery.

4.2. Carbohydrate, lipid, and hybrid self-assembling hydrogels

Polymeric polysaccharides including hyaluronic acid, dextran, chitosan, alginate, and others are popular components of covalently crosslinked hydrogel networks. Recently, self-assembling carbohydrate-based LMWHs have also been used to form non-covalent hydrogels. Many of these carbohydrate derived LMWHs append aromatic groups to monosaccharides to provide molecules that can exploit hydrogen-bonding, π–π, and hydrophobic interactions to form self-assembled hydrogel networks. The Shimizu group has utilized sugar-based hydrogelators (Fig. 11; **16**, **17**) that are composed of monosaccharides with appended aromatic and/or hydrophobic groups (**16**) or bolaamphiphiles in which two monosaccharides are linked by a bridging hydrophobic chain (**17**).[178–180] Self-assembly and hydrogelation of these molecules is driven by packing of the hydrophobic tails which are shielded in fibril

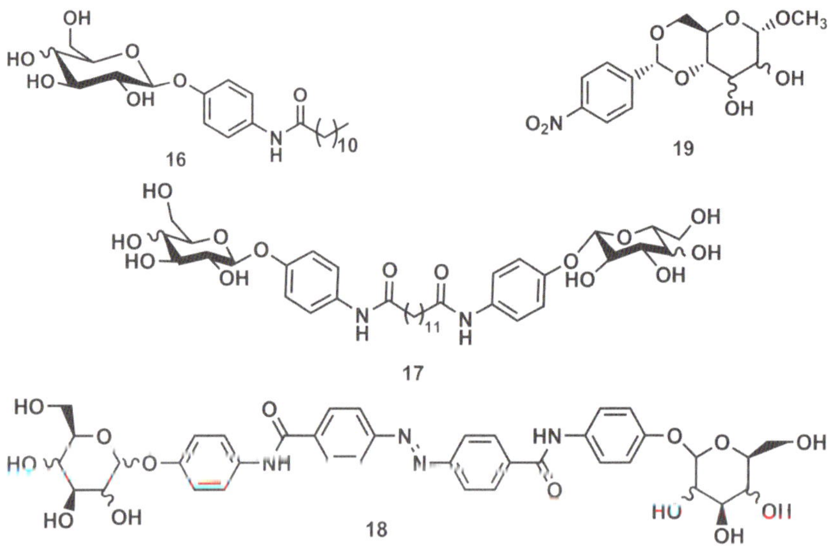

Fig. 11. Chemical structures of modified carbohydrates that have been used as LMWHs.

interiors by the appended hydrophobic carbohydrates.[178] Carbohydrate bolaamphiphiles have also integrated azobenzene as the hydrophobic linker group (Fig. 11; **18**) to create self-assembled hydrogels.[181,182] Benzylidene protected 1-*O*-methyl-4,6-*O*-benzylidene-monosaccharides undergo self-assembly and hydrogelation when the benzylidene includes *para*-nitro substitution (Fig. 11; **19**).[183] In contrast, *meta*- and *ortho*-nitro benzylidenes fail to undergo self-assembly and gelation. Hydrophobic and dipole–dipole interactions between stacked aromatic groups likely account for these observations.

Lipids have been extensively employed in the creation of self-assembling LMWHs.[184] As described previously, long chain alkanes are often appended to peptides or carbohydrates to create self-assembling amphiphiles. Cholesterol derivatives have also been used as modifiers in the design of amphipathic self-assembling hydrogelators. For example, tripodal cholic acid derivatives have been shown to form self-assembled hydrogels in the presence of appropriate counterions and organic co-solvents.[184] Cationic and neutral analogues of bile acids have also been reported to form thermoreversible hydrogels in the presence of NaCl salt or organic co-solvents.[179] Semi-fluorinated fatty acid functionalized amphiphiles also efficiently self-assemble into hydrogel network, presumably due to strong hydrophobic interactions between the fluorinated hydrocarbons.[185,186]

Gemini surfactants have been shown to be efficient amphiphiles for the design of self-assembling LMWHs. Inspired by their work with dibenzoyl cystine derivatives (Fig. 7, **1–3**), Menger and co-workers discovered that dodecyl alkane modified

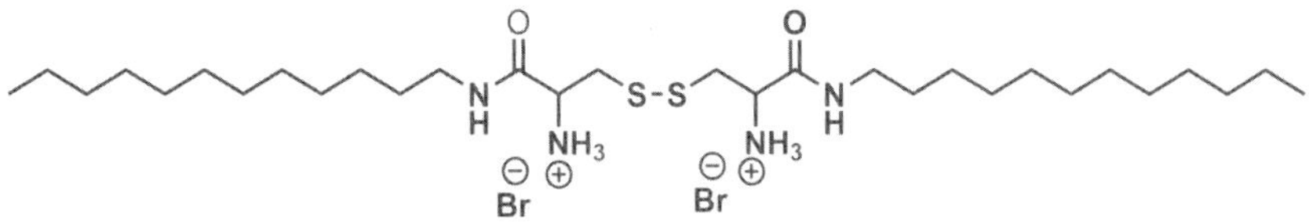

20

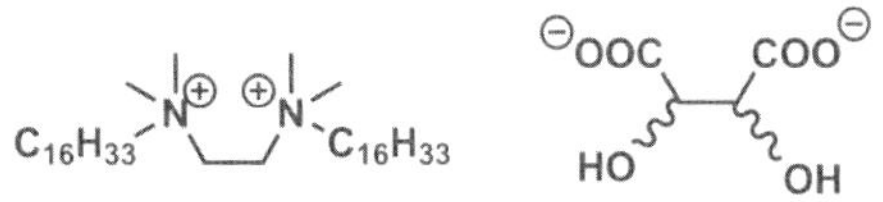

21

Fig. 12. Chemical structures of L-cystine hydrocarbon conjugates (**20**) and bis-(hexadecyldimethylammonium)ethane tartrate salts (**21**).

L-cystine (Fig. 12; **20**) also form stable self-assembled hydrogels. Changes in the hydrocarbon tail modify the hydrogelation potential of these amphiphiles.[187,188] Oda and co-workers have found that bis-(hexadecyldimethylammonium)ethane can be paired with tartrate counterions to form hydrogels (Fig. 12; **21**).[189] Similarly, Bhattacharya and De have found that bis-(hexadecyldimethylammonium)propane can also be used to form hydrogel when paired with palmitate.[182,190] Surfactants share important characteristics with LMWH molecules generally. They are amphipathic structures, with appropriately positioned hydrophobic and hydrophilic functionality.

Many of the self-assembling hydrogelators described in this chapter are hybrid molecules. Additional hybrid molecules have also been used as LMWHs. For example, Xu has been able to utilize nucleobases conjugated to short peptides, amino acids, and glycosides to form hybrid hydrogelators.[191–193] Attachment of bioactive molecules to amino acids to form LMWH hybrids that can be directly applied to biomedical drug delivery applications are described in some detail in the following section. Amino acid–carbohydrate hybrids, including *N*-acetyl–galactosamine appended to amino acid esters and carbohydrate esters at amino acid *C*-termini have also been adapted for the creation of LMWHs.[194] Creative hybrid LMWHs have the potential for application as multifunctional bioactive agents.

5. Self-Assembled Pharmaceutical Agent Hydrogels

Self-assembled hydrogels composed of pharmaceutical agents are highly desired biomaterials since they allow alteration of drug solubility and reduce harmful off-target effects by enabling the targeted delivery of the therapeutic agents to specific tissues and organs. Excellent reviews on these types of pro-drug hydrogels are available for detailed discussion of these materials.[195,196] Pharmaceutical hydrogels are composed of unaltered drugs or of modified prodrug forms of the therapeutic agents where the modifications promote π–π stacking, hydrophobic, and hydrogen bonding interactions that drive self-assembly and hydrogelation processes. Lantreotide (treatment for acromegaly), amygdalin (anticancer) conjugated with fatty acids, vancomycin (antibiotic) conjugated with pyrene at the *C*-terminus, gonadotropin, phosphorylated paclitaxel (anticancer), and D-glucosamine (osteoarthritis) conjugated with Nap–Phe are examples of prodrug molecules that form self-assembled hydrogels.[197–201] Therapeutic agents can be incorporated into multicomponent hydrogels by co-assembly. Xu and co-workers found that the osteoporosis suppressing drug, pamidronate forms co-gels with mixtures of Fmoc-L-Leu and *N*-ε-Fmoc-L-Lys.[202] Ibuprofen and acetaminophen attached to Gly–Gly dipeptides also form self-assembled hydrogels that can be degraded by carboxypeptidase to release the active forms of these drugs.[77,203] These hydrogels enable novel and promising strategies for drug delivery and release to targeted tissues.

6. Conclusions and Outlook

Self-assembling hydrogels have been shown to be attractive alternatives to covalently, chemically crosslinked polymer hydrogels. Self-assembling hydrogels either form spontaneously upon dissolution of the monomeric constituents into water or in response to environmental stimuli. Thus, self-assembling hydrogels are dynamic materials that are capable of reversibly undergoing sol–gel/gel–sol transitions. The self-assembly motifs are often bioinspired molecules, including peptides, proteins, oligonucleotides, carbohydrates, and functionalized amino acids. Thus, these materials are highly biocompatible and have been designed for use as drug delivery vectors, tissue culture matrices, and cell transplant materials. Many of these materials have been discovered serendipitously or have been developed using empirical approaches. Recent research has provided critical insight into the physicochemical basis for self-assembly/hydrogelation phenomena. Research that elucidates the relationships between self-assembled structures and their emergent properties will facilitate the design of next-generation materials that rival traditional polymer-based hydrogels.

Acknowledgments

This work was supported by the National Science Foundation (DMR-1148836) and by a University of Rochester Provost's Multidisciplinary Award.

References

1. S. Zhang, *Amino Acids Pept. Proteins*, **37**, 40–67 (2012).
2. S. Zhang, *Biotechnol. Adv.*, **20**, 321–339 (2002).
3. Z. Luo and S. Zhang, *Amyloid Fibrils and Prefibrillar Aggregates: Molecular and Biological Properties,* Ed. D. E. Otzen, Wiley–VCH Verlag GmbH & Co. KGaA, pp. 439–454 (2013).
4. C. Dobson, *Protein Misfolding, Aggregation, and Conformational Diseases*, Eds. V. Uversky and A. Fink, US: Springer, *Vol.* 4, pp. 21–41 (2006).
5. F. Chiti and C. M. Dobson, *Nat. Chem. Biol.*, **5**, 15–22 (2009).
6. D. M. Ryan and B. L. Nilsson, *Polym. Chem.*, **3**, 18–33 (2012).
7. J. P. Jung, J. Z. Gasiorowski, and J. H. Collier, *Biopolymers*, **94**, 49–59 (2010).
8. R. V. Ulijn and D. N. Woolfson, *Chem. Soc. Rev.*, **39**, 3349–3350 (2010).
9. N. Stephanopoulos, J. H. Ortony, and S. I. Stupp, *Acta Mater.*, **61**, 912–930 (2013).
10. J. B. Matson and S. I. Stupp, *Chem. Commun.*, **48**, 26–33 (2012).
11. N. A. Peppas, J. Z. Hilt, A. Khademhosseini, and R. Langer, *Adv. Mater.*, **18**, 1345–1360 (2006).
12. Z. Yang, G. Liang, and B. Xu, *Soft Matter*, **3**, 515–520 (2007).
13. M. C. Branco and J. P. Schneider, *Acta Biomater.*, **5**, 817–831 (2009).
14. H. Cui, M. J. Webber, and S. I. Stupp, *Biopolymers*, **94**, 1–18 (2010).
15. I. W. Hamley, *Angew. Chem. Int. Ed.*, **46**, 8128–8147 (2007).
16. W. T. Truong, Y. Su, J. T. Meijer, P. Thordarson, and F. Braet, *Chem. Asian. J.*, **6**, 30–42 (2011).
17. J. Chen, J. W. Kampf, and A. J. McNeil, *Langmuir*, **26**, 13076–13080 (2010).
18. M. L. Muro-Small, J. Chen, and A. J. McNeil, *Langmuir*, **27**, 13248–13253 (2011).
19. S. Debnath and R. V. Ulijn, *Functional Molecular Gels*, Eds. B. Escuder and J. F. Miravet, The Royal Society of Chemistry, pp. 95–116 (2014).
20. A. Bandiera, A. Markulin, L. Corich, F. Vita, and V. Borrelli, *Biomacromolecules*, **15**, 416–422 (2014).
21. T. Garg, S. Singh, and A. K. Goyal, *Crit. Rev. Ther. Drug*, **30**, 369–409 (2013).
22. R. P. Nagarkar, R. A. Hule, D. J. Pochan, and J. P. Schneider, *Biopolymers*, **94**, 141–155 (2010).
23. K. Y. Lee and D. J. Mooney, *Chem. Rev.*, **101**, 1869–1880 (2001).
24. E. C. Wu, S. Zhang, and C. A. E. Hauser, *Adv. Funct. Mater.*, **22**, 456–468 (2012).
25. J. Kopêck, *J. Polym. Sci. Part A*, **22**, 5929–5946 (2009).
26. Y. Gao, Z. Yang, Y. Kuang, M. L. Ma, J. Li, F. Zhao, and B. Xu, *Biopolymers*, **94**, 19–31 (2010).
27. J. Kopêck and J. Yang, *Angew. Chem. Int. Ed.*, **30**, 7396–7417 (2012).
28. L. Pan, G. Yu, D. Zhai, H. R. Lee, W. Zhao, N. Liu, H. Wang, B. C.-K. Tee, Y. Shi, Y. Cui, and Z. Bao, *Proc. Natl. Acad. Sci.*, **109**, 9287–9292 (2012).
29. T. Miyata, A. Jikihara, K. Nakamae, and A. S. Hoffman, *J. Biomater. Sci. Polym. Ed.*, **15**, 1085–1098 (2004).

30. J. H. Collier, J. S. Rudra, J. Z. Gasiorowski, and J. P. Jung, *Chem. Soc. Rev.*, **39**, 3413–3424 (2010).
31. H. Geckil, F. Xu, X. Zhang, S. Moon, and U. Demirci, *Nanomedicine*, **5**, 469–484 (2010).
32. F. Li and W. Liu, *Handbook of Hydrogels: Properties, Preparation & Applications*, Ed. D. B. Stein, Nova Publisher, pp. 365–396 (2006).
33. F. W. Kotch and R. T. Raines, *Proc. Natl. Acad. Sci.*, **103**, 3028–3033 (2006).
34. M. Rasmussen, M. Jacobsson, and L. Bjorck, *J. Biol. Chem.*, **278**, 32313–32316 (2003).
35. C. Yan and D. J. Pochan, *Chem. Soc. Rev.*, **39**, 3528–3540 (2010).
36. A. H. Clark and S. B. Rossmurphy, *Adv. Polym. Sci.*, **83**, 57–192 (1987).
37. L. E. R. O'Leary, J. A. Fallas, E. L. Bakota, M. K. Kang, and J. D. Hartgerink, *Nat. Chem.*, **3**, 821–828 (2011).
38. A. Altunbas and D. J. Pochan, *Top. Curr. Chem.*, **310**, 135–168 (2012).
39. T. Z. Grove and L. Regan, *Curr. Opin. Struct. Biol.*, **22**, 451–456 (2012).
40. J. Lee, *Recent Res. Dev. Polym. Sci.* **6**, 27–43 (2002).
41. L. Debelle, A. J. Alix, S. M. Wei, M. P. Jacob, J. P. Huvenne, M. Berjot, and P. Legrand, *Eur. J. Biochem.*, **258**, 533–539 (1998).
42. A. Pepe, B. Bochicchio, and A. M. Tamburro, *Nanomedicine*, **2**, 203–218 (2007).
43. S. M. Partridge, D. F. Elsden, and J. Thomas, *Nature*, **197**, 1297–1298 (1963).
44. D. L. Nettles, A. Chilkoti, and L. A. Setton, *Adv. Drug. Deliv. Rev.*, **62**, 1479–1485 (2010).
45. A. Chilkoti, T. Christensen, and J. A. MacKay, *Curr. Opin. Chem. Biol.*, **10**, 652–657 (2006).
46. D. W. Urry, *Angew. Chem. Int. Ed.*, **32**, 819–841 (1993).
47. D. W. Urry, *Trends Biotechnol.*, **17**, 249–257 (1999).
48. A. M. Jonker, D. W. P. M. Löwik, and J. C. M. van Hest, *Chem. Mater.*, **24**, 759–773 (2011).
49. T. Yamaoka, T. Tamura, Y. Seto, T. Tada, S. Kunugi, and D. A. Tirrell, *Biomacromolecules*, **4**, 1680–1685 (2003).
50. I. Massodi, E. Thomas, and D. Raucher, *Molecules*, **14**, 1999–2015 (2009).
51. U.-J. Kim, J. Park, C. Li, H.-J. Jin, R. Valluzzi, and D. L. Kaplan, *Biomacromolecules*, **5**, 786–792 (2004).
52. H. J. Jin and D. L. Kaplan, *Nature*, **424**, 1057–1061 (2003).
53. A. Nagarsekar, J. Crissman, M. Crissman, F. Ferrari, J. Cappello, and H. Ghandehari, *J. Biomed. Mater. Res.* **62**, 195–203 (2002).
54. C. Akkermans, P. Venema, A. J. van der Goot, H. Gruppen, E. J. Bakx, R. M. Boom, and E. van der Linden, *Biomacromolecules*, **9**, 1474–1479 (2008).
55. S. Yu, P. Yao, M. Jiang, and G. Zhang, *Biopolymers*, **83**, 148–158 (2006).
56. H. Yan, A. Nykanen, J. Ruokolainen, D. Farrar, J. E. Gough, A. Saiani, and A. F. Miller, *Faraday Discuss.*, **139**, 71–84 (2008).
57. C. J. Bowerman and B. L. Nilsson, *Biopolymers*, **98**, 169–184 (2012).
58. R. J. Swanekamp, J. T. Di Maio, C. J. Bowerman, and B. L. Nilsson, *J. Am. Chem. Soc.*, **134**, 5556–5559 (2012).

59. H. Yokoi, T. Kinoshita, and S. Zhang, *Proc. Natl. Acad. Sci.*, **102**, 8414–8419 (2005).
60. M. E. Davis, J. P. Motion, D. A. Narmoneva, T. Takahashi, D. Hakuno, R. D. Kamm, S. Zhang, and R. T. Lee, *Circulation*, **111**, 442–450 (2005).
61. D. M. Marini, W. Hwang, D. A. Lauffenburger, S. Zhang, and R. D. Kamm, *Nano Lett.*, **2**, 295–299 (2002).
62. S. Zhang, T. Holmes, C. Lockshin, and A. Rich, *Proc. Natl. Acad. Sci.*, **90**, 3334–3338 (1993).
63. W. Hwang, D. M. Marini, R. D. Kamm, and S. Zhang, *J. Chem. Phys.*, **118**, 389–397 (2003).
64. A. M. Smith and T. Scheibel, *Macromol. Chem. Phys.*, **211**, 127–135 (2010).
65. J. Kisiday, M. Jin, B. Kurz, H. Hung, C. Semino, S. Zhang, and A. J. Grodzinsky, *Proc. Natl. Acad. Sci.*, **99**, 9996–10001 (2002).
66. T. Wang, X. Zhong, S. Wang, F. Lv, and X. Zhao, *Int. J. Mol. Sci.*, **13**, 15279–15290 (2012).
67. A. Schneider, J. A. Garlick and C. Egles, *PLoS ONE*, **3**, e1410 (2008).
68. Z. Luo and S. Zhang, *Chem. Soc. Rev.*, **41**, 4736–4754 (2012).
69. R. G. Ellis-Behnke, Y. X. Liang, D. K. Tay, P. W. Kau, G. E. Schneider, S. Zhang, W. Wu and K. F. So, *Nanomedicine*, **2**, 207–215 (2006).
70. M. R. Caplan, P. N. Moore, S. Zhang, R. D. Kamm, and D. A. Lauffenburger, *Biomacromolecules*, **1**, 627–631 (2000).
71. M. R. Caplan, E. M. Schwartzfarb, S. Zhang, R. D. Kamm, and D. A. Lauffenburger, *Biomaterials*, **23**, 219–227 (2002).
72. K. Wang, J. D. Keasling, and S.J . Muller, *Int J. Biol. Macromolec.*, **36**, 232–3 (2005)
73. J. B. Guilbaud, C. Rochas, A. F. Miller, and A. Saiani, *Biomacromolecules*, **14**, 1403–1411 (2013).
74. D. Roberts, C. Rochas, A. Saiani, and A. F. Miller, *Langmuir*, **28**, 16196–16206 (2012).
75. C. J. Bowerman, W. Liyanage, A. J. Federation, and B. L. Nilsson, *Biomacromolecules*, **12**, 2735–2745 (2011).
76. C. J. Bowerman, D. M. Ryan, D. A. Nissan, and B. L. Nilsson, *Mol. BioSyst.*, **5**, 1058–1069 (2009).
77. P. K. Vemula, G. A. Cruikshank, J. M. Karp, and G. John, *Biomaterials*, **30**, 383–393 (2009).
78. J. P. Schneider, D. J. Pochan, B. Ozbas, K. Rajagopal, L. Pakstis, and J. Kretsinger, *J. Am. Chem. Soc.*, **124**, 15030–15037 (2002).
79. B. Ozbas, J. Kretsinger, K. Rajagopal, J. P. Schneider, and D. J. Pochan, *Macromolecules*, **37**, 7331–7337 (2004).
80. K. Rajagopal, B. Ozbas, D. J. Pochan, and J. P. Schneider, *Eur. Biophys. J.*, **35**, 162–169 (2006).
81. L. A. Haines, K. Rajagopal, B. Ozbas, D. A. Salick, D. J. Pochan, and J. P. Schneider, *J. Am. Chem. Soc.*, **127**, 17025–17029 (2005).
82. D. J. Pochan, J. P. Schneider, J. Kretsinger, B. Ozbas, K. Rajagopal, and L. Haines, *J. Am. Chem. Soc.*, **125**, 11802–11803 (2003).
83. L. Haines-Butterick, K. Rajagopal, M. Branco, D. Salick, R. Rughani, M. Pilarz, M. S. Lamm, D. J. Pochan, and J. P. Schneider, *Proc. Natl. Acad. Sci.*, **104**, 7791–7796 (2007).

84. A. S. Veiga, C. Sinthuvanich, D. Gaspar, H. G. Franquelim, M. A. Castanho and J. P. Schneider, *Biomaterials*, **33**, 8907–8916 (2012).
85. R. V. Rughani, D. A. Salick, M. S. Lamm, T. Yucel, D. J. Pochan, and J. P. Schneider, *Biomacromolecules*, **10**, 1295–1304 (2009).
86. R. P. Nagarkar, R. A. Hule, D. J. Pochan, and J. P. Schneider, *J. Am. Chem. Soc.*, **130**, 4466–4474 (2008).
87. K. J. Nagy, M. C. Giano, A. Jin, D. J. Pochan, and J. P. Schneider, *J. Am. Chem. Soc.*, **133**, 14975–14977 (2011).
88. L. Aulisa, H. Dong, and J. D. Hartgerink, *Biomacromolecules*, **10**, 2694–2698 (2009).
89. K. M. Galler, L. Aulisa, K. R. Regan, R. N. D'Souza, and J. D. Hartgerink, *J. Am. Chem. Soc.*, **132**, 3217–3223 (2010).
90. E. L. Bakota, L. Aulisa, K. M. Galler, and J. D. Hartgerink, *Biomacromolecules*, **12**, 82–87 (2010).
91. S. I. Stupp, R. H. Zha, L. C. Palmer, H. Cui, and R. Bitton, *Faraday Discuss*, **166**, 9–30 (2013).
92. G. A. Silva, C. Czeisler, K. L. Niece, E. Beniash, D. A. Harrington, J. A. Kessler, and S. I. Stupp, *Science*, **303**, 1352–1355 (2004).
93. S. E. Paramonov, H. -W. Jun, and J. D. Hartgerink, *J. Am. Chem. Soc.*, **128**, 7291–7298 (2006).
94. J. C. Stendahl, M. S. Rao, M. O. Guler, and S. I. Stupp, *Adv. Funct. Mater.*, **16**, 499–508 (2006).
95. M. A. Greenfield, J. R. Hoffman, M. Olvera de la Cruz, and S. I. Stupp, *Langmuir*, **26**, 3641–3647 (2009).
96. J. D. Hartgerink, E. Beniash, and S. I. Stupp, *Science*, **294**, 1684–1688 (2001).
97. V. M. Yuwono and J. D. Hartgerink, *Langmuir*, **23**, 5033–5038 (2007).
98. H. Cui, T. Muraoka, A. G. Cheetham, and S. I. Stupp, *Nano Lett.*, **9**, 945–951 (2009).
99. K. Rajangam, M. S. Arnold, M. A. Rocco, and S. I. Stupp, *Biomaterials*, **29**, 3298–3305 (2008).
100. K. Rajangam, H. A. Behanna, M.. J. Hui, X. Han, J. F. Hulvat, J. W. Lomasney, and S. I. Stupp, *Nano Lett.*, **6**, 2086–2090 (2006).
101. M. J. Webber, J. Tongers, M. -A. Renault, J. G. Roncalli, D. W. Losordo, and S. I. Stupp, *Acta Biomater.*, **6**, 3–11 (2010).
102. V. M. Tysseling-Mattiace, V. Sahni, K. L. Niece, D. Birch, C. Czeisler, M. G. Fehlings, S. I. Stupp, and J. A. Kessler, *J. Neurosci.*, **28**, 3814–3823 (2008).
103. H. A. Behanna, J. J. J. M. Donners, A. C. Gordon, and S. I. Stupp, *J. Am. Chem. Soc.*, **127**, 1193–1200 (2005).
104. K. L. Niece, J. D. Hartgerink, J. J. J. M. Donners, and S. I. Stupp, *J. Am. Chem. Soc.*, **125**, 7146–7147 (2003).
105. A. Aggeli, M. Bell, N. Boden, J. N. Keen, T. C. B. McLeish, I. Nyrkova, S. E. Radford, and A. Semenov, *J. Mater. Chem.*, **7**, 1135–1145 (1997).
106. S. Maude, D. E. Miles, S. H. Felton, J. Ingram, L. M. Carrick, R. K. Wilcox, E. Ingham, and A. Aggeli, *Soft Matter* **7**, 8085–8099 (2011).

107. C. W. G. Fishwick, A. J. Beevers, L. M. Carrick, C. D. Whitehouse, A. Aggeli, and N. Boden, *Nano Lett.*, **3**, 1475–1479 (2003).
108. A. Aggeli, M. Bell, L. M. Carrick, C. W. Fishwick, R. Harding, P. J. Mawer, S. E. Radford, A. E. Strong, and N. Boden, *J. Am. Chem. Soc.*, **125**, 9619–9628 (2003).
109. L. Carrick, M. Tassieri, T. A. Waigh, A. Aggeli, N. Boden, C. Bell, J. Fisher, E. Ingham, and R. M. L. Evans, *Langmuir*, **21**, 3733–3737 (2005).
110. L. M. Carrick, A. Aggeli, N. Boden, J. Fisher, E. Ingham, and T. A. Waigh, *Tetrahedron*, **63**, 7457–7467 (2007).
111. J. H. Collier, B. H. Hu, J. W. Ruberti, J. Zhang, P. Shum, D. H. Thompson, and P. B. Messersmith, *J. Am. Chem. Soc.*, **123**, 9463–9464 (2001).
112. J. P. Jung, A. K. Nagaraj, E. K. Fox, J. S. Rudra, J. M. Devgun, and J. H. Collier, *Biomaterials*, **30**, 2400–2410 (2009).
113. J. P. Jung, J. L. Jones, S. A. Cronier and J. H. Collier, *Biomaterials*, **29**, 2143–2151 (2008).
114. J. H. Collier and P. B. Messersmith, *Bioconjugate Chem.*, **14**, 748–755 (2003).
115. M. J. Krysmann, V. Castelletto, A. Kelarakis, I. W. Hamley, R. A. Hule, and D. J. Pochan, *Biochemistry*, **47**, 4597–4605 (2008).
116. D. N. Woolfson, *Biopolymers*, **94**, 118–127 (2010).
117. J. G. Adamson, N. E. Zhou, and R. S. Hodges, *Curr. Opin. Biotechnol.*, **4**, 428–437 (1993).
118. E. F. Banwell, E. S. Abelardo, D. J. Adams, M. A. Birchall, A. Corrigan, A. M. Donald, M. Kirkland, L. C. Serpell, M. F. Butler, and D. N. Woolfson, *Nat. Mater.*, **8**, 596–600 (2009).
119. J. Walshaw and D. N. Woolfson, *J. Mol. Biol.*, **307**, 1427–1450 (2001).
120. F. H. C. Crick, *Acta Crystallogr.*, **6**, 689–697 (1953).
121. D. N. Woolfson, *Advances in Protein Chemistry*, Eds. A. D. P. David and M. S. John, Academic Press, Vol. 70, pp. 79–112 (2005).
122. W. A. Petka, J. L. Harden, K. P. McGrath, D. Wirtz, and D. A. Tirrell, *Science*, **281**, 389–392 (1998).
123. W. Shen, J. A. Kornfield, and D. A. Tirrell, *Soft Matter*, **3**, 99–107 (2007).
124. C. Xu and J. Kopecek, *Pharm. Res.*, **25**, 674–682 (2008).
125. C. Xu, V. Breedveld, and J. Kopecek, *Biomacromolecules*, **6**, 1739–1749 (2005).
126. M. G. Ryadnov and D. N. Woolfson, *Nat. Mater.*, **2**, 329–332 (2003).
127. D. Papapostolou, A. M. Smith, E. D. T. Atkins, S. J. Oliver, M. G. Ryadnov, L. C. Serpell, and D. N. Woolfson, *Proc. Natl. Acad. Sci.*, **104**, 10853–10858 (2007).
128. A. Dasgupta, J. H. Mondal, and D. Das, *RSC Adv.*, **3**, 9117–9149 (2013).
129. H. Dong, S. E. Paramonov, and J. D. Hartgerink, *J. Am. Chem. Soc.*, **130**, 13691–13695 (2008).
130. Z. G. Wang and B. Ding, *Adv. Mater.* **25**, 3905–3914 (2013).
131. H. Gu, J. Chao, S.-J. Xiao, and N. C. Seeman, **4**, 245–248 (2009).
132. N. C. Seeman, *Nature*, **421**, 427–431 (2003).
133. N. Park, J. S. Kahn, E. J. Rice, M. R. Hartman, H. Funabashi, J. Xu, S. H. Um, and D. Luo, *Nat. Protoc.*, **4**, 1759–1770 (2009).

134. J. B. Lee, S. Peng, D. Yang, Y. H. Roh, H. Funabashi, N. Park, E. J. Rice, L. Chen, R. Long, M. Wu, and D. Luo, *Nat. Nano*, **7**, 816–820 (2012).
135. S. H. Um, J. B. Lee, N. Park, S. Y. Kwon, C. C. Umbach, and D. Luo, *Nat. Mater.*, **5**, 797–801 (2006).
136. Y. Xing, E. Cheng, Y. Yang, P. Chen, T. Zhang, Y. Sun, Z. Yang, and D. Liu, *Adv. Mater.*, **23**, 1117–1121 (2011).
137. E. Cheng, Y. Xing, P. Chen, Y. Yang, Y. Sun, D. Zhou, L. Xu, Q. Fan, and D. Liu, *Angew. Chem. Int. Ed.*, **48**, 7660–7663 (2009).
138. J. Raeburn, A. Zamith Cardoso, and D. J. Adams, *Chem. Soc. Rev.*, **42**, 5143–5156 (2013).
139. M. de Loos, B. L. Feringa, and J. H. van Esch, *Eur. J. Org. Chem.*, **2005**, 3615–3631 (2005).
140. R. A. Gotner and W. F. Hoffman, *J. Am. Chem. Soc.*, **43**, 2199–2202 (1921).
141. F. M. Menger, Y. Yamasaki, K. K. Catlin, and T. Nishimi, *Angew. Chem. Intl. Ed.*, **34**, 585–586 (1995).
142. R. Vegners, I. Shestakova, I. Kalvinsh, R. M. Ezzell, and P. A. Janmey, *J. Pept. Sci.*, **1**, 371–378 (1995).
143. M. Reches and E. Gazit, *Science*, **300**, 625–627 (2003).
144. A. Mahler, M. Reches, M. Rechter, S. Cohen, and E. Gazit, *Adv. Mater.*, **18**, 1365–1370 (2006).
145. V. Jayawarna, M. Ali, T. A. Jowitt, A. F. Miller, A. Saiani, J. E. Gough, and R. V. Ulijn, *Adv. Mater.*, **18**, 611–614 (2006).
146. A. M. Smith, R. J. Williams, C. Tang, P. Coppo, R. F. Collins, M. L. Turner, A. Saiani, and R. V. Ulijn, *Adv. Mater.*, **20**, 37–41 (2008).
147. M. Hughes, P. W. J. M. Frederix, J. Raeburn, L. S. Birchall, J. Sadownik, F. C. Coomer, I. H. Lin, E. J. Cussen, N. T. Hunt, T. Tuttle, S. J. Webb, D. J. Adams, and R. V. Ulijn, *Soft Matter*, **8**, 5595–5602 (2012).
148. D. J. Adams, M. F. Butler, W. J. Frith, M. Kirkland, L. Mullen, and P. Sanderson, *Soft Matter*, **5**, 1856–1862 (2009).
149. V. Jayawarna, S. M. Richardson, A. R. Hirst, N. W. Hodson, A. Saiani, J. E. Gough, and R. V. Ulijn, *Acta Biomater.*, **5**, 934–943 (2009).
150. Z. Yang, H. Gu, D. Fu, P. Gao, J. K. Lam, and B. Xu, *Adv. Mater.*, **16**, 1440–1444 (2004).
151. Z. Yang, G. Liang, M. Ma, Y. Gao, and B. Xu, *Small*, **3**, 558–562 (2007).
152. J. Gao, H. Wang, L. Wang, J. Wang, D. Kong, and Z. Yang, *J. Am. Chem. Soc.*, **131**, 11286–11287 (2009).
153. D. M. Ryan, S. B. Anderson, F. T. Senguen, R. E. Youngman, and B. L. Nilsson, *Soft Matter*, **6**, 475–479 (2010).
154. D. M. Ryan, S. B. Anderson, and B. L. Nilsson, *Soft Matter*, **6**, 3220–3231 (2010).
155. D. M. Ryan, T. M. Doran, and B. L. Nilsson, *Langmuir*, **27**, 11145–11156 (2011).
156. D. M. Ryan, T. M. Doran, S. B. Anderson, and B. L. Nilsson, *Langmuir*, **27**, 4029–4039 (2011).
157. D. M. Ryan, T. M. Doran, and B. L. Nilsson, *Chem. Commun.*, **47**, 475–477 (2011).

158. G. Cheng, V. Castelletto, R. R. Jones, C. J. Connon, and I. W. Hamley, *Soft Matter*, **7**, 1326–1333 (2011).
159. V. Castelletto, C. M. Moulton, G. Cheng, I. W. Hamley, M. R. Hicks, A. Rodger, D. E. Lopez-Perez, G. Revilla-Lopez, and C. Aleman, *Soft Matter*, **7**, 11405–11415 (2011).
160. R. Orbach, L. Adler-Abramovich, S. Zigerson, I. Mironi-Harpaz, D. Seliktar, and E. Gazit, *Biomacromolecules*, **10**, 2646–2651 (2009).
161. Z. Yang, G. Liang, and B. Xu, *Chem. Commun.*, 738–740 (2006).
162. Z. Yang, G. Liang, M. Ma, Y. Gao, and B. Xu, *J. Mater. Chem.*, **17**, 850–854 (2007).
163. L. Chen, S. Revel, K. Morris, L. C. Serpell, and D. J. Adams, *Langmuir*, **26**, 13466–13471 (2010).
164. R. J. Mart, R. D. Osborne, M. M. Stevens, and R. V. Ulijn, *Soft Matter*, **2**, 822–835 (2006).
165. M. Zelzer, S. J. Todd, A. R. Hirst, T. O. McDonald, and R. V. Ulijn, *Biomater. Sci.*, **1**, 11–39 (2013).
166. Y. Gao, F. Zhao, Q. Wang, Y. Zhang, and B. Xu, *Chem. Soc. Rev.*, **39**, 3425–3433 (2010).
167. X. Qin, W. Xie, S. Tian, J. Cai, H. Yuan, Z. Yu, G. L. Butterfoss, A. C. Khuong, and R. A. Gross, *Chem. Commun.*, **49**, 4839–4841 (2013).
168. S. Toledano, R. J. Williams, V. Jayawarna, and R. V. Ulijn, *J. Am. Chem. Soc.*, **128**, 1070–1071 (2006).
169. A. K. Das, R. Collins, and R. V. Ulijn, *Small*, **4**, 279–287 (2008).
170. D. J. Adams and P. D. Topham, *Soft Matter*, **6**, 3707–3721 (2010).
171. M. Hughes, L. S. Birchall, K. Zuberi, L. A. Aitken, S. Debnath, N. Javid, and R. V. Ulijn, *Soft Matter*, **8**, 11565–11574 (2012).
172. J. Shi, Y. Gao, Z. Yang, and B. Xu, *Beilstein J. Org. Chem.*, **7**, 167–172 (2011).
173. T. M. Doran, E. A. Anderson, S. E. Latchney, L. A. Opanashuk, and B. L. Nilsson, *ACS Chem. Neurosci.*, **3**, 211–220 (2012).
174. S. Roy, N. Javid, P. W. J. M. Frederix, D. A. Lamprou, A. J. Urquhart, N. T. Hunt, P. J. Halling, and R. V. Ulijn, *Chem. Eur. J.*, **18**, 11723–11731 (2012).
175. S. Roy, N. Javid, J. Sefcik, P. J. Halling, and R. V. Ulijn, *Langmuir*, **28**, 16664–16670 (2012).
176. C. J. Bowerman and B. L. Nilsson, *J. Am. Chem. Soc.* **132**, 9526–9527 (2010).
177. L. Lv, H. Liu, X. Chen, and Z. Yang, *Colloid s Surf. B*, **108**, 352–357 (2013).
178. J. H. Jung, S. Shinkai, and T. Shimizu, *Chem. Eur. J.*, **8**, 2684–2690 (2002).
179. G. C. Maity, *J. Phy. Sci.*, **12**, 173–186 (2008).
180. T. Shimizu and M. Masuda, *J. Am. Chem. Soc.*, **119**, 2812–2818 (1997).
181. H. Kobayashi, A. Friggeri, K. Koumoto, M. Amaike, S. Shinkai, and D. N. Reinhoudt, *Org. Lett.*, **4**, 1423–1426 (2002).
182. S. Bhattacharya, U. Maitra, S. Mukhopadhyay, and A. Srivastava, *Molecular Gels*, Eds. R. Weiss and P. Terech, Netherlands: Springer, pp. 613–647 (2006).
183. O. Gronwald and S. Shinkai, *J. Chem. Soc. Perkin Trans.*, 1933–1937 (2001).
184. U. Maitra, S. Mukhopadhyay, A. Sarkar, P. Rao, and S. S. Indi, *Angew. Chem. Int. Ed.*, **40**, 2281–2283 (2001).

185. S. Pang and D. Zhu, *Chem. Phys. Lett.*, **358**, 479–483 (2002).
186. T. Imae, K. Funayama, M. P. Krafft, F. Giulieri, T. Tada, and T. Matsumoto, *J. Colloid Interface Sci.*, **212**, 330–337 (1999).
187. F. M. Menger, H. Zhang, K. L. Caran, V. A. Seredyuk, and R. P. Apkarian, *J. Am. Chem. Soc.* **124**, 1140–1141 (2002).
188. F. M. Menger, V. A. Seredyuk, R. P. Apkarian, and E. R. Wright, *J. Am. Chem. Soc.*, **124**, 12408–12409 (2002).
189. R. Oda, I. Huc, and S. J. Candau, *Angew. Chem. Int. Ed.*, **37**, 2689–2691 (1998).
190. S. Bhattacharya and S. De, *Langmuir*, **15**, 3400–3410 (1999).
191. X. Li, X. Du, Y. Gao, J. Shi, Y. Kuang, and B. Xu, *Soft Matter*, **8**, 7402–7407 (2012).
192. X. Li, Y. Kuang, and B. Xu, *Soft Matter*, **8**, 2801–2806 (2012).
193. X. Li, Y. Kuang, H. -C. Lin, Y. Gao, J. Shi, and B. Xu, *Angew. Chem. Int. Ed.*, **50**, 9365–9369 (2011).
194. S. Kiyonaka, S. Shinkai, and I. Hamachi, *Chem. Eur. J.*, **9**, 976–983 (2003).
195. F. Zhao, M. L. Ma, and B. Xu, *Chem. Soc. Rev.*, **38**, 883–891 (2009).
196. P. K. Vemula, N. Wiradharma, J. A. Ankrum, O. R. Miranda, G. John, and J. M. Karp, *Curr. Opin. Biotechnol.*, **24**, 1174–1182 (2013).
197. C. Valéry, M. Paternostre, B. Robert, T. Gulik-Krzywicki, T. Narayanan, J.-C. Dedieu, G. Keller, M.-L. Torres, R. Cherif-Cheikh, P. Calvo, and F. Artzner, *Proc. Natl. Acad. Sci.*, **100**, 10258–10262 (2003).
198. B. Xing, C. W. Yu, K. H. Chow, P. L. Ho, D. Fu, and B. Xu, *J. Am. Chem. Soc.*, **124**, 14846–14847 (2002).
199. S. K. Maji, D. Schubert, C. Rivier, S. Lee, J. E. Rivier, and R. Riek, *PLoS Biol.*, **6**, 240–252 (2008).
200. Z. Yang, G. Liang, M. Ma, A. S. Abbah, W. W. Lu, and B. Xu, *Chem. Commun.*, 843–845 (2007).
201. X. Lin, L. Deng, Y. Xu, and A. Dong, *Soft Matter*, **8**, 3470–3477 (2012).
202. Z. Yang, K. Xu, L. Wang, H. Gu, H. Wei, M. Zhang, and B. Xu, *Chem. Commun.* 4414–4416 (2005).
203. S. Bhuniya, Y. J. Seo, and B. H. Kim, *Tetrahedron Lett.*, **47**, 7153–7156 (2006).

Chapter 10

Environment Responsive Hydrogels

Yanzhen Yin*, Chao Lang†, Shufei Jiao*, and Junqiu Liu†
**College of Chemistry and Chemical Engineering,*
Qinzhou University, Qinzhou, Guangxi 535000, P. R. China
†State Key Laboratory of Supramolecular Structure and Materials,
College of Chemistry, Jilin University, Changchun 130012, P. R. China

Hydrogels are special three-dimensional (3D) polymer networks crosslinked by chemical bonds or physical nodes, which exhibit the unique property of swollen behaviors but not dissolved in water. Considering that responsive hydrogels can function as the amazing scaffolds for the fabrication of smart devices to investigate the physiological processes in living system, responsive hydrogels have attracted researcher's special attentions. Benefited from the development of the innovated synthesis methods and self-assembly protocols, a wide variety of responsive hydrogels are continuously constructed and the responsive mechanisms are deeply investigated. Typically, versatile responsive hydrogels with pH responsive, temperature responsive, light responsive properties are constructed. Beside the exploration of construction methods and responsive mechanism of hydrogels, the applications of responsive hydrogels are also extensively investigated. This chapter reviewed the construction methods, responsive mechanisms and related applications of the responsive hydrogels in the past few years, which may provide a significant guide in the redesign and application of responsive hydrogels.

1. Introduction

With the typical structure of three-dimensional (3D) networks crosslinked by chemical bonds or physical nodes, hydrogels are extensively investigated in the past decades.[1–3] Hydrogels are endowed with the unique property of swollen behavior but not dissolved in water. Usually, hydrogels can absorb lots of water with the water content as high as 20,000 times of the weight of dry polymer network. The remarkable water holding capacity of hydrogels are endowed from the anchored hydrophilic groups in polymer chains.[2] To provide the basic guides for the understanding of hydrogels and to further promote the application of it, based on the prior mean-field theory[4] and Flory–Rehner theory,[5] wide theoretical researches are carried out.[6–11] Combining these hydrogel theories and application requirements, various hydrogels are developed, such as imprinted hydrogels,[12,13] microgels,[14,15] supramolecular hydrogels,[16,17] responsive hydrogels,[18,19] and so on. Especially, hydrogels have gained diverse applications in giant biomimetic systems,[14,20] self-assembled systems,[16,21] regenerative medicines,[22,23] biosensors,[24,25] drug delivery systems[26,27], and composite materials.[28,29] Among the versatile designed hydrogels, responsive hydrogels have attracted researcher's special attentions because they can function as the amazing scaffolds for the fabrication of smart devices to investigate the physiological processes in living system.[3,30–33] Usually, the response to stimuli is a basic phenomenon in living systems. Therefore, the mimic research of this stimuli responsive behavior of living systems can offer a ready solution to many of the current-day biomedical problems.[32] Considering that the wonderful similarity between the stimuli responsive behavior of responsive hydrogels and that of living systems, the construction and investigation of responsive hydrogels with excellent responsive behaviors have become a long-term and significant aim.

Commonly, the polymeric networks of responsive hydrogels can rapidly change their swelling equilibrium with the external stimuli(temperature, light, pH, etc.) from environment.[2] Recently, as the innovated synthesis methods and self-assembly protocols are developed, a wide variety of responsive hydrogels are continuously constructed and the responsive mechanisms are deeply investigated. Typically, the widely applied Atom Transfer Radical Polymerization (ATRP) technique[34] allows to synthesize the controlled hydrogels with a narrow molecular weight distribution and defined end-groups.[35,36] One-pot polymerization method make the synthesis processes of responsive hydrogel more simple and efficient.[37,38] Interface assisted synthesis technique allows polymerization to take place at high temperature over a long period of time and the desired monomers can be trapped in hydrogel particles upon polymerization.[39,40] The imprinting procedure can endow the responsive hydrogel with unique recognition ability for specific protein or molecule.[12,41] Photo-crosslinkable synthesis method is used to construct the polymer networks of responsive hydrogels after irradiation without physical contact.[42,43] Supramolecular self-assembly protocols consisting of host–guest interaction,[21] electrostatic interaction,[44] hydrophobic interaction[45] can assemble the building block to form diverse responsive hydrogels in a simple and efficient manner. Additionally, enzymatic reaction,[46] electrospinning technique,[47] microcontact printing,[35] microfluidic approach,[48] dipole–dipole interaction[49] are all proved to be the excellent construction approaches for responsive hydrogels. Benefited from the innovated methods mentioned above, novel smart hydrogels are prepared, such as hydrogel capsules,[50–53] hydrogel films,[1,43,54,55] composites hydrogels,[29,56–58] hydrogel actuators[59–62] and so on. Moreover, apart from the researches of construction methods of responsive hydrogels, the theory researches related to the responsive mechanism of smart hydrogels are simultaneously carried out.[3,6–9] Significantly, both the investigation of the construction methods of responsive hydrogels and theory research of them play important roles in the exploration and application of novel smart responsive hydrogels materials.

As the smart materials, responsive hydrogels exhibit the rapidly responsive ability and sharp volume phase transitions according to the external stimuli from environment. Hydrogels demonstrate large-scale volumetric changes in response to small levels of stimuli.[1] To the best of our knowledge, the most typical external stimuli factors related to responsive behaviors of smart hydrogels are pH,[63–68] temperature,[39,45,69–71] light,[46,53,72–74] and multi-factors.[75–79] Additionally, the responsive hydrogels based on enzyme responsive,[59,80] calcium responsive,[81,82] glucose responsive,[83,84] redox responsive,[85,86] ionic-strength responsive,[9,32] chemical responsive[87] are also exhibited amazing responsive abilities. Usually, the changes of structures and functions of responsive hydrogels are caused by the changes of polymer networks when the stimuli responsive processes are occurred. Based on the extensive researches mentioned above, many useful insights into the structures, responsive mechanisms and functions of responsive hydrogels are revealed. Among these insights, several features of responsive hydrogels are particularly important. Firstly, the responsiveness of responsive hydrogels is determined by induced structural changes in the materials. The changes include crosslinking density, electrostatic interactions and molecular conformation.[59] Secondly, the external stimuli factors usually cause a change in phase, shape, mechanics, refractive index, permeability, elastic modulus and interfacial tension. And the changes subsequently can be reversed to their original state.[1] Thirdly, the reversible change of the parameters of responsive hydrogels provide the wonderful platform for the construction of novel smart materials, such as nanoreactor,[51] glasses coatings,[88] nano-valve,[89] biosensor,[90] derived material,[91] injectable hydrogels,[92] biomarker material,[93] microlens[94], and so on. From the perspective of structures, responsive mechanisms and functions, these features highlight the pivotal importance of the responsive property of smart hydrogels. Significantly, these features also provide a significant guide in the redesign and application of responsive hydrogels.

This chapter gives an overview of the fundamentals of hydrogels. The research related to the construction methods, responsive mechanisms and applications of responsive hydrogels in the past few years are reviewed. In view of the different responsive behaviors, we summarize the investigation of responsive hydrogels and divide them into several categories, starting from pH responsive hydrogel expanding to temperature responsive hydrogel, photo responsive hydrogel, multi responsive hydrogel, and other responsive hydrogel. Moreover, the applications of such smart responsive hydrogels are also summarized. Herein, other excellent hydrogels without responsive property are not discussed.[16,95,96] Regenerative medicine, drug delivery system and nanosensors constructed based on responsive hydrogels are summarized in other chapters and not discussed in this chapter.

2. Construction and Responsive Mechanism of Hydrogel

Hydrogels can exhibit the remarkable water holding capacity, which usually absorb lots of water with the water content as high as 20,000 times of the weight of dry polymer network. The unique water holding capacity and rapidly responsive behaviors of responsive hydrogels have attracted more attentions of researchers. Especially, researchers are actively interested in the synthesis of novel responsive hydrogels and investigation of their responsive mechanisms. Not only versatile responsive hydrogels with external stimuli responsive behaviors are constructed but also wide theoretical researches are carried out.

2.1. pH responsive hydrogel

By incorporating the special monomer units into polymer backbones, the phase transition and solubility of responsive hydrogel can be changed dependent on the change of pH. Such hydrogel exhibits the typical pH responsive behavior.[2] Section 2.1 is divided into three parts from the perspective of research foci, including *commonly construction method*, *construction of composite hydrogel* and *hydrogel pH responsive mechanism*.

2.1.1. *Commonly construction method*

Herein, most scientists focus on the preparation of pH responsive hydrogels based on bio-related molecules, such as saccharide derivative,[97] amino acid,[67] peptide,[63] DNA[18], and so on. Usually, not only the traditional polymerization method but also the photo-emulsion polymerization[65] and supramolecular self-assembled method[68] are employed to prepare pH responsive hydrogels.

Chen *et al.* synthesized a new saccharide-derived hydrogelator (methyl-4,6-O-(4′-aldehydephenylidene)-α-*d*-glucopyranoside).[97] Based on this hydrogelator, they obtained the pH responsive hydrogel. The resulting hydrogel not only showed thermal responsiveness but also exhibited cysteine and pH responsiveness. Commonly, amino acid and short peptide derivatives have unique propertied of self-assemble into regular structures, which provide the basement for the preparation of hydrogels. For example, Nanda *et al.* anchored a pyrene into phenylalanine and obtained the phenylalanine derivative, which was a superhydrogel in nature and showed a thixotropic property.[67] This phenylalanine derivative formed a hydrogel in a wide range of aqueous solutions of pH (7.46–14). Additionally, the pH responsive hydrogel based on peptide was developed by Fletcher's group.[63] They reported the design of α-helical peptide that formed self-healing hydrogels at weight fractions below 0.1%. It also indicated that gelation occurred when the peptide self-assembles into soluble coiled–coil fibrils.

Meanwhile, based on the self-assembled property of peptide derivative, Dey and co-workers designed six L-histidine-based amphiphiles with different hydrocarbon chain lengths and examined their abilities to gelate water. It was observed that π–π stacking, hydrophobic interaction, amide hydrogen bonding, and solubility factor contributed to the stability and strength of the hydrogels. Furthermore, using DNA as building block, the pH responsive DNA hydrogel with three-armed DNA nanostructures was constructed by Cheng and co-workers. This DNA hydrogel can be switched to the non-gel state in one minute by simply environmental pH changes.[18] Interestingly, Reppas and co-workers reported an oil-in-water photo-emulsion polymerization method, which allowed for the facile synthesis of sub-100 nm hydrogel particles of poly(ethylene glycol) methyl ether methacrylate without specialized conditions requisite for RAFT or ATRP.[65]

2.1.2. *Construction of composite hydrogel*

Composite hydrogel was originally prepared based on covalently inter-linked microgels by Hu and co-workers.[98] Usually, composite hydrogels consist of hydrogels and other functional materials, such as cellulose,[99] alginate,[100] graphene oxide (GO),[57] nanotube,[101] polyaniline[102], and so on.

Liu *et al.* prepared ultrafine fibrous composite hydrogel nanofibers with ultrafine diameters combining poly[styrene-*co*-(maleic sodium anhydride)] and cellulose.[99] The crosslinked hydrogel nanofibers supported on cellulose showed a fast pH response and improved dimensional stability. Alginate is extracted from brown seaweed, which is one of the most abundant polysaccharides and exhibits unique properties in biodegradability, biocompatibility, and physicochemical behavior. Considering that alginate exhibited the promising properties, various composite hydrogels were prepared based on it.[100,103] Typically, Neufeld and co-workers prepared semisynthetic network alginate polymer and obtained an acetal-linked network polymer hydrogel by reaction with glutaraldehyde. Banerjee's group prepared pH sensitive alginate-methyl cellulose blend hydrogel beads based on single water-in-water (w/w) emulsion gelation method in a complete aqueous environment.[103]

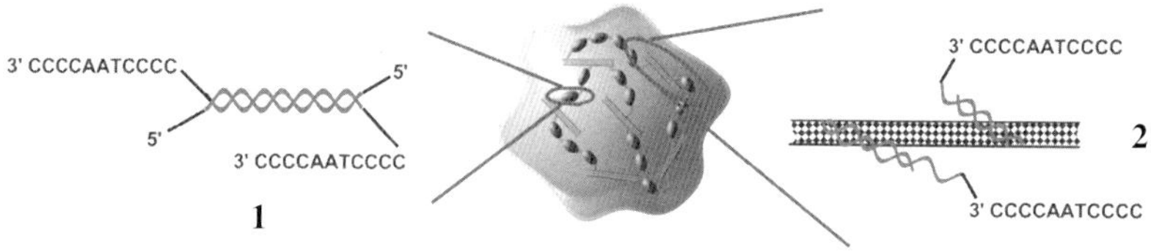

Fig. 1. The structure of DNA–SWNT hybrid hydrogel.

GO is a two-dimensional (2D) carbon material with a large number of hydrophilic oxygenated functional groups. Using graphene oxide as functional material, Xu and co-workers prepared a series of novel graphene oxide/poly(acrylic acid-co-acrylamide) super-absorbent composite hydrogels.[57] They exhibited significant improvement of swelling capacity in neutral medium, and could also retain relatively higher swelling capacities to a certain degree at acidic and basic solutions. Similarly, single walled carbon nanotube (SWNT) is also a commonly used inorganic material for composite materials. Liu *et al.* constructed a novel DNA–SWNT hybrid hydrogel based on linear DNA (Fig. 1; **1**) and crosslinking SWNT (Fig. 1; **2**), which could be switched to sol state by pH change. The illustration of the structure of DNA–SWNT hybrid hydrogel was given in Fig. 1.[101] This research was a helpful exploration to introduce inorganic ingredient into pure DNA hydrogel system. Additionally, the composite hydrogels based on polyaniline nanofibers[102] and doubly crosslinked microgels[104] were constructed.

2.1.3. *Hydrogel pH responsive mechanism*

To investigate the responsive mechanisms of pH responsive hydrogel, a series of pH responsive hydrogels were constructed employing the methods of chemical crosslinking,[11,105] layer-by-layer assembly,[106,107] and double hydrogen bonding interaction.[64] The responsive behaviors including swelling response, shape response, permeability were deeply investigated. Furthermore, the theory researches of the pH responsive mechanism were also carried out.[7,8,108]

Kong *et al.* prepared pH responsive hydrogels with varying molecular weight. It proved that the number of crosslinkers and the molecular weight of the crosslinkers played critical roles in determining the responsiveness and the structural integrity.[109] Additionally, they also reported the influence of the physical properties and hydrolysis rates of hydrogels by the substituents present in three novel 1,3,5-triazaadamantane crosslinkers. To achieve the excellent mechanical strength and high sensitivity to pH changes, Spinks and co-workers prepared a new hydrogel with double network.[66] Such hydrogel displayed significant improvement in strength, which was likely due to the double network topology and hydrogen bonded clusters from poly(acrylic acid). Similarly, Liu *et al.* also focused on the improvement in mechanical strength of pH responsive hydrogel based on double hydrogen bonding interaction.[64] Using two hydrogen-bonding motif-containing monomers, the hydrogel polymer (Fig. 2; **3**) was synthesized (Fig. 2). This hydrogel exhibited both high tensile and compressive strengths over a broad pH range. Additionally, benefit of the optical and AFM techniques, the mechanical property of hollow capsules with varying degrees of crosslinking was investigated.[110]

As the layer-by-layer methods are used to prepared pH-hydrogels, the further investigation of the responsive behavior can be achieved.[52,106,107] Kozlovskaya *et al.* tuned the swelling pH transitions of hydrogel hollow capsules.[52] Recently, they further investigated the pH-triggered shape response of cubical ultrathin hydrogel capsules.[106] Meanwhile, Matsuyama's group studied the influence of consecutive polyelectrolyte adsorption treatment on the pH responsive changes.[107] It indicated that polycation characteristics strongly influenced the properties of these microgels. Additionally, the effect of monovalent sodium salts on the molecular equilibrium swelling was also reported.[111]

As the significant complements for the experimental study of the responsive mechanism, the theory researches also play important roles in the revealing of the responsive behavior. Suo and co-workers developed the theory of constrained swelling of a pH-sensitive hydrogel.[7] This theory was firstly used to compare several cases of homogenous swelling. Li *et al.* presented a modeling study for analyzing the effect of the ionic valence of the environmental solution on the mechanical behavior of a smart hydrogel.[108] Recently, they improved the multieffect-coupling pH-stimulus model.[8] And the performance of the smart hydrogel was simulated for responding to the environmental solution pH stimulus.

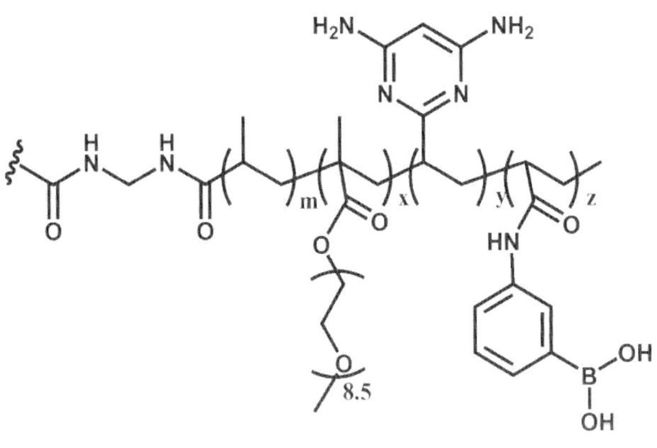

3

Fig. 2. The structure of hydrogel based on two hydrogen-bonding motif-containing monomers.

2.2. Temperature responsive hydrogel

Among all the stimuli responsive hydrogels, temperature responsive hydrogel probably belong to one of the largest classes. The section is also divided into three parts, including *commonly construction method*, *construction of composite hydrogel* and *hydrogel temprature responsive mechanism*.

2.2.1. *Commonly construction method*

The temperature responsive hydrogels introduced in this section are mainly prepared based on the scaffolds of supramolecular assembled structures,[96,112–114] hydrogel films[42] and hydrogel spheres.[70,71] Additionally, the temperature responsive hydrogels constructed employing the novel techniques are also summarized.[35,38,39]

Ritter and co-workers pioneered in construction of temperature responsive hydrogel using *N*-isopropylacrylamide as monomer.[112] As illustrated in Fig. 3, based on the host–guest interaction between adamantyl group and cyclodextrin, the thermosensitive hydrogel (Fig. 3; **4**) was prepared. Similarly, based on the host–guest interaction between D3-symmetric tris(spiroborate) cyclophane and $[Ir(tpy)_2](PF_6)_3$ complex, the assembled chain structure was obtained by Yamaguchi *et al.*[113] Moreover, employing the host–guest interaction between cucurbit[8]uril (CB[8]) and viologen/naphthoxy, a thermo-sensitive supramolecular polymer hydrogel (Fig. 3; **5**) was prepared by Scherman and co-workers.[96] Typically, as the dynamic crosslink of CB[8]/viologen/naphthoxy, this hydrogel exhibited thermal reversibility. Additionally, the temperature responsive hydrogels based on hydrophobic interaction of dipeptides[114] and cyclic macromonomer crosslinking interaction[19] were also reported.

Using a photo-crosslinkable benzophenone unit, Knoll and co-workers prepared the responsive hydrogel films by photo-crosslink method based on poly(*N*-isopropylacrylamide) (PNIPAM) copolymers.[42] To fabricate hydrogel nanoparticles

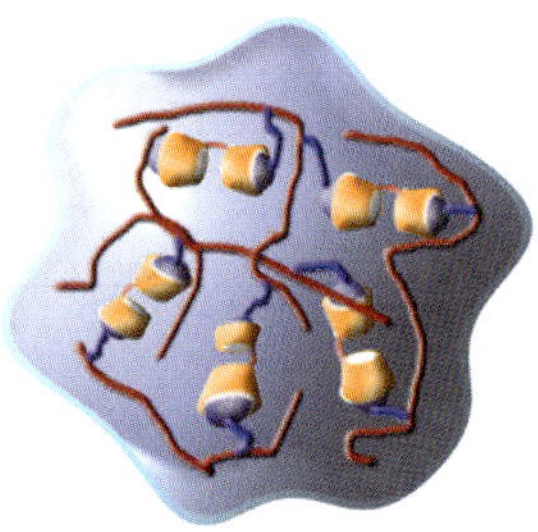

4

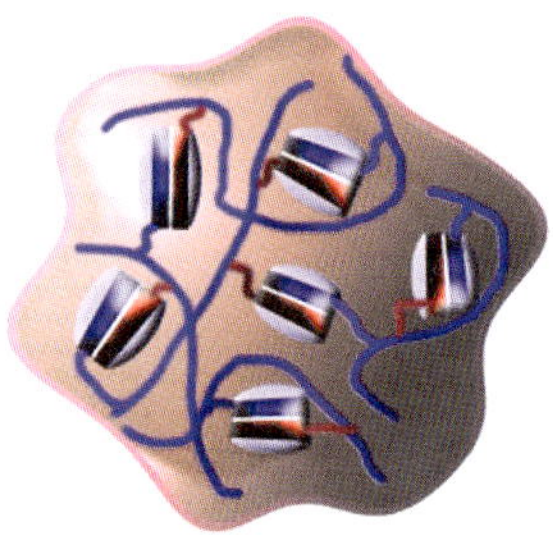

5

Fig. 3. Temperature responsive hydrogel constructed using supramolecular self-assembled method.

with ultrafine nanosized hair, Yang's group developed a simple self-developed approach consisting of a two-step photo-induced polymerization of crosslinked polyacrylamide soft hydrogel nanoparticles (5–10 nm in diameter) grafted with PNIPAM chains.[71] A fast association process was observed at approximately 33–34°C during the heating process. Additionally, Macdonald and co-workers reported an efficient method for fabricating monodisperse PNIPAM microgels enclosed by a single, continuous, impermeable lipid bilayer.[70]

Furthermore, the novel construction protocols and developed techniques have largely enhanced the innovation of preparation methods of temperature responsive hydrogel. Kiriy *et al.* reported the preparation of PNIPAM hydrogel microcapsules by an one pot synthesis method.[38] Then, Hilt and co-workers developed the controlled synthesis method for responsive hydrogel nanostructures *via* microcontact printing and ATRP.[35] Based on the interface assisted synthesis method, the functional hydrogel particles were prepared by Serpe's group.[39] This approach might be used to synthesize particles with a variety of different functionalities and compositions.

2.2.2. *Construction of composite hydrogel*

As the functional materials are anchored into the composite hydrogels, the properties of composited hydrogel such as structural stability, mechanical strength and response behaviors are significantly improved. Usually, the functional materials including silicon-containing molecules,[115] iron oxide,[116] starch,[117] liposome,[118] alginate[119] are employed.

As shown in Fig. 4, to fabricate a thermosensitive hybrid hydrogel thin film, Du's group reported a facile method from a crosslinkable hydrid copolymer using

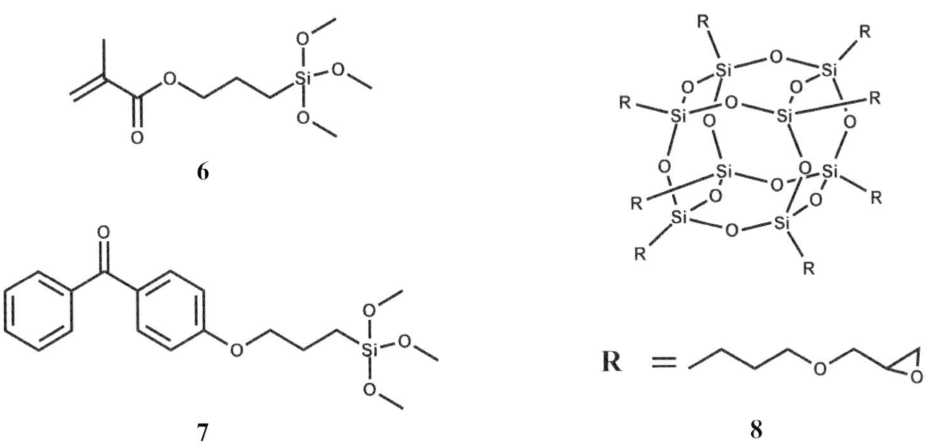

Fig. 4. The silicon-containing molecules used to prepare crosslinkable composite hydrogels.

silicon-containing monomer (Fig. 4; **6**).[115] After hydrolysis of the methoxysilyl groups and subsequent condensation of the silanol groups, the hybrid hydrogel was formed. Using silicon-containing molecule bearing benzophenone groups (Fig. 4; **7**) as material, Brom *et al.* prepared a new temperature responsive hydrogel by photo-crosslinking using UV irradiation.[58] This composite was very stable and exhibited excellent responsive properties. Additionally, combining a polyhedral oligomeric silsesquioxane (Fig. 4; **8**) possessing eight epoxide groups and commercial PNIPAM, Lin *et al.* constructed the thermo responsive hydrogel nanofibers.[47] These nanofibres showed excellent hydrogel characteristics with fast swelling and de-swelling responses triggered by temperature changes.

To obtain thermo responsive composite microcapsules, potential of which will be used in remotely delivery system, Štěpánek and co-workers synthesized the responsive microcapsules consisting of PNIPAM hydrogel and hydrophilic citrate-stabilized super-paramagnetic iron oxide nanoparticles.[116] And they described a novel method of synthesizing composite PNIPAM/alginate particles that changed their optical properties in response to a temperature change but kept both, their original shape and size.[119] Moreover, Wang and co-workers presented a novel approach for fabricating the thermo responsive PNIPAM hydrogels based on starch-based nanospheres using derivable allyl groups as nanoscale crosslinkers.[117] The obtained hydrogels possessed an extremely high mechanical strength and a remarkably rapid shrinking time. Additionally, Hong *et al.* demonstrated a microfluidic method to direct the assembly of liposome–PNIPAM hybrid nanoparticles.[118] Based on a radical-induced graft polymerization technique, Park's group prepared a new series of thermo responsive graft copolymers, which exhibited thermo responsive sol-to-gel transitions depending on chain length of the grafted PNIPAM.

2.2.3. *Hydrogel temperature responsive mechanism*

Herein, the temperature responsive mechanisms of hydrogels including switching kinetics,[120] permeability,[121] revival thermodynamics,[122] mechanical and surface properties[123] were investigated. Various methods including atomic force microscopy,[123] visualizing method[124] and theory research[121] were employed.

Typically, Müller-Buschbaum and co-workers investigated the switching kinetics of thin thermo responsive hydrogel films.[120] They proved that the collapse transition proceeds could be seen as three steps. The first step was the shrinkage of the initially swollen film by a release of water. In the second step, the thickness remained constant with water molecules embedded in the film. In the third step, water was reabsorbed from the vapor atmosphere, thereby giving rise to a relaxation process.

Furthermore, to investigate the swelling, permeability, and mobility of tracer molecules in thermo responsive hydrogel films, Raccis and co-workers employed fluorescence correlation spectroscopy to carry out the related researches.[121] Moreover, Knoll's group studied the thermo responsive behavior of hydrogels with different thicknesses in MilliQ water by the surface plasmon diffraction technique.[125] Furthermore, employing atomic force spectroscopy as analysis method, Jonas deeply investigated the temperature-induced structural and adhesive changes.[55] And they also achieved the simultaneous measurement of mechanical and surface properties in thermo responsive hydrogel films using atomic force spectroscopy. [123]

Additionally, near-infrared multispectral imaging microscope was used to measure images and spectra of individual hydrogel directly and simultaneously.[124,126] It was possible to determine lower critical solution temperature (LCST) values based on monitoring either change in the spectra or the volume of the hydrogel particle. Moreover, Wu *et al.* investigated precise chain collapse and revival thermodynamic mechanism of PNIPAM using 2D correlation infrared spectroscopy and a newly developed perturbation correlation moving window technique. It indicated that in the heating process, PNIPAM hydrogel occurred to collapse along the backbone before water molecules were expelled outside the network. In the sequential cooling process, PNIPAM hydrogel had water molecules diffusing into the network first before the chain revival along the backbone occurred.

Commonly, responsive hydrogels based on supramolecular assembled structures are endowed with property of reversible transformation. To reveal the transition mechanisms between self-assembled structures (micelle,[127] vesicle,[128] ribbon[45]) and hydrogels, several investigated were carried out. Additionally, Frank[129] and Zhu[130] devoted themselves in exploring the interaction mechanisms between hydrogels and the surrounding hydrogel matrix.

2.3. Photo responsive hydrogel

Among the stimuli hydrogels, photo responsive hydrogels are promising ones as the unique properties of remotely input in a spatially and temporally controlled without physical contact. Such properties motivated researchers to develop various construction methods for photo responsive hydrogels.[46,53,73,74,131–134]

Typically, using molecular recognition of α-cyclodextrin, Harada *et al.* have successfully constructed a photo responsive hydrogel system by combination of α-cyclodextrin, dodecyl (C12)-modified poly(acrylic acid), and a photo responsive competitive guest.[73] The gel–sol transition occurred repeatedly by repetitive irradiations of UV or visible light. Equally, Hamachi and co-workers discovered several new photo responsive supramolecular hydrogelators bearing fumaric amide as a

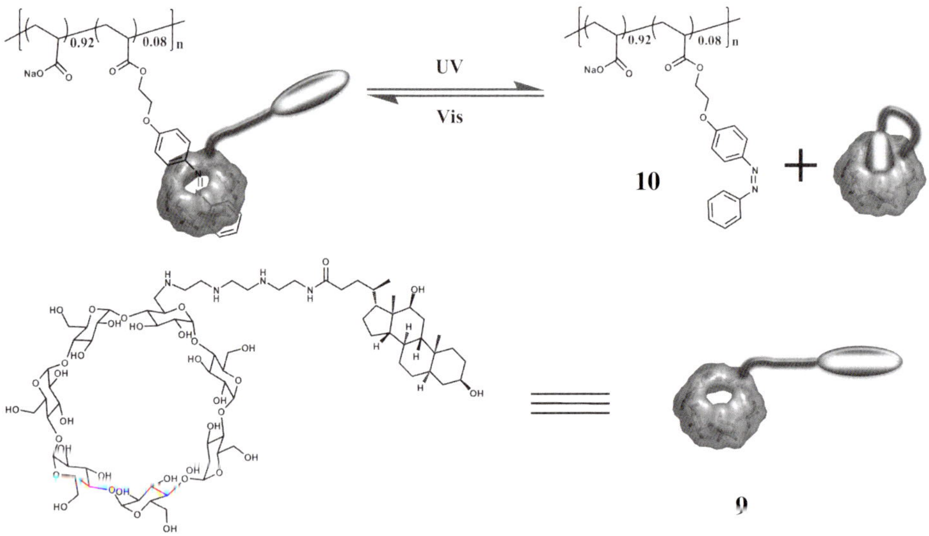

Fig. 5. Photo responsive hydrogel system based on the supramolecular inclusion complex from deoxycholated-β-cyclodextrin derivative and azobenzene-branched poly(acrylic acid) copolymer.

trans–cis photo switching module.[132] Based on this hydrogelators, the gel–sol/sol–gel transition was achieved by reversibly induced by light. Stoddart's group constructed the azobenzene-based light responsive hydrogel system based on the host–guest interaction between the deoxycholated-β-cyclodextrin derivative (Fig. 5; **9**) and azobenzene-branched poly(acrylic acid) copolymer (Fig. 5; **10**). The competitive mechanism during the sol-to-gel phase transition cycles was illustrated in Fig. 5. The hydrogel can be recovered from the sol phase by photo-irradiation with visible light of 450 nm. Moreover, using the similar host–guest competitive mechanism, Jiang and co-workers prepared the photo-responsive pseudopolyrotaxane hydrogels, which boded well for future applications in various fields.

Furthermore, the light initiating photopolymerization technology was employed to construct photo responsive hydrogels. Based on this technology, the typical hydrogels using acryloylacetone,[133] 4-[(4-acryloyloxy) phenylazo] benzene-sulfonic acid,[74] 4-methyl-[7-(methacryloyl)oxyethyloxy]coumarin[131] as photo responsive molecules were prepared. Moreover, Xu and co-workers reported the first example of the use of an enzymatic reaction to generate photo responsive supramolecular hydrogel.[46] Kim *et al.* established a straightforward method for the fabrication of uniform poly(vinylamine) hydrogel capsules without using templates.[53] They showed that subtle changes in the permeability of hydrogel capsules could be achieved through the modification of their charged surfaces with negatively charged biopolymers.

2.4. Multi responsive hydrogel

As the unique advantages of multi responsive behaviors could be regulated by multiple ways, multi responsive hydrogels attracted special research attentions. Up to now, various multi responsive hydrogels have been constructed. Herein, the summarization of multi responsive hydrogels is divided into three parts, including *commonly construction method, construction of composite hydrogel* and *hydrogel multi responsive mechanism.*

2.4.1. *Commonly construction method*

Similar to the construction of pH, temperature and photo responsive hydrogels, the preparation of multi responsive hydrogels also employed supramolecular self-assembled technique as the main construction method. As shown in Fig. 6, Liu and co-workers synthesized a four PEG-branched porphyrin molecule end-decorated with benzaldehyde (Fig. 6; **11**), which formed physical pseudo-polyrotaxane hydrogels in the presence of α-cyclodextrin.[135] Based on the pH responsive schiff-base reaction and the photo responsive host–guest system consisting of PEG block, α-cyclodextrin and 1-[p-(phenylazo)benzyl]-bromide (Fig. 6; **12**), the cycles of

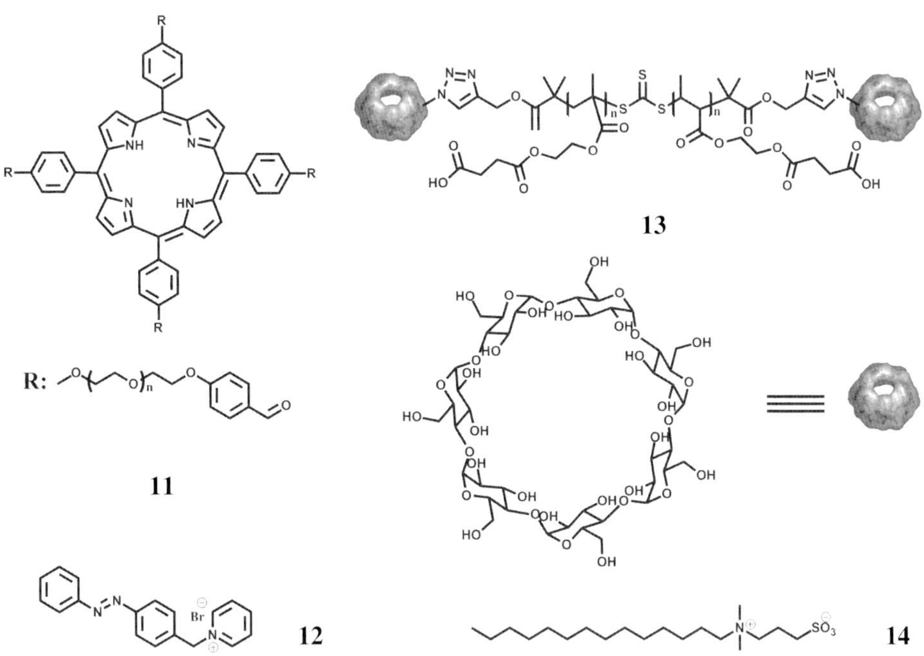

Fig. 6. The building block prepared for photo responsive supramolecular hydrogels.

gel–sol transitions were achieved through pH and photo stimuli. Kang *et al.* synthesized the β-cyclodextrin-capped poly(2-(methacryloyloxy)ethyl succinate) (Fig. 6; **13**) *via* controlled RAFT polymerization and click chemistry.[136] Based on this molecule and PEG-containing polymer, the hydrogel networks were prepared by UV-initiated thiolene click reaction and host–guest inclusion complexation. The hydrogels with threaded sliding rings exhibited both pH and temperature dependent equilibrium swelling ratios in aqueous media. Using the commercially zwitterionic surfactant (Fig. 6; **14**) as guest molecule, Huang and co-workers reported a hydrogel system based on the host–guest interaction of (Fig. 6; **14**) and β-cyclodextrin with temperature, pH, urea, and a competitive guest responsive abilities.[137] This hydrogels showed excellent mechanical properties with an elastic modulus $>10\times10^4$ Pa and yield stress>100 Pa.

Additionally, Dey's group firstly demonstrated the heat and pH responsive hydrogel of sodium dodecyl sulfate and sodium *N*-(*N* dodecyl-2-aminoethanol)-L-valinate with very low minimum gelation concentration. The gelation occurred as a result of entanglement of helical ropes formed from twisted ribbon-like structures generated by the ion pair complex. Then, based on the hydrogen bonding interaction[44] and hydrophobic interaction,[138] the temperature and pH responsive hydrogels were reported. Also, the sodium and pH responsive hydrogel formed based on an aryl extended calix[4]pyrrole receptor and the tetramethylammonium guest was reported.[139]

Moreover, Ibarz *et al.* constructed the polymer hydrogels of poly(4-vinyl pyridine) using very simple modified nanoprecipitation technique.[140] These hydrogels were shown to be pH and ionic strength responsive, undergoing swelling with equilibration times in the range of days. Szilágyi and co-workers prepared pH and temperature responsive co-network hydrogel by the reaction of allylamine-grafted polysuccinimide and *N*-isopropylacrylamide in organic medium and a subsequent hydrolysis.[141] Furthermore, Yang *et al.* reported multi responsive hydrogel based on polyacrylamide functionalized with thymine derivatives.[142] These hydrogels responded to the changes of pH and thymine.

2.4.2. *Construction of composite hydrogel*

Herein, the multi responsive composite hydrogels are mainly constructed combining hydrogel and quantum dot,[79,143] alginate,[77,144] cellulose,[145,146] graphene oxide,[78,147] carbon nanotube(CNT),[29] and chitosan.[148]

Jiang *et al.* pioneered in preparing the composite hydrogels based on the host–guest inclusion complexation of β-cyclodextrin-modified CdS quantum dots and functional guest polymers.[79,143] They constructed the composite hydrogel based on quantum dots and an azobenzene end functionalized block copolymer.

The inclusion complex complexation and the domains of the collapsed PNIPAM chains served as two distinct crosslinks and rendered the hydrogel excellent dual sensitivity to competitive hosts/guests substitution and to temperature variation. Similarly, they prepared another composite hydrogel based on the quantum dots and ferrocene-containing polymer. This hydrogel exhibited satisfactory temperature-reversible sol–gel transitions as well as the responsiveness to chemical oxidization and supramolecular competition.

Furthermore, the multi responsive composite hydrogels were prepared using alginate-based materials. Xiao *et al.* prepared sodium alginate-based physically crosslinked dual responsive hydrogel using poly(vinyl alcohol) as a controllable gelator.[77] The swelling test showed that such hydrogels were endowed with the properties of pH responsive and electric responsive. Li and co-workers reported a kind of biocompatible hydrogel composed of alginate-g-β-cyclodextrin and ferrocene-terminated pluronic F127, which showed gel–sol phase transformations in response to temperature, oxidizing agents, and glucose because of the reversible association–dissociation of ferrocene-β-cyclodextrin inclusions and F127 micelles.[144]

Moreover, a temperature and pH sensitive composite hydrogel was constructed based on carboxylated methyl cellulose and poly(vinyl alcohol) mixed in aqueous solution.[145] And a series of pH and saline responsive composite hydrogels were prepared by a facile free radical graft copolymerization amongst hydroxyethyl cellulose, sodium acrylate and medicinal stone.[146]

Using graphene oxide as composite material, Wu and co-workers developed a facile one-step strategy for graphene oxide interpenetrating PNIPAM hydrogel networks by covalently bonding graphene oxide sheets and PNIPAM microgels directly in water.[78] This hydrogel exhibited dual thermal and pH response with good reversibility. Jiang and co-workers demonstrated a new light and thermal responsive PNIPAM hydrogel incorporating glycidyl methacrylate functionalized graphene oxide instead of metallic nanoparticle fillers.[147] Additionally, Javey described the fabrication of reversible, thermally and optically responsive hydrogel utilizing composites of PNIPAM loaded with SWCNT.[29] Payne developed a new method for covalently crosslinking chitosan by chemically oxidizing catechol to *o*-quinone.[148] The crosslinked chitosan film showed the pH and voltage responsive properties.

2.4.3. *Hydrogel multi responsive mechanism*

To reveal the influence of the grafted chain length on responsive behavior, the grafted poly(*N*,*N*-diethylacrylamide-co-(2-dimethylamino)ethyl methacrylate) hydrogel with the temperature and pH responsive was prepared by Liu and co-workers.[149] The comb-type grafted hydrogel having the different lengths of the grafted chains was synthesized in the presence of crosslinker. The hydrogel showed quite fast re-swelling and de-swelling behaviors in response to temperature and pH stimuli, which was because of the introduction of side chains with freely mobile ends in the comb-type grafted hydrogels made the mobility of the networks increased, and the responsive rates of the grafted hydrogel were controlled by modifying the length of the grafted chains. Frank and co-workers also prepared a temperature and pH responsive hydrogel, which functioned to investigate the swelling behavior and transition temperatures of the photo-crosslinked hydrogels.[11]

Schulz and co-workers prepared pH and ionic-strength responsive polyelectrolytic hydrogel and investigated its responsive behavior using a piezoresistive microsensor.[150] This polyelectrolytic hydrogel showed a very sharp volume phase transition at pH values below 7.4, which was in the range of the physiological pH. The time-dependent sensor response was measured for small changes in pH and ionic strength, respectively. Both sensor types showed asymmetric swelling behaviors between the swelling and the de-swelling cycle as well as different time constants. Similarly, Howse *et al.* investigated the pH and counter-ion response of hydrogels using laser light scattering on imprinted micron scale topography. A quartz diffraction grating was used to create a micron-sized periodic structure on the surface of a thin film of the polymer. And the resulting diffraction pattern was used to calculate the swelling ratio of the polymer film *in situ*. This technique has been proven to be an inexpensive and effective analytical tool for measuring hydrogel response on the microscopic scale. Additionally, Jonas *et al.* investigated the optical gradient profiles during temperature and salt dependent swelling of thin responsive hydrogel films using surface plasmon resonance/optical waveguide mode spectroscopy.[151]

2.5. Other responsive hydrogel

Except the responsive hydrogels mentioned above, various amazing hydrogels with other responsive behaviors were investigated, such as ionic-strength,[9] redox responsive,[85] glucose responsive,[83] enzyme responsive,[59] chemically responsive,[87] and so on.

To analyze the effect of initial fixed charge density on ionic strength response of smart hydrogel, Li *et al.* presented a multi-effect-coupling ionic-strength-stimulus model.[6] The parameter study was then conducted for analysis of influence of the initial fixed charge density on responsive characteristics of ionic-strength-sensitive hydrogel including ionic transport, electrical potential, and displacement. Then, they also analyzed the responsive characteristics of ionic-strength-sensitive hydrogel with consideration of the effect of equilibrium constant by a chemo–electro–mechanical model.[9]

Zheng and co-workers fabricated size and shape controlled stimuli responsive asymmetric hydrogels.[32] The reversible ion responsive hydrogel microcantilevers exhibited attractive and controllable bending behavior due to their asymmetric deformation to external ions. Additionally, Chu *et al.* developed a novel ion-imprinted strategy for synthesizing responsive hydrogels with rapid response to potassium ions.[41] Daunert *et al.*[82] and Banta *et al.*[81] developed the hydrogels with Calcium responsive behavior respectively.

As shown in Fig. 7, Tong *et al.* developed a redox responsive gel–sol transition system based on an aqueous poly(acrylic acid) solution containing an Fe(III)-citrate complex.[152] When Fe(III) ions in poly(acrylic acid) hydrogel containing citric acid were reduced to Fe(II) by light irradiation, the hydrogel dissolved to solution. The poly(acrylic acid) solution could be recovered to the homogeneous hydrogel again by oxidating Fe(II) to Fe(III). This reversible transition was indicated chromatically by Fe(III) ions and could be repeated many times provided there was enough citric acid. Moreover, Hempenius and co-workers synthesized a rapidly forming redox responsive poly(ferrocenylsilane)–poly(ethyleneglycol)-based hydrogel.[85] Harada *et al.* reported the redox responsive hydrogel system using the molecular recognition of β-cyclodextrin and ferrocenecarboxylic acid.[86]

Li and co-workers developed a model concerning the diffusion and enzyme reaction simultaneously to characterize the equilibrium behavior of the glucose responsive hydrogel.[83] The effect of Young's modulus of the hydrogel was investigated on the distributive concentrations of reacting and diffusive species and the deformation of the glucose-sensitive hydrogels. Moreover, Daunert *et al.*

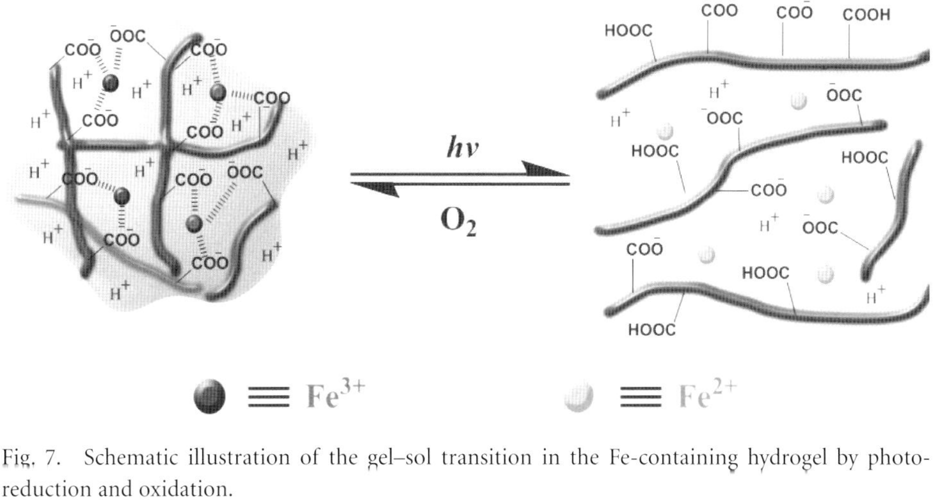

Fig. 7. Schematic illustration of the gel–sol transition in the Fe-containing hydrogel by photo-reduction and oxidation.

described one smart glucose responsive hydrogel material prepared by immobilizing the glucose/galactose binding protein within an acrylamide hydrogel network.[84] This hydrogel demonstrated a quantitative "accordion"-like dynamic response in the presence of glucose.

Additionally, Ulijn *et al.* demonstrated the preparation of enzyme responsive poly(ethylene glycol) acrylamide hydrogel microparticles functionalized by solid phase synthesis with new branched peptide actuators.[59] Stokke and co-workers prepared an oligonucleotide-polymer hybrid hydrogel with swelling response depending on specific stimuli by probe oligonucleotides.[153] The hydrogel acted as a transducer of the specific recognition of DNA sequences into micro- and macro-scale mechanics. Harada *et al.* reported the chemically responsive sol–gel transition of supramolecular single-walled carbon nanotubes hydrogel made by hybrids of single-walled carbon nanotubes and cyclodextrins.

3. Application of Responsive Hydrogel

The reversible responsive behavior of responsive hydrogel provides a wonderful platform for the construction of novel smart materials, such as nanoreactor,[51] glasses coating,[88] nano-valve,[89] biosensor,[90] derived material,[91] injectable hydrogel,[92] biomarker material,[93] microlense,[94] and so on. Herein, in the view of the scaffolds of hydrogels, the applications of responsive hydrogels summarized in this section are divided into several categories, starting from pH responsive hydrogel expanding to temperature responsive hydrogel, photo responsive hydrogel, multi responsive hydrogel, and other responsive hydrogel.

3.1. pH responsive hydrogel

Except the applications of pH responsive hydrogels in the regenerative medicine, drug delivery system and nanosensors, the functional film,[154] nanoreactor,[51] and coating[88] based on pH responsive hydrogels are prepared and described in this section.

Minko *et al.* fabricated ion crosslinked porous alginate thin films from mixtures of sodium alginate and polyvinyl alcohol in an aqueous solution.[154] Rinsing of the films in calcium chloride solutions yielded porous hydrogel film membranes on solid substrates. The porous membranes were pH sensitive materials whose pore diameters could be tuned by changes in pH. Gleason and co-workers prepared surface-tethered pH responsive hydrogel thin films as size-selective layers on nanoporous asymmetric membrane. They confirmed that the deposited film bridged the pore openings of the alumina supports, and little pore infiltration occurred.[155] Membrane permeability was controlled through variation of the thickness and composition of hydrogel. Zhang's group fabricated a graphene oxide hydrogel *via* suspending the GO in water without any additional processing steps.[156] The hydrogel/air interface, a well-defined hydrogel membrane was formed once the solvent was removed by vacuum drying. The microstructure of the resulting film was tailored by different dehydration approaches. This film exhibited pH responsiveness and good mechanical property.

Tsukruk *et al.* demonstrated the pH responsive layered hydrogel microcapsules as gold nanoreactors, which could facilitate gold nanoparticles within hydrogel walls under ambient conditions.[51] The *in situ* synthesis of gold nanoparticles within the ultrathin and pH responsive shells could be potentially used to straightforward fabricate the hybrid organic-gold nanomaterials. Additionally, inspired by biological actuators, Aizenberg and co-workers developed a novel chemo–mechanical hybrid actuation system that swelled and contracted in response to chemical signals.[60] Khutoryanskiy *et al.* developed the multilayered hydrogel coatings covalently-linked to glass surfaces showing the potential application of mimicking mucosal tissues.[88] Using initiated chemical vapor deposition, Mao and coworkers reported an all-dry fabrication method of the hybrid structure that consisting of pH responsive hydrogel and CNT arrays. The hydrogel coating imparted pH responsiveness to the nanotube arrays, and it significantly enhanced the surface wet ability.

3.2. Temperature responsive hydrogel

Herein, in the view of the scaffolds of temperature responsive hydrogels, the applications of them are divided into *composite hydrogel* and *other hydrogel.*

3.2.1. *Composite hydrogel*

The applications of the composite hydrogel with temperature responsive significantly focused on the preparation of bio-related materials. Disease-associated blood biomarkers exist in exceedingly low concentrations within complex mixtures of high-abundance proteins such as albumin. Liotta *et al.* prepared biomarker based on the smart hydrogel by introducing an affinity bait molecule into *N*-isopropylacrylamide.[93] The hydrogel performed three independent functions within minutes: (a) molecular size sieving, (b) affinity capture of all solution-phase target molecules, (c) complete protection of harvested proteins from enzymatic degradation. Akaike *et al.* regulated the cellular morphology using temperature responsive hydrogel for integrin-mediated mechanical force stimulation.[157] During gel swelling, changes of cell shape were clearly observed. And it proved that cells formed filopodia-like structures in response to mechanical cues, suggesting that mechanical forces facilitated actin polymerization at the peripheral region. Bhattacharyya's group reported the synthesis of reactive Fe and Fe/Pd nanoparticles in a temperature responsive hydrogel.[158] These nanoparticles were stabilized in the hydrogel network and the de-chlorination reactivity in water was enhanced and controllable in the temperature range of 30–34°C. Additionally, the methylcellulose based thermally reversible hydrogel system for tissue engineering applications was developed by Devireddy and co-workers.[159]

Moreover, Wells *et al.* prepared the temperature responsive microcapsules with variable optical signatures based on the incorporation of quantum dots into a highly biocompatible hydrogel.[50] The resulting microcapsules displayed temperature responsive behavior, as the optical signature displayed a linear dependence on temperature over the range of 20–45°C. Inci anchored the boradiazaindacene dye molecules to a polyethylene glycol (PEG)-based hydrogel with different concentrations using a picosecond time-resolved spectroscopic technique.[160] Based on this hydrogel, they investigated the dynamics of the fluorescence mechanism of boradiazaindacene dye molecules.

Hilt *et al.* presented a demonstration of remote controlled flow regulation in a microfluidic device using a hydrogel nanocomposite valve.[161] The swelling and collapse of the resultant hydrogel nanocomposite was remotely controlled by application of an alternating magnetic field. Moreover, Xu and co-workers prepared the graphene oxide/poly(acrylic acid-*co*-acrylamide) super-absorbent hydrogel nanocomposites.[56] Interestingly, the hydrogel nanocomposites exhibited significant improvement of swelling capacity in neutral medium although they just contained 0.10 wt.% of graphene oxide, and they could also retain relatively higher swelling capacities to a certain degree at acidic and basic solutions. Additionally, Ulbricht *et al.* prepared novel hydrogel pore-filled composite membranes with tunable and temperature responsive size-selectivity based on PNIPAM hydrogel.[162]

3.2.2. *Other hydrogel*

Liu and co-workers introduced the active sites of glutathione peroxidase into temperature responsive PNIPAM hydrogel scaffolds.[14] Similarly to the catalytic behavior of glutathione peroxidase with the ability of scavenging of reactive oxygen species and protecting cells from oxidative damage, the functional hydrogels exhibited the typical glutathione peroxidase catalytic behavior. More importantly, the catalytic activity of this microgel enzyme model displayed an obvious temperature responsive characteristic. Typically, the catalytic activity of the microgel could be turned on and off reversibly by changing the temperature (see Fig. 8).

Suzuki and co-workers firstly applied PNIPAM hydrogel as a particulate steric stabilizer in the dispersion polymerization of styrene.[163] It proved that some of the

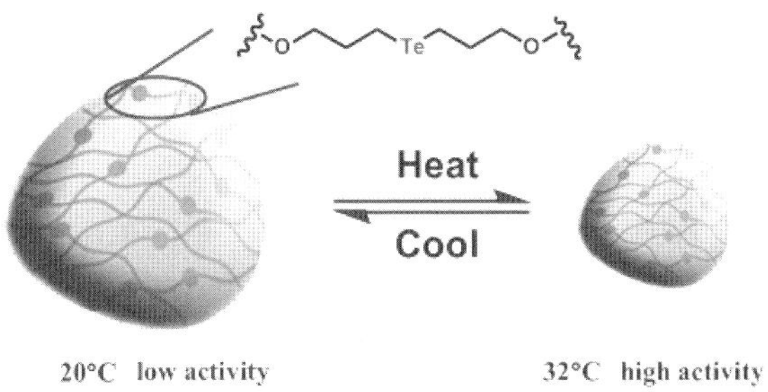

Fig. 8. The temperature responsive microgel with catalytic behavior of glutathione peroxidase.

resultant polystyrene particles were covered with hydrogel particles. Yu *et al.* synthesized a thermo and pH responsive hydrogel using *N*-isopropylacrylamide and potassium 4-(acryloyloxy) pyridine-2, 6-dicarboxylate as monomers.[164] This hydrogel functioned as scaffold for supported-palladium catalyst of copper-free Sonogashira reaction in aqueous media.

Hu and co-workers prepared the monodisperse spheres composed of PNIPAM and used them as building blocks for a thin hydrogel film.[54] This film not only absorbed a large amount of water like conventional hydrogel but also exhibited iridescent colors due to long range ordered microgel arrays. Zhang *et al.* developed thermosensitive macroporous hydrogel showing selectivity for the lysozyme based on metal coordinate interaction.[12] In the recognition process of the protein, the interaction of the imprinted thermosensitive hydrogel to protein can be switched between the coordinate effect and the electrostatic effect by adding or not adding Cu ions. Moreover, based on the special recognition property of designed hydrogels, the absorption of bovine serum albumin[165] and reusable nickel(II) ions[166] were achieved using thermosensitive hydrogels. Additionally, thermosensitive hydrogels used to activate adaptive liquid microlense were also developed.[94,167]

3.3. Photo responsive hydrogel

Sumaru *et al.* reported the quick photoresponse of thin hydrogel layers composed of thermo responsive PNIPAM with an anchored acrylated spirobenzopyran chromophore. And they prepared rewritable microrelief on this photo responsive hydrogel layers.[168] The instant formation of microrelief on a thin hydrogel layer was demonstrated by means of micropatterned light irradiation. Then, they demonstrated novel on-chip fluid control strategies, on-demand formation of arbitrary microchannels and parallel control of multiple microvalves by micropatterned light irradiation of a photo responsive hydrogel sheet.[18]

Lam and co-workers prepared the photo responsive molecularly imprinted hydrogel, which applied in the repetitive controlled release and uptake of substrates.[169] The imprinted hydrogel was found to afford good optical transparency in thee aqueous media, reasonable substrate binding affinity, and the fast photorespond rate. Nandi *et al.* prepared a light harvesting hydrogel consisting of a two component supramolecular complex of melamine and 6,7-dimethoxy-2,4[1H,3H]-quinazolinedione (donor) with riboflavin (acceptor), which worked in a wide range of temperature and pH.[170] It showed that a gradual quenching and red shift of the acceptor emission peak with the increase in its concentration through a co-assembly process. Furthermore, to prepare hydrogel with semiconducting behavior, Banerjee *et al.* employed a pH responsive hydrogel from an amino acid-based perylene bisimide. Interestingly, this hydrogel showed excellent photo-switching behavior with a high photo response value.[171]

3.4. Multi responsive hydrogel

The hydrogels with both pH and temperature responsive are widely investigated among multi responsive hydrogel. Typically, based on these hydrogels, the application of immobilized glucose oxidase,[172,173] microfluidic chip,[174] surface modification,[175] photopatterned actuators[62] were achieved. Hu and co-workers prepared the triply switchable bioelectrocatalysis based on hydrogel films. And these hydrogel films were used to immobilize glucose oxidase and explore the application in biosensors.[172,173] Schöning *et al.* developed a microfluidic chip with integrated microvalves based on temperature and pH responsive hydrogel thin films.[174] Moreover, the surface modification of cotton fabric with dual responsive PNIPAAm/chitosan nano hydrogel was achieved by Hemmatinejad's group. Gracias and co-workers fabricated the photopatterned actuators composed of stimuli responsive hydrogel bilayers made from *N*-isopropylacrylamide, acrylic acid and poly-ethylene oxide diacrylate.

Additionally, the full-color indicator was constructed based on an electro and thermochromic hydrogel. The external rapid tuning in the structural color of this hydrogel was successfully achieved by introducing a periodically ordered interconnecting porous structure.[176] Chu *et al.* developed a new type of glucose responsive hydrogel with rapid response to blood glucose concentration change at physiological temperature based on the scaffold of PNIPAM.[177] Zhao and co-workers prepared a novel stimuli responsive protein imprinted polymer for selective recognition of bovine serum albumin.[178] It was shown that the charge effect and the shape memory effect were the major factors affecting the imprint formation and template recognition.

3.5. Other responsive hydrogel

To prepare the ultrafiltration membranes for protein bioseparation, Ghosh and co-workers modified a commercial microporous membrane with a hydrogel composed of poly-*N*-vinyllactams crosslinked with bisacrylamide.[179] Then, the parameter scanning ultrafiltration technique was then used to examine the feasibility of separating a binary model protein mixture of equine ferritin and human immunoglobulin G. It demonstrated that these membranes could potentially be used in multi-component protein separation. Then, they achieved the chromatographic separation of proteins using hydrophobic membrane shielded with an environment responsive hydrogel.[180]

Furthermore, the smart hydrogels response to various enzymes were constructed and applied in several fields. Plunkett *et al.* prepared a chymotrypsin responsive hydrogel.[181] This hydrogel was applied in a coupled reaction of methacrylamide groups and cysteine residues in the presence of amines and alcohols. Hamachi *et al.* developed the supramolecular hydrogels exhibiting reversible thermochromism concurrently with gel-to-sol transition from four glycolipids.[17] These hydrogels also showed similar color change in response to glycosidases, which might be employed to construct a colorimetric sensor array chip for sensing glycosidases with the naked eye. Maitz and co-workers prepared a blood coagulation responsive hydrogel system that could deliver heparin in amounts triggered by the environmental levels of thrombin.[182]

Moreover, Hart and co-workers prepared the hydrogel-driven carbon nanotube microtransducers based on composites of 3D CNT frameworks and hydrogel.[183] The composite hydrogels exhibited a moisture response by changing the ambient humidity, which was also predicted by a finite element model of the composite system. Additionally, Desimone *et al.* designed reductively responsive siRNA-conjugated hydrogel nanoparticles for gene silencing.[184] Post and co-workers developed an electrosensitive and biocompatible hydrogel-based smart device composed of acrylic acid and fibrin, which was used as tissue engineered construct to mechanically stimulate cells.[185]

4. Conclusions and Outlook

With special 3D polymer network crosslinked by chemical bonds or physical nodes, hydrogels exhibited the unique property of swollen behavior. Commonly, responsive hydrogels can function as the amazing scaffolds for the fabrication of smart devices to investigate the physiological processes in living system and have attracted researcher's special attentions. Herein, both the theory researches and exploration of construction methods of responsive hydrogels are summarized in this chapter. Moreover, the applications of responsive hydrogels are also summarized, which may provide a significant guide in the redesign and application of responsive hydrogels. Usually, the main applications of hydrogels are focused on the regenerative medicine, drug delivery system, and nanosensors and the other applications are less investigated. Therefore, to expand the application fields of responsive hydrogels and to construct more amazing smart materials based on responsive hydrogels, more efforts are still needs to be done.

Acknowledgments

Financial support from the Natural Science Foundation of China (Grant Nos. 51303088, 21234004, 91027023, and 21221063, 21004028), the Natural Science Foundation of Guangxi Province (Grant No. 2013GXNSFBA019043), the Natural Science Foundation of Education Bureau of Guangxi Province (No. 2013YB254).

References

1. I. Tokarev and S. Minko, *Soft Matter*, **511** (2009).
2. Y. Samchenko, Z. Ulberg, and O. Korotych, *Adv. Colloid. Interface Sci.*, **247** (2011).
3. E. M. White, J. Yatvin, J. B. Grubbs, J. A. Bilbrey, and J. Locklin, *J. Polym. Sci. Part B: Polym. Phys.*, **1084** (2013).
4. M. L. Huggins, *J. Chem. Phys.*, **440** (1941).
5. P. J. Flory and J. Rehner Jr., *J. Chem. Phys.*, **521** (1943).
6. F. Lai and H. Li, *Soft Matter*, **311** (2010).
7. R. Marcombe, S. Cai, W. Hong, X. Zhao, Y. Lapusta, and Z. Suo, *Soft Matter*, **784** (2010).
8. H. Li and Y. K. Yew, *Polym. Eng. Sci.*, **429** (2010).
9. H. Li, F. Lai, and R. Luo, *Langmuir*, **13142** (2009).
10. T. Tanaka, S. T. Sun, Y. Hirokawa, S. Katayama, J. Kucera, Y. Hirose, and T. Amiya, *Nature*, **796** (1987).
11. M. E. Harmon, D. Kuckling, and C. W. Frank, *Macromolecules*, **162** (2003).
12. L. Qin, X. W. He, W. Zhang, W. Y. Li, and Y. K. Zhang, *Anal. Chem.*, **7206** (2009).
13. G. Wulff, B. O. Chong, and U. Kolb, *Angew. Chem. Int. Ed.*, **2955** (2006).
14. X. Huang, Y. Yin, Y. Tang, X. Bai, Z. Zhang, J. Xu, J. Liu, and J. Shen, *Soft Matter*, **1905** (2009).
15. H. Kawaguchi, K. Fujimoto, and Y. Mizuhara, *Colloid. Polym. Sci.*, **53** (1992).
16. K. L. Liu, Z. Zhang, and J. Li, *Soft Matter*, **11290** (2011).
17. R. Ochi, K. Kurotani, M. Ikeda, S. Kiyonaka, and I. Hamachi, *Chem. Commun.*, **2115** (2013).
18. E. Cheng, Y. Xing, P. Chen, Y. Yang, Y. Sun, D. Zhou, L. Xu, Q. Fan, and D. Liu, *Angew. Chem. Int. Ed.*, **7660** (2009).

19. K. Ishida, T. Uno, T. Itoh, and M. Kubo, *Macromolecules*, **6136** (2012).
20. Y. Gao, C. Hou, L. Zhou, D. Zhang, C. Zhang, L. Miao, L. Wang, Z. Dong, Q. Luo, and J. Liu, *Macromol. Biosci.*, **808** (2013).
21. C. Koopmans and H. Ritter, *Macromolecules*, **7418** (2008).
22. Z. Ma, D. M. Nelson, Y. Hong, and W. R. Wagner, *Biomacromolecules*, **1873** (2010).
23. K. L. Fujimoto, Z. Ma, D. M. Nelson, R. Hashizume, J. Guan, K. Tobita, and W. R. Wagner, *Biomaterials*, **4357** (2009).
24. L. M. Bonanno and L. A. DeLouise, *Adv. Funct. Mater.*, **573** (2010).
25. J. Sorber, G. Steiner, V. Schulz, M. Guenther, G. Gerlach, R. Salzer, and K. F. Arndt, *Anal. Chem.*, **2957** (2008).
26. I. Tomatsu, K. Peng and A. Kros, *Adv. Drug. Delivery. Rev.*, **1257** (2011).
27. X. Kang, Z. Cheng, D. Yang, P. Ma, M. Shang, C. Peng, Y. Dai, and J. Lin, *Adv. Funct. Mater.*, **1539** (2012).
28. F. H. A. Rodrigues, A. G. B. Pereira, A. R. Fajardo, and E. C. Muniz, *J. Appl. Polym. Sci.*, **3480** (2013).
29. X. Zhang, C. L. Pint, M. H. Lee, B. E. Schubert, A. Jamshidi, K. Takei, H. Ko, A. Gillies, R. Bardhan, J. J. Urban, M. Wu, R. Fearing, and A. Javey, *Nano Lett.*, **3239** (2011).
30. D. E. Discher, D. J. Mooney, and P. W. Zandstra, *Science*, **1673** (2009).
31. X. Li, E. Katsanevakis, X. Liu, N. Zhang, and X. Wen, *Prog. Polym. Sci.*, **1105** (2012).
32. Z. Xiong, M. L. Zheng, X. Z. Dong, W. Q. Chen, F. Jin, Z. S. Zhao, and X. M. Duan, *Soft Matter*, **10353** (2011).
33. C. de las Heras Alarcón, S. Pennadam, and C. Alexander, *Chem. Soc. Rev.*, **276** (2005).
34. K. Matyjaszewski and J. Xia, *Chem. Rev.*, **2921** (2001).
35. H. D. Chirra, D. Biswal, and J. Z. Hilt, *Polym. Adv. Technol.*, **773** (2011).
36. H. D. Chirra and J. Z. Hilt, *Langmuir*, **11249** (2010).
37. M. A. Haque, T. Kurokawa, and J. P. Gong, *Soft Matter*, **8008** (2012).
38. M. Horecha, V. Senkovskyy, M. Stamm, and A. Kiriy, *Macromolecules*, **5811** (2009).
39. L. Hu, Z. Chen, and M. J. Serpe, *Soft Matter*, **10095** (2012).
40. Z. Chen, L. Hu, and M. J. Serpe, *J. Mater. Chem.*, **20998** (2012).
41. H. G. Wu, X. J. Ju, R. Xie, Y. M. Liu, J. G. Deng, C. H. Niu, and L. Y. Chu, *Polym. Adv. Technol.*, **1389** (2011).
42. P. W. Beines, I. Klosterkamp, B. Menges, U. Jonas, and W. Knoll, *Langmuir*, **2231** (2007).
43. D. Matsukuma, K. Yamamoto, and T. Aoyagi, *Langmuir*, **5911** (2006).
44. B. Roy, A. Saha,A. Esterrani, and A. K. Nandi, *Soft Matter*, **3337** (2010).
45. A. Nakagawa, F. Steiniger, W. Richter, A. Koschella, T. Heinze, and H. Kamitakahara, *Langmuir*, **12609** (2012).
46. X. Li, Y. Gao, Y. Kuang, and B. Xu, *Chem. Commun*, **5364** (2010).
47. J. Wang, A. Sutti, X. Wang, and T. Lin, *Soft Matter*, **4364** (2011).
48. S. Sugiura, A. Szilagyi, K. Sumaru, K. Hattori, T. Takagi, G. Filipcsei, M. Zrinyi, and T. Kanamori, *Lab. Chip.*, **196** (2009).
49. C. E. Brubaker and P. B. Messersmith, *Biomacromolecules*. **4326** (2011).

50. D. Hardison, H. U. Deepthike, W. Senevirathna, T. Pathirathne, and M. Wells, *J. Mater. Chem.*, **5368** (2008).
51. V. Kozlovskaya, E. Kharlampieva, S. Chang, R. Muhlbauer, and V. V. Tsukruk, *Chem. Mater.*, **2158** (2009).
52. V. Kozlovskaya, A. Shamaev, and S. A. Sukhishvili, *Soft Matter*, **1499** (2008).
53. J. Kim, H. J. Lim, Y. K. Hwang, H. Woo, J. W. Kim, and K. Char, *Langmuir*, **11899** (2012).
54. J. Zhou, G. Wang, M. Marquez, and Z. Hu, *Soft Matter*, **820** (2009).
55. M. J. N. Junk, R. D. Berger, and U. Jonas, *Langmuir*, **7262** (2010).
56. A. Khan, A. M. E. Toni, and M. Alhoshan, *Mater. Lett.*, **12** (2012).
57. Y. Huang, M. Zeng, J. Ren, J. Wang, L. Fan, and Q. Xu, *Colloids. Surf. A*, **97** (2012).
58. C. R. van den Brom, I. Anac, R. F. Roskamp, M. Retsch, U. Jonas, B. Menges, and J. A. Preece, *J. Mater. Chem.*, **4827** (2010).
59. T. O. McDonald, H. Qu, B. R. Saunders, and R. V. Ulijn, *Soft Matter*, **1728** (2009).
60. L. D. Zarzar, P. Kim, and J. Aizenberg, *Adv. Mater.*, **1442** (2011).
61. T. Guan, F. Godts, F. Ceyssens, E. Vanderleyden, K. Adesanya, P. Dubruel, H. P. Neves, and R. Puers, *Sens. Actuators. A*, **184** (2012).
62. N. Bassik, B. T. Abebe, K. E. Laflin, and D. H. Gracias, *Polymer*, **6093** (2010).
63. N. L. Fletcher, C. V. Lockett, and A. F. Dexter, *Soft Matter*, **10210** (2011).
64. H. Gao, N. Wang, X. Hu, W. Nan, Y. Han, and W. Liu, *Macromol. Rapid Commun.*, **63** (2013).
65. W. B. Liechty, R. L. Scheuerle, and N. A. Peppas, *Polymer*, **3784** (2013).
66. S. Naficy, J. M. Razal, P. G. Whitten, G. G. Wallace, and G. M. Spinks, *J. Polym. Sci. Part B: Polym. Phys.*, **423** (2012).
67. J. Nanda, A. Biswas, and A. Banerjee, *Soft Matter*, **4198** (2013).
68. T. Patra, A. Pal, and J. Dey, *Langmuir*, **7761** (2010).
69. B. G. Choi, S. H. Cho, H. Lee, M. H. Cha, K. Park, B. Jeong, and D. K. Han, *Macromolecules*, **2269** (2011).
70. Q. Saleem, B. Liu, C. C. Gradinaru, and P. M. Macdonald, *Biomacromolecules*, **2364** (2011).
71. S. Lv, L. Liu, and W. Yang, *Langmuir*, **2076** (2009).
72. S. Matsumoto, S. Yamaguchi, A. Wada, T. Matsui, M. Ikeda, and I. Hamachi, *Chem. Commun.*, **1545** (2008).
73. I. Tomatsu, A. Hashidzume, and A. Harada, *Macromolecules*, **5223** (2005).
74. J. Liu, J. Nie, Y. Zhao, and Y. He, *J. Photochem. Photobiol. A*, **20** (2010).
75. D. Khatua, R. Maiti, and J. Dey, *Chem. Commun*, **4903** (2006).
76. L. Li, X. Xing, and Z. Liu, *J. Appl. Polym. Sci.*, **1128** (2012).
77. C. Xia and C. Xiao, *J. Appl. Polym. Sci.*, **2244** (2012).
78. S. Sun and P. Wu, *J. Mater. Chem.*, **4095** (2011).
79. P. Du, J. Liu, G. Chen, and M. Jiang, *Langmuir*, **9602** (2011).
80. P. D. Thornton, G. McConnell, and R. V. Ulijn, *Chem. Commun.*, **5913** (2005).
81. K. Dooley, Y. H. Kim, H. D. Lu, R. Tu, and S. Banta, *Biomacromolecules*, **1758** (2012).

82. J. D. Ehrick, S. K. Deo, T. W. Browning, L. G. Bachas, M. J. Madou, and S. Daunert, *Nat. Mater.*, **298** (2005).
83. H. Li and R. Luo, *Biosens. Bioelectron.*, **3630** (2009).
84. J. D. Ehrick, M. R. Luckett, S. Khatwani, Y. Wei, S. K. Deo, L. G. Bachas, and S. Daunert, *Macromol. Biosci.*, **864** (2009).
85. X. Sui, L. van Ingen, M. A. Hempenius, and G. J. Vancso, *Macromol. Rapid Commun.*, **2059** (2010).
86. I. Tomatsu, A. Hashidzume, and A. Harada, *Macromol. Rapid Commun.*, **238** (2006).
87. T. Ogoshi, Y. Takashima, H. Yamaguchi, and A. Harada, *J. Am. Chem. Soc.*, **4878** (2007).
88. O. V. Khutoryanskaya, M. Potgieter, and V. V. Khutoryanskiy, *Soft Matter*, **551** (2010).
89. J. Wu and M. J. Sailor, *Adv. Funct. Mater.*, **733** (2009).
90. Y. Zhang and C. Ji, *Anal. Chem.*, **5275** (2010).
91. H. Zhang, A. Qadeer, D. Mynarcik, and W. Chen, *Biomaterials*, **890** (2011).
92. A. Sahu, W. I. Choi, and G. Tae, *Chem. Commun*, **5820** (2012).
93. A. Luchini, D. H. Geho, B. Bishop, D. Tran, C. Xia, R. L. Dufour, C. D. Jones, V. Espina, A. Patanarut, W. Zhou, M. M. Ross, A. Tessitore, E. F. Petricoin, and L. A. Liotta, *Nano Lett.*, **350** (2007).
94. J. Kim, S. Nayak, and L. A. Lyon, *J. Am. Chem. Soc.*, **9588** (2005).
95. A. Shundo, K. Mizuguchi, M. Miyamoto, M. Goto, and K. Tanaka, *Chem. Commun.*, **8844** (2011).
96. E. A. Appel, F. Biedermann, U. Rauwald, S. T. Jones, J. M. Zayed, and O. A. Scherman, *J. Am. Chem. Soc.*, **14251** (2010).
97. Q. Chen, Y. Lv, D. Zhang, G. Zhang, C. Liu, and D. Zhu, *Langmuir*, **3165** (2009).
98. Z. Hu, X. Lu, J. Gao, and C. Wang, *Adv. Mater.*, **1173** (2000).
99. S. Cao, B. Hu, and H. Liu, *Polym. Int.*, **545** (2009).
100. A. W. Chan, R. A. Whitney, and R. J. Neufeld, *Biomacromolecules*, **609** (2009).
101. E. Cheng, Y. Li, Z. Yang, Z. Deng, and D. Liu, *Chem. Commun.*, **5545** (2011).
102. Y. Xia and H. Zhu, *Soft Matter*, **9388** (2011).
103. S. Banerjee, S. Singh, S. S. Bhattacharya, and P. Chattopadhyay, *Int. J. Biol. Macromol.*, **297** (2013).
104. C. Supasuteekul, A. H. Milani, J. M. Saunders, S. Lally, T. Freemont, and B. R. Saunders, *Soft Matter*, **7234** (2012).
105. R. E. Kohman, C. Cha, S. C. Zimmerman, and H. Kong, *Soft Matter*, **2150** (2010).
106. V. Kozlovskaya, Y. Wang, W. Higgins, J. Chen, Y. Chen, and E. Kharlampieva, *Soft Matter*, **9828** (2012).
107. A. Fujii, T. Maruyama, T. Sotani, Y. Ohmukai, and H. Matsuyama, *Colloids. Surf. A*, **159** (2009).
108. R. Luo and H. Li, *Acta Biomater.*, **2920** (2009).
109. J. H. Jeong, J. J. Schmidt, C. Cha, and H. Kong, *Soft Matter*, **3930** (2010).
110. J. P. Best, M. P. Neubauer, S. Javed, H. H. Dam, A. Fery, and F. Caruso, *Langmuir*, **9814** (2013).

111. J. M. G. Swann, W. Bras, P. D. Topham, J. R. Howse, and A. J. Ryan, *Langmuir*, **10191** (2010).
112. O. Kretschmann, S. W. Choi, M. Miyauchi, I. Tomatsu, A. Harada, and H. Ritter, *Angew. Chem. Int. Ed.*, **4361** (2006).
113. H. Danjo, K. Hirata, S. Yoshigai, I. Azumaya, and K. Yamaguchi, *J. Am. Chem. Soc.*, **1638** (2009).
114. I. W. Hamley, G. Cheng, and V. Castelletto, *Macromol. Biosci.*, **1068** (2011).
115. Z. Cao, B. Du, T. Chen, H. Li, J. Xu, and Z. Fan, *Langmuir*, **5543** (2008).
116. V. Tokarova, A. Pittermannova, J. Cech, P. Ulbrich, and F. Stepanek, *Soft Matter*, **1087** (2012).
117. Y. Tan, K. Xu, P. Wang, W. Li, S. Sun, and L. Dong, *Soft Matter*, **1467** (2010).
118. J. S. Hong, S. M. Stavis, S. H. DePaoli Lacerda, L. E. Locascio, S. R. Raghavan, and M. Gaitan, *Langmuir*, **11581** (2010).
119. A. Zadražil and F. Štěpánek, *Colloids. Surf. A*, **115** (2010).
120. Q. Zhong, E. Metwalli, G. Kaune, M. Rawolle, A. M. Bivigou-Koumba, A. Laschewsky, C. M. Papadakis, R. Cubitt, and P. Muller-Buschbaum, *Soft Matter*, **5241** (2012).
121. R. Raccis, R. Roskamp, I. Hopp, B. Menges, K. Koynov, U. Jonas, W. Knoll, H. J. Butt, and G. Fytas, *Soft Matter*, **7042** (2011).
122. S. Sun, J. Hu, H. Tang, and P. Wu, *J. Phys. Chem. B*, **9761** (2010).
123. K. A. Melzak, A. Mateescu, J. L. Toca-Herrera, and U. Jonas, *Langmuir*, **12871** (2012).
124. I. Mejac and C. D. Tran, *Anal. Chem.*, **3520** (2011).
125. N. Zhang and W. Knoll, *Anal. Chem.*, **2611** (2009).
126. I. Mejac, H. H. Park, W. W. Bryan, T. R. Lee, and C. D. Tran, *Anal. Chem.*, **1698** (2010).
127. Y. Lin, Y. Qiao, Y. Yan, and J. Huang, *Soft Matter*, **3047** (2009).
128. J. Zhang and X. Shen, *J. Phys. Chem. B*, **1451** (2013).
129. M. Yanagioka and C. W. Frank, *Langmuir*, **5927** (2009).
130. W. Song, Y. Guan, Y. Zhang, and X. X. Zhu, *Soft Matter*, **2629** (2013).
131. J. He, X. Tong, and Y. Zhao, *Macromolecules*, **4845** (2009).
132. S. Matsumoto, S. Yamaguchi, S. Ueno, H. Komatsu, M. Ikeda, K. Ishizuka, Y. Iko, K. V. Tabata, H. Aoki, and S. Ito, *Chem-Eur. J.*, **3977** (2008).
133. T. Watanabe, M. Akiyama, K. Totani, S. M. Kuebler, F. Stellacci, W. Wenseleers, K. Braun, S. R. Marder, and J. W. Perry, *Adv. Funct. Mater.*, **611** (2002).
134. X. Liao, G. Chen, X. Liu, W. Chen, F. Chen, and M. Jiang, *Angewandte Chemie.*, **4511** (2010).
135. L. Zhou, J. Li, Q. Luo, J. Zhu, H. Zou, Y. Gao, L. Wang, J. Xu, Z. Dong, and J. Liu, *Soft Matter*, **4635** (2013).
136. T. Cai, W. J. Yang, Z. Zhang, X. Zhu, K. G. Neoh, and E. T. Kang, *Soft Matter*, **5612** (2012).
137. L. Jiang, Y. Yan, and J. Huang, *Soft Matter*, **10417** (2011).
138. A. Pal, S. Shrivastava, and J. Dey, *Chem. Commun.*, **6997** (2009).
139. B. Verdejo, F. Rodriguez-Llansola, B. Escuder, J. F. Miravet, and P. Ballester, *Chem. Commun.*, **2017** (2011).
140. A. Arizaga, G. Ibarz, and R. Piñol, *J. Colloid. Interface Sci.*, **668** (2010).

141. Á. Némethy, K. Solti, L. Kiss, B. Gyarmati, M. A. Deli, E. Csányi, and A. Szilágyi, *Eur. Polym. J.*, **2392** (2013).
142. K. Yang and M. Zeng, *New J. Chem.*, **920** (2013).
143. J. Liu, G. Chen, M. Guo, and M. Jiang, *Macromolecules*, **8086** (2010).
144. L. Tan, Y. Liu, W. Ha, L. S. Ding, S. L. Peng, S. Zhang, and B. J. Li, *Soft Matter*, **5746** (2012).
145. C. Xiao, C. Xia, Y. Ma, and X. He, *J. Appl. Polym. Sci.*, **4750** (2013).
146. W. Wang, J. Wang, Y. Kang, and A. Wang, *Compos. Part B-Eng.*, **809** (2011).
147. C. W. Lo, D. Zhu, and H. Jiang, *Soft Matter*, **5604** (2011).
148. Y. Zhang, Y. Thomas, E. Kim, and G. F. Payne, *J. Phys. Chem. B*, **1579** (2012).
149. J. Chen, M. Liu, N. Zhang, P. Dai, C. Gao, L. Ma, and H. Liu, *Sens. Actuators. B*, **34** (2010).
150. V. Schulz, M. Guenther, G. Gerlach, J. J. Magda, P. Tathireddy, L. Rieth, and F. Solzbacher, *Smart Struct Mater Nondestruct Eval Health Monit Diagn*, (2009).
151. M. J. N. Junk, I. Anac, B. Menges and U. Jonas, *Langmuir*, **12253** (2010).
152. F. Peng, G. Li, X. Liu, S. Wu, and Z. Tong, *J. Am. Chem. Soc.*, **16166** (2008).
153. K. Gawel and B. T. Stokke, *Soft Matter*, **4615** (2011).
154. V. Gopishetty, I. Tokarev, and S. Minko, *J. Mater. Chem.*, **19482** (2012).
155. W. E. Tenhaeff and K. K. Gleason, *Chem. Mater.*, **4323** (2009).
156. S. Y. Qin, X. J. Liu, R. X. Zhuo, and X. Z. Zhang, *Macromol. Chem. Phys.*, **2044** (2012).
157. K. Yamaki, I. Harada, M. Goto, C. S. Cho, and T. Akaike, *Biomaterials*, **1421** (2009).
158. L. Xiao, A. B. Isner, J. Z. Hilt, and D. Bhattacharyya, *J. Appl. Polym. Sci.*, **1804** (2013).
159. S. Thirumala, J. M. Gimble, and R. V. Devireddy, *Cells*, **460** (2013).
160. S. Acikgoz, G. Aktas, M. N. Inci, H. Altin, and A. Sanyal, *J. Phys. Chem. B*, **10954** (2010).
161. N. S. Satarkar, W. Zhang, R. E. Eitel, and J. Z. Hilt, *Lab Chip*, **1773** (2009).
162. N. Adrus and M. Ulbricht, *J. Mater. Chem.*, **3088** (2012).
163. D. Suzuki and S. Yamakawa, *Langmuir*, **10629** (2012).
164. J. Yang, X. Zhang, W. Yu, W. Liu and F. Bian, *React. Funct. Polym.*, **710** (2013).
165. X. Zhu, X. Gu, L. Zhang, and X. Z. Kong, *Nanoscale Res. Lett.*, **7** (2012).
166. F. Yan, M. Wang, D. Cao, S. Guo, and L. Chen, *J. Polym. Sci. Part A: Polym. Chem.*, **2401** (2013).
167. L. Dong, A. K. Agarwal, D. J. Beebe, and H. Jiang, *Nature*, **551** (2006).
168. A. Szilágyi, K. Sumaru, S. Sugiura, T. Takagi, T. Shinbo, M. Zrínyi, and T. Kanamori, *Chem. Mater.*, **2730** (2007).
169. C. Gong, K. L. Wong, and M. H. Lam, *Chem. Mater.*, **1353** (2008).
170. P. Bairi, B. Roy, and A. K. Nandi, *Chem. Commun.*, **10850** (2012).
171. S. Roy, D. Kumar Maiti, S. Panigrahi, D. Basak, and A. Banerjee, *RSC Advances*, **11053** (2012).
172. Y. Liang, H. Liu, K. Zhang, and N. Hu, *Electrochim. Acta*, **456** (2012).
173. Y. Liang, S. Song, H. Yao, and N. Hu, *Electrochim. Acta*, **5166** (2011).
174. M. Bäcker, M. Raue, S. Schusser, C. Jeitner, L. Breuer, P. Wagner, A. Poghossian, A. Förster, T. Mang, and M. J. Schöning, *Physica Status Solidi (a)*, **839** (2012).

175. A. Bashari, N. Hemmatinejad, and A. Pourjavadi, *Polym. Adv. Technol.*, (2013).
176. K. Ueno, K. Matsubara, M. Watanabe, and Y. Takeoka, *Adv. Mater.*, **2807** (2007).
177. S. B. Zhang, L. Y. Chu, D. Xu, J. Zhang, X. J. Ju, and R. Xie, *Polym. Adv. Technol.*, **937** (2008).
178. Z. Hua, Z. Chen, Y. Li, and M. Zhao, *Langmuir*, **5773** (2008).
179. R. Huang, L. K. Kostanski, C. D. M. Filipe, and R. Ghosh, *J. Membr. Sci.*, **42** (2009).
180. R. Huang, K. Z. Mah, M. Malta, L. K. Kostanski, C. D. M. Filipe, and R. Ghosh, *J. Membr. Sci.*, **177** (2009).
181. K. N. Plunkett, K. L. Berkowski, and J. S. Moore, *Biomacromolecules*, **632** (2005).
182. M. F. Maitz, U. Freudenberg, M. V. Tsurkan, M. Fischer, T. Beyrich, and C. Werner, *Nature communications*, **1** (2013).
183. M. De Volder, S. H. Tawfick, D. Copic, and A. J. Hart, *Soft Matter*, **9844** (2011).
184. S. S. Dunn, S. Tian, S. Blake, J. Wang, A. L. Galloway, A. Murphy, P. D. Pohlhaus, J. P. Rolland, M. E. Napier, and J. M. DeSimone, *J. Am. Chem. Soc.*, **7423** (2012).
185. N. Rahimi, D. G. Molin, T. J. Cleij, M. A. van Zandvoort, and M. J. Post, *Biomacromolecules*, **1448** (2012).

Index